An official publication of

THE AMERICAN SOCIOLOGICAL ASSOCIATION

N. J. DEMERATH, III, *Executive Officer*

SOCIOLOGICAL
METHODOLOGY
1970

Edgar F. Borgatta

EDITOR

George W. Bohrnstedt

ASSOCIATE EDITOR

SOCIOLOGICAL METHODOLOGY 1970

 Jossey-Bass Inc., Publishers
615 Montgomery Street • San Francisco • 1970

SOCIOLOGICAL METHODOLOGY 1970
Edgar F. Borgatta, *Editor*
George W. Bohrnstedt, *Associate Editor*

Copyright © 1970 by Jossey-Bass, Inc., Publishers

Copyright under Pan American and Universal
Copyright Conventions. All rights reserved. No part of
this book may be reproduced in any form—except for brief
quotation (not to exceed 1,000 words) in a review or scholarly
book—without written permission from the publishers. All
inquiries should be addressed to:

Jossey-Bass, Inc., Publishers
615 Montgomery Street
San Francisco, California 94111

Library of Congress Catalog Card Number 74-110635

International Standard Book Number ISBN 0-87589-070-9

Printed in the United States of America
Composed and printed by York Composition Company, Inc.
Bound by Chas. H. Bohn & Co., Inc.

JACKET DESIGN BY WILLI BAUM, SAN FRANCISCO

FIRST EDITION

Code 7025

THE JOSSEY-BASS BEHAVIORAL SCIENCE SERIES

SOCIOLOGICAL METHODOLOGY 1970

EDITOR Edgar F. Borgatta*

ASSOCIATE EDITOR George W. Bohrnstedt*

ADVISORY EDITORS Howard S. Becker*

Hubert M. Blalock, Jr.**

Otis Dudley Duncan***

Richard J. Hill*

Robert McGinnis**

Peter Rossi***

* Term ends with 1970 volume
** Term ends with 1971 volume
*** Term ends with 1972 volume

CONSULTANTS

PROLOGUE

The prologue to *Sociological Methodology 1969* contained impressions of how sociological methodology had developed in the past several decades and where it stood in 1969. In a way, this prologue continues those same themes, with some attention given to developments that might occur in the future.

If any one methodological emphasis dominated the first volume of *Sociological Methodology*, it was a concern with models for causal analysis. It is apparent from conversations with editors of substantive journals that these techniques are coming into vogue, since more and more papers carry titles prefaced with "A Causal Analysis of . . ." or "A Path Analysis of. . . ." Clearly, the current methodological fad is to construct path diagrams and to examine the fit of data to the causal model. While causal analysis ought to be an important tool for sociologists, its limitations need to be understood. One limitation of which researchers should be reminded is that "theories" should not be tested on data from which they are derived. Thus, when a set of data fit a causal model resonably well, the presumed parameters should then be tested in a replication. This testing of theory by replication is conspicuously absent in most articles that use causal models.

Although abuses are inevitable with any fad in the field, we must not make the opposite mistake—undervaluing the technique. The value of models to show researchers the limitations of their theories and their data should not be underestimated. If the rigor of testing assertions in causal models were to become a prerequisite for publication, most sociologists might find themselves writing less and some of the "new" sociologists might be tongue-tied. Causal analysis has become an important tool in the development of methodology itself, as well as in data analysis per se. Thus, three chapters in the current volume use path analysis in the development of new methodological strategies—Heise, Heise and Bohrnstedt, and Althauser and Heberlein—and other such examples, both published and unpublished, exist. Causal analysis indeed has become important for sociologists, in spite of abuses that are bound to occur.

No one methodological area dominates the current volume, but the presence of the section on "Measurement, Reliability, and Validity" deserves brief discussion. While nontechnical presentations of the measurement problem have occurred in sociology, relatively explicit technical papers have for the most part been absent. All the statistical techniques that are applied in estimation procedures assume perfect measurement, although measurement in sociology probably has been as poor as in any other discipline, if not poorer. The effects of errors in measurement have received attention in some disciplines, especially educational psychology, but have largely been ignored in sociology. It is hoped that the next decade will see progress in this very crucial area.

Although it may not be entirely clear from this volume, one of the most exciting trends in methodology is the convergence of techniques in the several social sciences. Economists, psychologists, and sociologists are borrowing methodological tools from one another and applying them freely to problems in their own fields. Perhaps the social sciences are coming of age as scientific disciplines. But, more importantly, channels of communication appear more open and drafts of papers circulate more freely. From these varied sources perhaps a unified methodology of the social sciences will emerge rather than a methodology for each of the separate disciplines. We note this trend in several methodological and statistically oriented journals, and in our own use of consultants for *Sociological Methodology*.

Clearly, techniques exist other than those mentioned above. Some may hold promise for sociology but have been largely ignored. In this volume introductions to two such topics are presented— Bayesian Statistics and Uncertainty Analysis. While only time will reveal the utility of these approaches for sociological analysis, it is clear that sociologists have not fully explored the use of these and many other approaches to analysis. Despite the bandwagon effect with which new techniques are widely adopted, it is encouraging to see that presumably it is more difficult to publish by merely applying a new technique. Apropos of this, this prologue can end with the same sentence as last year's: "These fads come and go; ultimately, however, these tools are only as good as the scientific intuition and imagination of the researcher using them."

Madison   EDGAR F. BORGATTA
August 1970   GEORGE W. BOHRNSTEDT

CONTENTS

PART FOUR: MATHEMATICAL SOCIOLOGY

SOCIOLOGICAL
METHODOLOGY
❧ 1970 ❧

PART ONE

THEORY BUILDING
AND CAUSAL MODELS

1

CAUSAL INFERENCE
FROM PANEL DATA

David R. Heise
QUEENS COLLEGE

The author is grateful to Arthur S. Goldberger, Otis Dudley Duncan, and George Bohrnstedt for helpful comments concerning earlier papers on this topic. They share no responsibility for inadequacies of this presentation. Work on this project was partially supported by grant OE-5-10-292 from the Office of Education. Computer analyses were supported by funds from the Wisconsin Alumni Research Foundation and the National Science Foundation.

A variety of procedures and analytic models for causal analysis in sociology already is available. Campbell and Stanley (1966) present designs for experiments and quasi-experiments; Blalock (1964), Duncan (1966), Land (1969), and Heise (1969), among others, have discussed recursive models for analyzing cross-sectional correlations, and Blalock (1969) has discussed block-recursive models; and numerous essays exist on the analysis of longitudinal data (Lipset et al., 1954; Campbell and Clayton, 1961; Campbell, 1963; Coleman, 1964; Pelz and Andrews,

1964; Coleman, 1968; Bohrnstedt, 1969; Rozelle and Campbell, 1969; Duncan, 1969). Since the different procedures and models are associated with different restrictions on applicability and different ambiguities in interpretation, it is desirable to maintain and even extend this kind of diversity.

The present paper presents a model for obtaining causal inferences from longitudinal data and evaluates the performance of the model when applied to realistic data. The model is for application to survey-type data with measurements made on the same variables and the same sample at two times. This model is developed through the use of path analysis (Wright, 1934; Wright, 1960; Duncan, 1966; Duncan, 1969), and, for the sake of clarity, attention focuses initially on a two-variable problem. One variable is called x-odd; the first set of measurements on this variable is represented specifically as x_1 and the second set as x_3. The other variable is x-even, and the measurements at two times on this variable are represented as x_2 and x_4.

CAUSAL ANALYSIS OF TWO-WAVE DATA

Different measurements on the same variable are treated here as hypothetically different variables. For example, x_1 and x_3 are construed as distinct variables even though they actually are only measurements at different times on the same variable (x-odd). Therefore, in the path analysis, the two-variable, two-wave situation is treated as a four-variable problem.

There would be no hope of using empirical correlations to estimate path coefficients for every conceivable path among four variables (Heise, 1969), but the time-ordering of the data allows several of the logically possible paths to be discarded. Because later states cannot determine earlier states,[1] four paths can be eliminated immediately as plausible possibilities because x_3 and x_4 represent states occurring after x_1 and x_2. (The eliminated paths are: $x_3 \rightarrow x_1$, $x_3 \rightarrow x_2$, $x_4 \rightarrow x_1$, and $x_4 \rightarrow x_2$.) Thus, out of the twelve logically possible paths in a four-variable system, only eight are plausible in time-ordered data. This still does not allow identification of path coefficients from data, however, since four variables yield six observed correlations, and one needs to

---

[1] This is a basic metatheoretical assumption in science. Sometimes humans seem to defy the principle—for example, we may see physicians obtaining an education (earlier state) because it is demanded by their occupation (later state). However, such cases are properly handled by considering psychological variables explicitly: that is, aspiration → education → occupation.

have at least as many observed correlations as unknown coefficients in order to estimate the values of the coefficients.

An assumption can be added that eliminates four more logically possible paths. It is assumed that if a change in x-odd effects a change in x-even (or vice versa), the effect does not occur instantaneously but rather after some finite time period. In particular, it is assumed that the period of causal lag is greater than the time required to measure one sampling unit on both x-odd and x-even. By this assumption, the values of x_1 do not affect the values of x_2 and the values of x_2 do not affect the values of x_1; similarly, x_3 does not affect x_4 or vice versa. Thereby, the following paths are eliminated from the model: $x_1 \rightarrow x_2$, $x_2 \rightarrow x_1$, $x_3 \rightarrow x_4$, and $x_4 \rightarrow x_3$.

Now four paths are left as possible connecting links, and the values of the path coefficients for these paths can be estimated from the observed correlations among x_1, x_2, x_3, and x_4. Two of the paths ($x_1 \rightarrow x_3$ and $x_2 \rightarrow x_4$) represent the temporal stability of x-odd and x-even during the period between measurements. If the path coefficients associated with these paths are large and positive, it would indicate that not much happened during the interval to disturb the original distributions on x-odd and x-even; or, in other words, the variations on each variable at time 1 determined to a large extent the variations on the same variable at time 2. Zero values of the coefficients would indicate the opposite—that the distributions on each variable changed a great deal between measurements.

The other two paths ($x_1 \rightarrow x_4$ and $x_2 \rightarrow x_3$) represent the impact of x-odd on x-even and of x-even on x-odd during the period between measurements. The path $x_1 \rightarrow x_4$, for example, refers to changes that occur in x-even by the time of the second measurement due to the particular values present in x-odd at the time of the first measurement. The path coefficients associated with these paths are the basis for causal inference. For example, if it is found that one of the path coefficients is zero, say the one for the path $x_1 \rightarrow x_4$, this indicates a lack of causal effect—x-odd does not determine x-even. Coefficients different from zero suggest the presence of causality and the size of the coefficient suggests the degree of relationship.

The actual path model for the two-variable, two-wave situation appears as Figure 1. All that has been said above is reflected in the diagram: the problem is treated as if it concerned a four-variable system in which only the illustrated four causal paths are plausible. In addition, the path diagram includes some features that have not yet been discussed.

From a path analytic standpoint, x_1 and x_2 are the predetermined

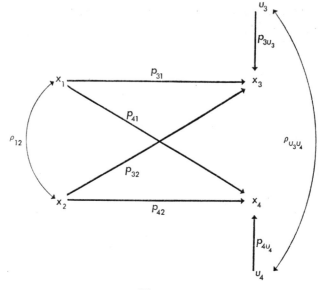

Figure 1

variables in the system. They affect other variables but no variables in the system affect them. While the predetermined variables are assumed to have no direct effect on each other, there is no necessity that they be uncorrelated. In fact, in this type of problem, a correlation would be expected because of the past operation of the system. The initial correlation between predetermined variables must be represented explicitly in a path model for analyses to be meaningful. This is done in Figure 1 by means of the curved line and the correlation ρ_{12}. This correlation, like the path coefficients, p_{31}, p_{41}, p_{32}, and p_{42}, is a basic parameter in the system, and, like the path coefficients, it is one of the unknowns to be estimated from empirical information.

Two new variables, u_3 and u_4, also are represented in Figure 1. These are hypothetical variables representing the aggregation of all outside disturbances affecting x-odd and x-even between measurements. The inclusion of these hypothetical variables indicates that while part of the variance in x_3 or x_4 is interpretable in terms of the original states, x_1 and x_2, not all of the variance is so explained. The path coefficients, p_{3u_3} and p_{4u_4}, indicate how much x_3 and x_4 are affected by outside disturbances. These coefficients are defined in terms of the variance in x_3 or x_4 which is *not* explained by x_1 and x_2. Therefore, once the other parameters of the system have been estimated, p_{3u_3} and p_{4u_4} can be obtained as residual quantities, and these coefficients do not constitute independent unknowns in the system. The curved line connecting u_3 and u_4 suggests that at any point of time the disturbances for different variables may be correlated without affecting the validity of the model.

The diagram in Figure 1 can be interpreted further to provide statements about a variety of special assumptions that are being made in this model. However, the assumptions will be considered in detail after considering how the parameters are estimated and how this model compares with other correlational procedures for causal inference.

Estimating Path Coefficients

The path model in Figure 1 could be used to write a series of equations expressing the value of each correlation between variables as a function of the basic parameters in the system. These equations then could be solved to express the parameters as functions of the correlations, thereby providing estimating formulas. In the two-variable, two-wave case this is easy to do, and the formulas are as follows:[2]

$$p_{31} = \frac{\rho_{13} - \rho_{12}\rho_{23}}{1 - \rho_{12}^2}$$

$$p_{32} = \frac{\rho_{23} - \rho_{12}\rho_{13}}{1 - \rho_{12}^2}$$

$$p_{41} = \frac{\rho_{14} - \rho_{12}\rho_{24}}{1 - \rho_{12}^2}$$

$$p_{42} = \frac{\rho_{24} - \rho_{12}\rho_{14}}{1 - \rho_{12}^2}$$

In an actual problem, one employs the empirically observed correlations among variables, r_{ij}, as sample estimates of the true correlations, ρ_{ij}.

When one is dealing with a multivariate problem, one obtains the estimates through a series of multiple regression analyses. The coefficients for all paths in which variable A is a dependent variable are obtained by regressing the time 2 values of A on the time 1 values of A, B, C, and so on. Similarly, the coefficients for all paths leading to B at time 2

[2] The parameters ρ_{12} and $\rho_{u_3u_4}$ also can be estimated from data. The estimate of ρ_{12} is simply the observed correlation r_{12}. The estimate of $\rho_{u_3u_4}$ requires complex manipulations defined by the general matrix formula: $\mathbf{R}_u = \mathbf{D}_u^{-1}(\mathbf{R}_2 - \mathbf{R}_{12}'[\mathbf{R}_1^{-1}]'\mathbf{R}_{12})\mathbf{D}_u^{-1}$. Quantities are defined as follows: $\mathbf{R}_u$ is the matrix of correlations among time 2 disturbances. $\mathbf{D}_u$ is a diagonal matrix in which element d_{ii} is defined as $\sqrt{1 - R_i^2}$, where R_i is the multiple correlation coefficient obtained by regressing the time 2 values of variable i on the values of all variables at time 1. $\mathbf{R}_1$ is the matrix of cross-section correlations among variables at time 1 and $\mathbf{R}_2$ is the matrix of cross-section correlations at time 2. $\mathbf{R}_{12}$ is the matrix of time-lagged correlations between variables at time 1 and variables at time 2.

are obtained by regressing time 2 values of B on time 1 values of A, B, C, and so on. The procedure is continued until the time 2 values of each variable in the system have been treated as a dependent variable in a regression analysis. The standardized partial regression coefficients resulting from these analyses are estimates of the path coefficients given the assumptions of the model. (Of course, the relation between the path coefficients and standardized partial regression coefficients also holds for the two-variable case; that is, $p_{31} = \beta_{31 \cdot 2}$, $p_{32} = \beta_{32 \cdot 1}$, $p_{41} = \beta_{41 \cdot 2}$, and $p_{42} = \beta_{42 \cdot 1}$.)

Comparison with Cross-Sectional Analysis

Results from the two-wave model provide a set of parameter estimates that can be used to make inferences about causation. It is of interest to consider how the information obtained from a path analysis of panel data that perfectly fit the above model compares with that derived from a causal analysis of cross-sectional data that perfectly fit a simple recursive model of analysis (see Heise, 1969).

First, by examining whether a particular path coefficient is zero, it can be inferred whether one variable has a direct effect on another. Cross-sectional analyses also allow one to infer the presence or absence of direct effects. Second, non-zero path coefficients not only indicate that causal relations exist but also suggest the relative magnitude of relationships when comparing different paths. Path coefficients from a cross-sectional analysis, though they are not directly comparable to the coefficients from a panel analysis, do provide similar information. Third, the panel analysis provides information on directionality of effects. For example, in the two-variable case, if p_{41} is non-zero and p_{32} is zero, then x-odd determines x-even; if p_{41} is zero and p_{32} is non-zero, then x-even determines x-odd. No information about directionality can be obtained from a cross-sectional analysis using a simple recursive model, and indeed, one must have this information before a meaningful cross-sectional analysis can be conducted. Fourth, the two-wave model provides information about mutual dependence. For example, in the two-variable case, if both p_{41} and p_{32} are non-zero, there is evidence that x-odd and x-even are mutually dependent. A cross-sectional analysis using a simple recursive model is not applicable to such complexities.

In sum, causal analysis of time-lagged correlations provides information similar to that yielded by inference from cross-sectional correlations using a recursive analytic model. In addition, it provides information about the directionality of causal influences, and it can be applied to systems of variables in which there are mutual dependencies.

Comparison with Inference from Cross-Lagged Correlations

The possibility of inferring causal relations from cross-lagged correlations in panel studies has intrigued a number of researchers. Given the path model for the two-variable, two-wave situation, it is easy to show that the raw correlations actually do not provide good information for causal inference, a conclusion that has been reached previously from another perspective (Pelz and Andrews, 1964).

According to the rules of path analysis as applied to Figure 1, the correlations ρ_{14} and ρ_{23} can be analyzed as follows:

$$\rho_{14} = p_{41} + \rho_{12}p_{42}$$
$$\rho_{23} = p_{32} + \rho_{12}p_{31}$$

Now it has been suggested that comparing the observed correlations ρ_{14} with ρ_{23} will indicate the direction of the dominant causal effect. That is, if ρ_{14} is greater than ρ_{23}, then presumably x-odd has a greater effect on x-even than x-even has on x-odd. However, the equations above indicate that such a conclusion may be unwarranted since ρ_{14} and ρ_{23} are not simple functions of the underlying causal parameters, p_{41} and p_{32}. In particular, this comparison of raw correlations could be upset if the stabilities of x-odd and x-even were moderately different. For example, ρ_{14} might be greater than ρ_{23} even if p_{41} is zero and p_{32} is different from zero, providing that ρ_{12} and p_{42} are large and p_{31} is small. Then, examining the raw correlations could lead to a conclusion just the opposite of what would be concluded from the path analysis. Another problem is that comparisons of the raw correlations at best provide information on the relative causal impact of x-odd and x-even and vice versa; it would not be possible to conclude that one variable does not affect the other as it would be using the path analysis approach.

Pelz and Andrews (1964) came to similar conclusions about the use of raw cross-legged correlations and settled on the comparison of partial cross-legged correlations as a technique for making causal inferences. The similarity of their approach to the path analysis approach can be seen by comparing the formulas for the relevant partials in terms of raw correlations with the formulas for the relevant path coefficients in terms of raw correlations.

$$\rho_{14\cdot2} = \frac{\rho_{14} - \rho_{12}\rho_{42}}{\sqrt{(1 - \rho_{12}^2)(1 - \rho_{42}^2)}} \qquad p_{41} = \frac{\rho_{14} - \rho_{12}\rho_{42}}{1 - \rho_{12}^2}$$

$$\rho_{23\cdot1} = \frac{\rho_{23} - \rho_{12}\rho_{31}}{\sqrt{(1 - \rho_{12}^2)(1 - \rho_{31}^2)}} \qquad p_{32} = \frac{\rho_{23} - \rho_{12}\rho_{31}}{1 - \rho_{12}^2}$$

Clearly, the partial correlations are closely related to the path coefficients: the numerators in each pair of equations are identical. In either case, one can determine whether one variable has an effect on the other: with the partial correlations as with the path coefficients, a near-zero value indicates no effect. However, given the differences in denominators, it is possible that the partial correlation approach and the path analysis approach could lead to different conclusions regarding the impact of x-odd on x-even and of x-even on x-odd. Given such a conflict, it would seem preferable to rely on the values of the path coefficients, since these are estimates of parameters in a specified model of change, whereas the partial correlations estimate no such parameters in any model yet proposed for panel data.

Underlying Assumptions

From what has been said so far, one might suppose that the two-wave model for causal analysis of time-lagged correlations is a completely unambiguous procedure for defining causal networks from survey data. Actually, the model involves a series of assumptions that limit applicability and that always demand tempering of conclusions. The remainder of this paper is devoted to examining these assumptions.

The model is developed within the framework of correlation and regression analysis, so familiar restrictions involved in these procedures are relevant for the model. *Linearity:* It is assumed that the relations between variables all can be described as linear functions. Thus, it is presumed, for example, that no variable is a function of the square or the logarithm of another variable and it is also presumed that interactions (such as $A = B \cdot C$) are absent. If the model is applied to a grossly nonlinear system, one is likely to draw faulty conclusions about the nature of causality in the system. Two further conditions are required to obtain reasonably reliable estimates of regression coefficients and path coefficients. *Homoscedasticity:* It is assumed that the variance of each variable is in no way a function of the values of other variables. *Noncolinearity:* It is assumed that correlations among variables are not so close to 1.0 that it is difficult to separate the effects of one variable from another.

Two other assumptions involved in the model relate to the generality of the causal processes being examined. *Constancy:* It is assumed that the causal relations in the system operate continuously and that the structure of the relationships does not change with time. *Equivalence:* It is assumed that all units in the sample are subject to the same causal laws. Usually neither of these assumptions is really restrictive, since interest typically focuses only on defining relationships that have generality over time and over subjects.

Another series of assumptions is concerned with the cause-effect lags in the system and the timing of measurements. *Finite Causal Lags:* As mentioned earlier in developing the model, it is assumed that there are no instantaneous effects in the system—that every cause-effect relationship exists across some finite time interval. The very notion of causality seems to imply a time lag, so this assumption by itself is not restrictive, although a possible restriction comes below when one tries to make the measurement period shorter than the lag period. *Equal Causal Lags:* In addition, in the model presented here, it is assumed that that the lag periods for all relationships are about the same. It should be noted that this is an important restriction on the range of systems to which the model can be applied. While the model could be adapted to varying lags in some cases by varying the measurement interval, this is not always true, and in general, the model should not be applied when the lag periods for different relationships are distinctly different. *Measurement Period:* It is assumed that the time required to measure one sample unit on all variables is less than the causal lag period. One example of a situation in which this assumption might be violated could arise in opinion surveys: a person's solicited opinion on one topic might affect another opinion before the interview is through. In such a case, measurements made "simultaneously" would not be causally independent, and it would be inappropriate to apply the model in Figure 1. Another instance in which the assumption might be violated is when variables are defined as rates based on an extended time unit (for example, yearly income). In such a case, the variable may interact with other variables during the period of measurement, and a model allowing for "instantaneous" effects should be employed (Duncan, 1969). *Measurement Interval:* Also, it is assumed that the time between measurements is approximately the same as the causal lag period. This means that one must have some notion of the time scale of events in the system before designing the panel study.

Finally, there are two assumptions concerning sources of extraneous variation in the data. *Measurement Error:* Since the model was developed under the assumption that measurements reflect precisely the true values on each variable, application of the model presumes that measurements are made without error. *Disturbances:* It is assumed that any one of the unmeasured variables symbolized by a u in Figure 1 correlates with none of the time one variables. As will be seen later, this amounts to the assumptions: (a) that *every* variable that interacts with the system is included explicitly in analyses; and (b) that, in addition, any *stable* variable having a significant effect on the system is considered explicitly, even if it is not affected by the system.

Thus, there are four major sets of assumptions underlying the two-wave path model for panel analysis: the assumptions involved in linear regression, the assumptions referring to generality of the causal dynamics, the assumptions about the timing of causal effects and of measurements, and the assumptions concerning extraneous sources of variance. The first three groups of assumptions are not considered further here.[3] The remaining sections of this paper are devoted to considering the problems posed by the assumptions concerning extraneous sources of variance.

MEASUREMENT IMPRECISION

A model that demands perfect measurements is of little utility in the social sciences. Extremely good social and behavioral measures have reliabilities around 0.95, but this is less than perfect, and typical measures have considerably lower reliabilities. Measurement imprecision must be accepted as a basic given in analyses of panel data, and if a model for causal analysis is to have any value, it must yield information in the presence of some measurement errors.

The impact of measurement errors on parameter estimates can be worked out mathematically, but the resulting formulas are extremely complicated and difficult to interpret in terms of practical applications. Hence, a simulation procedure is used below. A hypothetical system is created and used to generate a set of panel data. Specified amounts of "measurement error" then are added to the data, and the data are analyzed using the two-wave analytic model to assess how well it estimates system parameters given unreliable measurements.

The hypothetical system that is used in the simulations is defined by the following set of equations:

$$y_{1\theta} = 0.51y_{1t} + 0.23y_{3t} + 0.30w_\theta + 0.40v_{1\theta} + 0.57u_{1\theta} \tag{1}$$
$$y_{2\theta} = 0.09y_{1t} + 0.40y_{2t} + 0.11y_{3t} + 0.22y_{4t} + 0.30v_{2\theta} + 0.76u_{2\theta} \tag{2}$$
$$y_{3\theta} = 0.20y_{1t} + 0.27y_{2t} + 0.52y_{3t} + 0.20w_\theta + 0.10v_{3\theta} + 0.58u_{3\theta} \tag{3}$$
$$y_{4\theta} = 0.30y_{1t} - 0.34y_{2t} + 0.12y_{3t} + 0.58y_{4t} + 0.41v_{4\theta} + 0.50u_{4\theta} \tag{4}$$
$$y'_{1t} = 0.71y_{1t} + 0.71e_{1t}, \; y'_{1\theta} = 0.71y_{1\theta} + 0.71e_{1\theta} \tag{5}$$
$$y'_{2t} = 0.80y_{2t} + 0.60e_{2t}, \; y'_{2\theta} = 0.80y_{2\theta} + 0.60e_{2\theta} \tag{6}$$
$$y'_{3t} = 0.75y_{3t} + 0.66e_{3t}, \; y'_{3\theta} = 0.75y_{3\theta} + 0.66e_{3\theta} \tag{7}$$
$$y'_{4t} = 0.77y_{4t} + 0.64e_{4t}, \; y'_{4\theta} = 0.77y_{4\theta} + 0.64e_{4\theta} \tag{8}$$

The subscript t indicates "value at time 1" and the subscript θ stands for "value at time 2."

---

[3] The following paper in this volume by Donald C. Pelz and Robert A. Lew discusses some of the implications of violating assumptions.

Equations (1) through (4) define the relationships among the four central variables of the system, y_1 through y_4. For example, equation (1) indicates that the value of y_1 at time 2 is dependent on the value of y_1 at time 1 (there is a stability coefficient of 0.51) and also is dependent on the value of y_3 at time 1 (the effect parameter is 0.23). In addition, y_1 at time 2 is dependent on disturbances entered into the system at time 2—w_θ, $v_{1\theta}$, and $u_{1\theta}$. Disturbances are represented by three different terms for convenience in later discussion.

It should be mentioned that the coefficients associated with u's in equations (1) through (4) are defined in terms of residual sources of variance and were estimated after the system had operated for awhile so that cross-sectional correlations among variables were stable. Also note that one source of disturbance, w, affects two system variables, y_1 and y_3, so the disturbances for y_1 and y_3 at time 2 are correlated. Contemporaneous correlation among disturbances does not violate the assumptions of the model.

Equations (5) through (8) define the relations between true values and "measured" values at any given time. For example, from equation (5) it is seen that at both time 1 and time 2 the expected value of the measurement, y_1', is 0.71 times the true value of y_1, and differences between y_1 and y_1' are due to measurement errors, e_1. The square of the first coefficient in any one of these equations is the index of reliability for the given measurement.

In this system the quantities w_θ, $v_{i\theta}$, and $u_{i\theta}$, $i = 1, \ldots , 4$, are uncorrelated with each other and they also are uncorrelated with y_{it}, $i = 1, \ldots , 4$. The quantities e_{it} and $e_{i\theta}$, $i = 1, \ldots , 4$, are uncorrelated with each other or with any other variables in the system other than the y_{it}' or $y_{\theta t}'$ to which they are directly linked.

The stability and effect parameters relating the y variables are summarized for easy reference in Table 1. These are the system parameters that will be estimated from simulated data using multiple regression procedures.

TABLE 1
True Values of Path Coefficients Relating Central Variables[a]

	y_{1t}	y_{2t}	y_{3t}	y_{4t}
$y_{1\theta}$	0.51	0.00	0.23	0.00
$y_{2\theta}$	0.09	0.40	0.11	0.22
$y_{3\theta}$	0.20	0.27	0.52	0.00
$y_{4\theta}$	0.30	−0.34	0.12	0.58

[a] The subscript t stands for time t, and θ stands for time $t + 1$. Read by rows, the table indicates which variables at time 1 determine the value of a given variable at time 2 and the degree of the relationships. For example, $y_{1\theta}$ is a function of y_{1t} and y_{3t}, but not of y_{2t} and y_{4t}.

This system is purposely fairly complex and contains a variety of structural features. Two variables affect all others; two variables are dependent on all others; some pairs of variables are mutually dependent; in other cases the causal linkage is unidirectional; some path coefficients are moderate in size; others are fairly close to zero; one path coefficient is negative in value. Measurement reliabilities for different variables are similar in value but not identical, and the reliabilities are fairly low, ranging from 0.50 to 0.64 (that is, 0.71^2 to 0.80^2).

The causal linkages indicated in equations (1) through (8) create correlations among the measured variables when the system is set in operation. After the system has operated for awhile, an equilibrium state is reached, and from then on the correlations remain constant over time. The expected values of the equilibrium correlations among the measured variables are presented in Table 2. The first bank of numbers indicates the cross-sectional correlations; the second bank, the lagged correlations across one measurement interval.

TABLE 2
Expected Values of Cross-Sectional and Lagged Correlations
Generated by Equations (1) Through (8)

	y'_{1t}	y'_{2t}	y'_{3t}	y'_{4t}
y'_{1t}	1.00	0.13	0.26	0.15
y'_{2t}	0.13	1.00	0.22	0.09
y'_{3t}	0.26	0.22	1.00	0.10
y'_{4t}	0.15	0.09	0.10	1.00
$y'_{1\theta}$	0.31	0.11	0.25	0.10
$y'_{2\theta}$	0.17	0.32	0.20	0.20
$y'_{3\theta}$	0.27	0.30	0.40	0.11
$y'_{4\theta}$	0.24	−0.09	0.14	0.38

The expected values of the correlations resulting from this system were analyzed using the two-wave model. The results, presented in Table 3, illustrate the performance of the two-wave model when measurements are imprecise but sampling errors are not a complicating factor.

TABLE 3
Estimated Path Coefficients—Results Obtained from Correlations
Involving Large Measurement Errors But No Sampling Errors

	y_{1t}	y_{2t}	y_{3t}	y_{4t}
$y_{1\theta}$	0.26	0.04	0.18	0.04
$y_{2\theta}$	0.08	0.27	0.11	0.15
$y_{3\theta}$	0.16	0.21	0.31	0.03
$y_{4\theta}$	0.19	−0.16	0.09	0.35

Comparing Table 3 with Table 1, it is clear that substantial errors are present in parameter estimates based on unreliable measurements. However, it is also evident that the errors are not haphazard. There appears to be a close parallelism between the estimated values and the true values of the system parameters, and, in fact, the product-moment correlation between the two sets of coefficients is 0.99. This suggests that even though the two-wave model does not yield the actual values of the system parameters when measurements are imprecise, it might give a set of numbers that could be used for causal inference.

The impression is strengthened by graphing the estimates based on unreliable measures (Table 3) against the true values of the system parameters (Table 1); the graph appears as Figure 2. The solid line traced through the points reveals that the estimates have very close to a linear relationship to the true values. (It is interesting to note that this correspondence is strong even though the reliabilities for different measurements varied somewhat.) The most convenient way to interpret this linear relationship is to note that the ordering of estimates corresponds with the ordering of true values, so the estimates provide information about the relative magnitudes of true parameters. In addition, it is to be noted that although the regression line in Figure 2 does not pass exactly through the origin, it very nearly does. This means that when the true parameter value is zero, the estimate also is near zero in value. So, allowing for a certain margin of error, it is possible to infer which parameters are zero and, therefore, which causal linkages are absent in a system. In short, the parameter estimates based on measurements with error do permit causal inference even if they do not allow one to reconstruct the actual quantitative characteristics of the system.

The fact that the angle of the line in Figure 2 is less than 45° suggests another point of interest about the estimates as compared with true values. The estimates, even though they correspond directly with the true values, extend over a smaller range. For example, in this system the true values of parameters range from −0.34 to 0.58 but the range of the estimates is only −0.16 to 0.35. Since the estimates are homogenized or compressed into a smaller range, it is evident that the ordering of values is reflected by smaller differences among the estimated parameters than among the true parameters. Or, to put it differently, there is less interpretable variance in the set of estimates than in the set of true parameters. This fact takes on significance when it is remembered that in practical problems sampling variations always create an additional component of error in parameter estimates. Imagine two studies, one with imperfect measurements and one with perfect measurements, in which the extent of sampling error is the same. The study with imperfect measurements will be more confounded by the sampling errors because

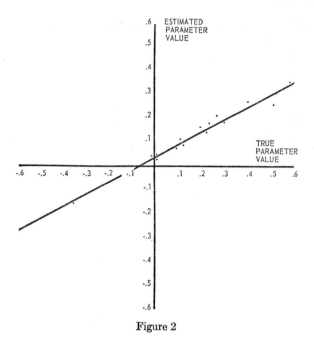

Figure 2

one is attempting to make sense of smaller expected differences. That is, the sampling errors will constitute a larger proportion of the total variance in estimates when one is using data containing measurement error.

Measurement Errors Plus Sampling Errors

One might attempt to work out mathematically the relationship between measurement error, sampling error, and interpretability of estimates, but resulting formulas would be complicated and hard to interpret. Instead, a Monte Carlo simulation was run in which the system in equations (1) through (8) was used to generate data, so that samples of varying sizes could be examined. That is, the equations were used to generate data by applying them repeatedly to sets of numbers drawn randomly from unit normal distributions. The original random values were modified again and again in accordance with the system, beyond the point at which equilibrium is reached, and then two more times to provide two waves of "observations." In this way, samples of observations of varying size were constructed, and correlations and lagged correlations among the four index variables were obtained for each sample. The estimating model then was applied to each set of correlations to derive estimates of the system parameters.

A summary of the results is presented in Table 4. The degree of correspondence between estimated parameters and true parameters drops substantially when samples are small. For example, the average correlation between estimates and true values is 0.83 when $N = 60$. For this comparison, this is quite a low correlation, indicating the obtained results are of poor quality and of little value as information about causal effects. Results improve as the sample size increases from 60 to 240: one sample of 240 yielded a correlation between estimates and true values of 0.94, the other, 0.95. Gains in accuracy seem to level off somewhat after 240: three of the four samples of 500 or 1000 also yielded 0.94 correlations between estimated and true parameters.

TABLE 4

Correlations Between Estimated Parameters and True Parameters—Summary Results of Analyzing Data with Large Measurement Errors and Sampling Errors[a]

Sample Size	Correspondence Between Estimated and True Parameters (Product-Moment Correlations)
60	0.81, 0.85
120	0.88, 0.91
240	0.94, 0.95
500	0.94, 0.94
1000	0.94, 0.97

[a] Results are presented for two samples of each size. Each sample is an independent random selection.

To appreciate the possibilities for causal inference using the larger samples, consider the degree of correspondence indicated by a 0.94 correlation. Results for "typical" data with this level of accuracy are presented in Table 5. These estimated coefficients again are to be compared with the true values in Table 1.

TABLE 5

Estimated Path Coefficients—Results Obtained from Typical Sample Data ($N = 500$) with Large Measurement Errors

	y_{1t}	y_{2t}	y_{3t}	y_{4t}
$y_{1\theta}$	0.22	0.06	0.23	0.00
$y_{2\theta}$	0.08	0.28	0.04	0.14
$y_{3\theta}$	0.16	0.23	0.29	0.00
$y_{4\theta}$	0.13	−0.15	0.05	0.41

To what extent could these data be used to answer questions of possible interest? For example, can one determine which parameters in the system are zero? In this particular sample, two of the zero-parameters (p_{14} and p_{34}) are estimated as zero, and a third (p_{12}) is estimated at 0.06. However, it must be noted that in other large samples the estimates of zero-parameters rarely were exactly zero, and they ranged in value up to 0.10. Thus, a range of values must be chosen as signifying zero-parameters occasionally. The size of the confidence interval would depend mainly on the sample size. In this particular instance one might ideally choose an interval of 0.06 units on either side of the expected value of estimates for zero parameters, giving the range -0.03 to 0.10.

A second question is: can one ascertain when a parameter is *not* zero? Suppose the above range was accepted as indicating zero parameters. Then, in this particular sample, three linkages that really do exist (p_{21}, p_{23}, p_{43}) would be assumed absent. However, the true values of these parameters are low, and in this sample no errors would be made concerning the larger causal linkages. Generally, one would be able to identify large causal effects with confidence, but small effects might be misinterpreted as zero relationships.

Finally, is there reliable information about the relative values of the parameters? First, it can be noted that the sign of the negative parameter is correctly indicated in this sample; in fact, the signs of parameters were identified correctly in every sample examined except those with $N = 60$. Beyond this, however, the results are not very impressive: one could not differentiate very reliably between medium and large effects given the numbers in Table 5.

Two-Wave Model with Good Measurements

The sampling studies above were carried out under the assumption that measurements were made with mediocre instruments having reliabilities in the range of 0.50 to 0.64. There is little point in studying instances in which measurements are perfect since perfect measures are not available. However, it is reasonable to consider cases where there are good, rather than mediocre, measurements. Accordingly, the system was modified by substituting equations (9) through (12) for (5) through (8) and another series of sampling studies was conducted.

$$y'_{1t} = 0.93 y_{1t} + 0.37 e_{1t} \qquad y'_{1\theta} = 0.93 y_{1\theta} + 0.37 e_{1\theta} \qquad (9)$$
$$y'_{2t} = 0.96 y_{2t} + 0.27 e_{2t} \qquad y'_{2\theta} = 0.96 y_{2\theta} + 0.27 e_{2\theta} \qquad (10)$$
$$y'_{3t} = 0.94 y_{3t} + 0.35 e_{3t} \qquad y'_{3\theta} = 0.94 y_{3\theta} + 0.35 e_{3\theta} \qquad (11)$$
$$y'_{4t} = 0.95 y_{4t} + 0.32 e_{3t} \qquad y'_{4\theta} = 0.95 y_{4\theta} + 0.32 e_{4\theta} \qquad (12)$$

A first point is that with reliabilities in the range 0.86 to 0.92, there is considerably less attenuation in the observed correlations, and the two-wave model applied to these correlations therefore should

TABLE 6
Estimated Path Coefficients—Results Obtained from Correlations Involving
Small Measurement Errors but No Sampling Errors

	y_{1t}	y_{2t}	y_{3t}	y_{4t}
$y_{1\theta}$	0.44	0.01	0.23	0.02
$y_{2\theta}$	0.09	0.37	0.11	0.20
$y_{3\theta}$	0.20	0.26	0.46	0.01
$y_{4\theta}$	0.27	−0.29	0.12	0.53

generally give better estimates of the parameters. Table 6, which shows
the expected values of parameter estimates based on the good measurements, reveals that this is so. In particular, it is worth noting that the
degree of homogenization of parameter estimates is far less than with
mediocre measurements.

Data for samples of various sizes were generated using equations
(1) through (4) and (9) through (12), and the sample data were analyzed
to estimate system parameters. Results are summarized in Table 7.
The table reveals that using good measures leads to a striking improve-
ment in the correspondence between estimates and true parameters.
Parameter estimates based on the sample of 500 and those based on the
sample of 1000 both correlate 0.99 with the true values.

TABLE 7
Correlations Between Estimated Parameters and True Parameters—Summary
Results of Analyzing Data with Small Measurement
Errors and Sampling Errors[a]

Sample Size	Correspondence Between Estimated and True Parameters (Product-Moment Correlations)
60	0.93
120	0.96
240	0.97
500	0.99
1000	0.99

[a] Results are presented for one sample of each size. Each sample is an independent random selection.

Table 8 shows the parameter estimates obtained from the sample
of 500, and again it is of interest to determine what these results could

TABLE 8
Estimated Path Coefficients—Results Obtained from Typical Sample
Data ($N = 500$) with Small Measurement Errors

	y_{1t}	y_{2t}	y_{3t}	y_{4t}
$y_{1\theta}$	0.48	0.03	0.19	0.07
$y_{2\theta}$	0.07	0.38	0.15	0.24
$y_{3\theta}$	0.17	0.22	0.49	0.05
$y_{4\theta}$	0.28	−0.37	0.09	0.52

tell about the causal dynamics of the system. It is clear that again an interval criterion must be used for deciding whether effects are absent since estimates of zero parameters take on values of 0.03, 0.07, and 0.05. However, since the expected value of the zero parameter estimates is closer to zero in the case of good measurements, the ideal interval might be adjusted downward a bit, say from −0.05 to 0.08. Also, it is evident that here again such an interval can lead one to eliminate linkages that exist but that are of low magnitude (for example, p_{21}).

The greatest benefit of using good measures comes in comparing the magnitudes of major effects. The figures in Table 8 provide good information not only about the signs of parameters, but also about the relative sizes of parameters—at least to the point of allowing classification of effects into medium and large. Good measures do not affect the random errors in estimation that are introduced by sampling, but they do decrease the overall homogenization of estimates, making it easier to compare different effects.

The above simulation studies indicate that unreliable measures do not eliminate the utility of the two-wave path model for causal inference although errors in measurement do increase the chance of erroneous conclusions. Since there is a direct correspondence between quality of measurements and the degree to which empirical results reflect actual processes, the best research strategy obviously is to use the best measuring instruments possible. The two-wave model has some utility when employed with poor measurements, but its efficiency is greater when employed with good measurements.

Once measurement errors are allowed as a possibility, there is another problem to be considered in research design. Every effort must be made to minimize correlations between measurement errors for different variables or different times. The practical effects of correlated errors on results using the model presented here have not been studied in detail, but a single simulation suggested that serially correlated errors can confound interpretations considerably. Correlated errors can be minimized by careful attention to measurement procedures, making them as independent as possible across variables and at different times. Or, one can work to maximize the reliabilities and validities of instruments so that the errors themselves are minimized.

DISTURBANCE CORRELATIONS

The second assumption about extraneous sources of variance requires that time 2 disturbances be uncorrelated with the values of variables at time 1. It will be shown that this assumption almost inevitably is violated in longitudinal data. Then, an example will be examined to determine how well the two-wave model performs when the assumption is not fulfilled.

For this discussion it is convenient to distinguish between variables that are considered explicitly in analyses and those that are ignored even though they have some impact on the system of interest. In equations (1) through (8) the y and y' variables are explicit variables because, either directly or indirectly, they are the focus of analyses. The variables labeled u, v, and w are implicit variables. Even though these are entered into the equations, they are not conceived to be an "interesting" part of the system. In fact, ordinarily the v and w variables would be included as part of the u aggregates and thereby relegated to the status of residual disturbances. (Their separate representation here is only for convenience.)

The assumption involved in the two-wave model is that time 2 values of the implicit variables are uncorrelated with time 1 values of the explicit variables. For this to be true, it is necessary that the implicit variables are all unaffected by the explicit variables, because otherwise direct paths would exist from an explicit variable at time 1 to an implicit variable at time 2, and a correlation obviously would exist. Hence, one implication of the assumption about disturbance correlations is that *the analysis must be inclusive in the sense of dealing with all relevant system variables.* This is an important requirement, but since theoretically it can be met through an elaborated research design, the issue will not be considered further.

Effects of Stable Implicit Variables

Although it may not be completely obvious, the assumption about disturbance correlations implies that all implicit variables have very low stability over time. Figure 3 illustrates why this is so and how stability in implicit variables leads to a violation of the assumption about disturbance correlations. (Note that Figure 3 is not a complete path diagram. For the sake of simplicity, a number of disturbance terms and some curved lines representing correlations among predetermined variables have been left out.)

In Figure 3 the disturbance variable d should be thought of as one of the variables ordinarily aggregated in a u term. Here it is considered by itself, and in particular, it is represented as having some stability over time (that is, arrows connect d_0 with d_1 and d_1 with d_2). This diagram allows one to see that stability in d leads to a correlation between x_1 and d_2 via the path $(x_1 \leftarrow d_1 \rightarrow d_2)$. Figure 3 reveals further that d_2 also would be correlated with x_2 via the path $(x_2 \leftarrow x_{-1} \leftarrow d_0 \rightarrow$

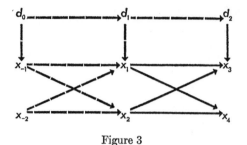

Figure 3

$d_1 \rightarrow d_2$). Thus, stability in this implicit variable leads to correlations between time 1 values of the explicit variables and time 2 disturbances, and in general, stable implicit variables create violations of the disturbance correlation assumption.

Previously, it has been assumed that the values of implicit variables change so rapidly that there is essentially no correlation between their values at one time and another. Now it is time to question this presumption that explicit variables may be somewhat stable over time, but the values of implicit variables change almost instantaneously.

In any particular problem it may be true that *some* of the implicit variables do change rapidly and may be considered to have essentially zero stability. On the other hand, it seems implausible that all implicit variables are unstable to this degree. Rather, it seems likely that most implicit variables are more or less comparable to the variables explicitly examined, and so implicit variables would have stability characteristics similar to those of explicit variables. So, in most real situations, there would be sufficient stability in the implicit variables to create correlations between explicit variables at one time and the disturbances at a later time, and thus, this assumption for the two-wave model would be violated in most real situations. The important issue, however, is how violating this assumption affects results.

Two-Wave Model with Disturbance Correlations

The system represented in equations (1) through (4) was modified by creating stability in the v disturbance variables. That is, the following equations were added to the system:

$$v_{1\theta} = 0.45v_{1t} + 0.89u_{v_{1\theta}} \tag{13}$$
$$v_{2\theta} = 0.50v_{2t} + 0.87u_{v_{2\theta}} \tag{14}$$
$$v_{3\theta} = 0.40v_{3t} + 0.92u_{v_{3\theta}} \tag{15}$$
$$v_{4\theta} = 0.45v_{4t} + 0.89u_{v_{4\theta}} \tag{16}$$

The addition of these equations to the system changes the coefficients for $u_{1\theta}$, $u_{2\theta}$, $u_{3\theta}$, and $u_{4\theta}$ in equations (1) through (4) to 0.46, 0.72, 0.55, and 0.37, respectively.

Once the system has operated for a time, this modification is sufficient to create noticeable correlations between time 1 values of the y variables and time 2 values of the disturbances. The system also was changed to one in which measurements are perfect—that is, equations (5) through (8) were not employed—so as to see more clearly the consequences of violating just the disturbance assumption. Then, the revised system was used to generate the expected values of equilibrium correlations, and these correlations were analyzed to estimate system parameters. Results are presented in Table 9.

TABLE 9
Estimated Path Coefficients—Results Obtained from Correlations Contaminated by Disturbance Correlations but No Measurement or Sampling Errors

	y_{1t}	y_{2t}	y_{3t}	y_{4t}
$y_{1\theta}$	0.64	0.00	0.18	−0.02
$y_{2\theta}$	0.09	0.46	0.10	0.20
$y_{3\theta}$	0.20	0.27	0.53	0.00
$y_{4\theta}$	0.26	−0.34	0.12	0.69

The disturbance correlations do interfere with parameter estimation, so that even without measurement errors or sampling errors, the estimated values deviate from the true values. Especially noticeable is an increase in the estimated size of stability coefficients, although a few other parameters also are affected slightly. Nevertheless, the pattern of estimated values seems to correspond well with the pattern of true values, and this observation is verified by a correlation of 0.99 between the two sets of values.

Of course, it can be objected that the above example is unrealistic since perfect measurements were assumed. So, the analysis was repeated allowing for imperfect, but good, measurements—that is, equations (9) through (12) were added to the system. The correlation between parameter estimates and true values was still 0.99. The analysis again was repeated using low quality measures—equations (5) through (8)—and the correlation between estimates and true values was 0.99 again.

In the above examples, each of the stable implicit variables affected just one explicit variable. Suppose a stable variable that affects two of those in the system is ignored. To represent this, the system was modified further by adding stability not just to the v variables but also to w, according to the following equation:

$$w_\theta = 0.40w_t + 0.93u_{w_\theta} \tag{17}$$

The addition of equations (13) through (17) to the system changes the coefficients for $u_{1\theta}$, $u_{2\theta}$, $u_{3\theta}$, and $u_{4\theta}$ in equations (1) through (4) to 0.35, 0.71, 0.48, and 0.36 respectively.

The analyses were repeated using poor measurements—equations (5) through (8)—and the parameter estimates in Table 10 were obtained. These clearly are not accurate estimates of the true values, but again the pattern among the estimates corresponds closely with the true pattern. The correlation is 0.99.

TABLE 10

Estimated Path Coefficients—Results Obtained from Correlations Contaminated by Disturbance Correlations and Large Measurement Errors but No Sampling Errors

	y_{1t}	y_{2t}	y_{3t}	y_{4t}
$y_{1\theta}$	0.32	0.04	0.19	0.05
$y_{2\theta}$	0.09	0.30	0.12	0.14
$y_{3\theta}$	0.19	0.22	0.32	0.04
$y_{4\theta}$	0.18	−0.15	0.10	0.42

Finally, a problem was set up in which v and w were assigned stability as above, and allowance was made for good measurements rather than mediocre measurements—equations (9) through (12) in place of (5) through (8). The expected values of the correlations yielded by this system were obtained and analyzed, and the results are presented in Table 11. Comparing the values in Tables 1 and 11 gives an idea of the kinds of distortions in parameter estimates that would occur in well-designed longitudinal studies.[4] Of course, the results from an actual study also would involve sampling errors, as discussed previously.

These studies suggest that stability in implicit variables is not an absolute barrier to use of the two-wave model for causal inference.

TABLE 11

Estimated Path Coefficients—Results Obtained from Correlations Contaminated by Disturbance Correlations and Small Measurement Errors but No Sampling Errors

	y_{1t}	y_{2t}	y_{3t}	y_{4t}
$y_{1\theta}$	0.58	0.00	0.21	0.01
$y_{2\theta}$	0.09	0.43	0.11	0.19
$y_{3\theta}$	0.23	0.26	0.47	0.01
$y_{4\theta}$	0.24	−0.29	0.12	0.63

[4] See the following paper in this volume for further discussion of the effects of unmeasured variables. Pelz and Lew deal with the problem in terms of "long-term stability."

Implicit variables are at least once removed from the observed system, and their impact on analyses seems to be relatively slight. Combined with measurement imprecision, the effects of stable implicit variables do prevent one from obtaining unbiased estimates of the system parameters. However, results from a two-wave analysis appear adequate for assessing the relative magnitudes of different parameters, allowing one to make the inferences about the causal nature of the system.

CONCLUSIONS

The model presented here is appropriate for analyzing systems having the following properties: (1) Variables in the system influence one another over some finite lag period, and the lag periods for all relationships are of the same magnitude. (2) The dependency of any one variable on others can be described by means of a linear equation. (3) The causal structuring among variables is stable over time and applicable to all units in the observational population.

To apply the model in a particular instance, one must know the magnitude of causal lags in the system. Then, one can approximate a study design meeting the following specifications: (4) The time required to measure an observational unit on all variables is less than the causal lag period. (5) The interval between time 1 measurements and time 2 measurements is approximately the same as the causal lag period. (6) The set of variables considered includes all those which are in mutual interaction with the system. (7) All stable or relatively unchanging variables affecting two or more of those in the system are included in analyses.

Given that conditions 1 through 7 are approximated, the two-wave panel analysis model provides a relatively simple procedure for examining causality. Its advantage over path analysis of cross-sectional correlations is that it can provide information on the direction of causation and information about mutual dependencies among variables.

A series of studies were run to examine the effect of violating certain assumptions involved in the model. It was found that measurement imprecision leads to biased estimates of system parameters; in particular, estimates of large parameters tend to be too small in absolute value. As one would expect, the effects are less when measurement reliabilities are high than when they are low. However, even with good measurements, the bias is pronounced enough to prevent a completely accurate reconstruction of the quantitative aspects of a system. Thus, because measurement error always is a problem, system parameters never can be estimated exactly, and in particular, the size of major effects will tend to be underestimated. (This, incidentally, is true of path analyses in general, not just longitudinal studies.)

Even though the parameter estimates are biased when imprecise measures are used, the relative values of the estimates parallel very closely the relative values of the true parameters, and so the pattern of estimates can be examined to obtain information about the pattern of true parameters. The estimates can be used to assess which relations in a system are of negligible magnitude since such relations are associated with parameter estimates that are near zero in value. In other words, a two-wave panel analysis can be used to infer whether there is a causal link from one variable to another.

Sampling errors complicate interpretation of results, but not prohibitively when samples are large (say 500 or more) and measurements are good. The overall effect of sampling errors is to create some confusion in comparing the magnitudes of different parameters, but still it is possible to determine the signs of parameters and to differentiate effects into classes of negligible, moderate, or large. With mediocre measurements, the potential for making such distinctions is less.

In almost any problem, latent variables probably are just as stable as variables considered explicitly. Stable latent variables create disturbance correlations, and so one assumption for the two-wave model is violated in practically every problem. However, simulation studies showed that typical violations of the assumption do not lead to distortions much in excess of those already introduced by measurement imprecision. In other words, either measurement errors or disturbance correlations prevent one from obtaining exact estimates of system parameters, but both of these conditions combined do not negate the possibility of making causal inferences of a more qualitative nature.

Thus, this particular path model for two-wave panel analysis would seem to be a useful tool for causal inference in sociology. One of its outstanding features is its ease of application, since the estimating procedures make use of standard multiple regression programs. However, it must be emphasized that special problems may demand different models. Duncan (1969) has discussed a variety of models for analyzing two-wave panel data that researchers may find useful, and in the future, it may be worth developing multiple-wave models to deal with certain issues.

REFERENCES

BLALOCK, H. M., JR.
    1964   *Causal Inferences in Nonexperimental Research.* Chapel Hill: University of North Carolina Press.
    1969   *Theory Construction.* Englewood Cliffs, N.J.: Prentice-Hall.

BOHRNSTEDT, G. W.
  1969 "Some observations on the measurement of change." Pp. 113–133 in
        E. F. Borgatta and G. W. Bohrnstedt (Eds.), *Sociological Methodology
        1969*. San Francisco: Jossey-Bass.
CAMPBELL, D. T.
  1963 "From description to experimentation: Interpreting trends as quasi-
        experiments." Pp. 212–242 in C. W. Harris (Ed.), *Problems in Measuring
        Change*. Madison: University of Wisconsin Press.
CAMPBELL, D. T. AND CLAYTON, K. N.
  1961 "Avoiding regression effects in panel studies of communication impact."
        Studies in Public Communication No. 3. Chicago: University of Chicago
        Department of Sociology, 99–118.
CAMPBELL, D. T. AND STANLEY, J. C.
  1966 *Experimental and Quasi-Experimental Designs for Research*. Chicago:
        Rand McNally.
COLEMAN, J. S.
  1964 *Models of Change and Response Uncertainty*. Englewood Cliffs, N.J.:
        Prentice-Hall.
  1968 "The mathematical study of change." Pp. 428–478 in H. M. Blalock
        and A. B. Blalock (Eds.), *Methodology in Social Research*. New York:
        McGraw-Hill.
DUNCAN, O. D.
  1966 "Path analysis: Sociological examples." *American Journal of Sociology*
        72:1–16.
  1969 "Some linear models for two-wave, two-variable panel analysis." *Psy-
        chological Bulletin*, 77:177–182.
HEISE, D. R.
  1969 "Problems in path analysis and causal inference." Pp. 38–73 in E. F.
        Borgatta and G. W. Bohrnstedt (Eds.), *Sociological Methodology 1969*.
        San Francisco: Jossey-Bass.
LAND, K. C.
  1969 "Principles of path analysis." Pp. 3–37 in E. F. Borgatta and G. W.
        Bohrnstedt (Eds.), *Sociological Methodology 1969*. San Francisco: Jossey-
        Bass.
LIPSET, S. M., LAZARSFELD, P. F., BARTON, A. H. AND LINZ, J.
  1954 "The psychology of voting: An analysis of political behavior." Pp.
        1124–1175 in G. Lindzey (Ed.), *Handbook of Social Psychology*. Cam-
        bridge, Mass.: Addison-Wesley.
PELZ, D. C. AND ANDREWS, F. M.
  1964 "Detecting causal priorities in panel study data." *American Sociological
        Review* 29:836–848.
ROZELLE, R. M. AND CAMPBELL, D. T.
  1969 "More plausible rival hypotheses in the cross-lagged panel correlation
        technique." *Psychological Bulletin* 71:74–80.
WRIGHT, S.
  1934 "The method of path coefficients." *Annals of Mathematical Statistics*,
        5:161–215.
  1960 "The treatment of reciprocal interaction, with or without lag, in path
        analysis." *Biometrics*, 16:423–445.

HEISE'S CAUSAL MODEL
APPLIED

Donald C. Pelz

UNIVERSITY OF MICHIGAN

Robert A. Lew

UNIVERSITY OF MASSACHUSETTS

In the preceding paper David R. Heise proposed a two-wave path analysis model as a "useful tool for causal inference in sociology." Since his assumptions coincide with those that we have utilized in a two-variable computerized simulation, his procedures were applied to several sets of data with known properties, to test their efficacy in detecting causal influences.[1]

[1] Further details on the simulation and its observed outputs are given in an unpublished report by Pelz *et al.* (1968), prepared under a grant from the National Science Foundation, GS-1873, with supplementary aid from the National Broadcasting Company. The original simulation program was written by Spyros Magliveras. Fruitful suggestions have been given by Graham Kalton. Arthur S. Goldberger (personal correspondence) has indicated alternative ways of deriving theoretical expressions.

In our simulated data, Heise's x-odd variable is represented by a time series x_{it} generated for each individual i in a population of N individuals at times $t = 1, 2, 3, \ldots$ in successive operations of the computer program, by the recursion equation:

$$x_{it} = p_{xx}x_{i(t-1)} + u_x \tag{1}$$

where p_{xx}, equivalent to Heise's path coefficient p_{31}, governs the degree to which x_{it} depends upon the prior value $x_{i(t-1)}$. The coefficient is constant over t and i, and may be set between 0 and ± 1. If $p_{xx} > |1|$, the variance of x_{it} will not remain stationary over time; and where u_x (subscript i understood) is equivalent to Heise's outside disturbance factor u_3 for the x-odd variable. It is a random error term uncorrelated across individuals and across time, with mean equal to 0 and variance constant over t and i. To achieve stationary variance in x_{it}, the variance of u_x must be set equal to $(1 - p_{xx}^2)\sigma_{x_{it}}^2$.

Heise's x-even variable is represented by another time series y_{it} generated by the recursion equation:

$$y_{it} = p_{yy}y_{i(t-1)} + u_y \tag{2}$$

where p_{yy}, equivalent to Heise's path coefficient p_{42}, governs the dependence of y_{it} upon the prior value of y, and u_y is equivalent to the random outside disturbance factor u_4 for the x-even variable.

The coefficients p_{xx} and p_{yy} are equal to the theoretical autocorrelation between adjacent values of the Markov series x_t and y_t (see Kendall and Stuart, 1966, pp. 405 ff.). They will be called *coefficients of of short-term stability*, and govern the stability of each variable from one time to the next. Another source of stability having rather different properties, called long-term stability, is discussed later.

Either variable can also be made dependent on (causally influenced by) the other variable. To represent the situation in which x influences y (symbolized $x \rightarrow y$), a modified y is created as in equation (2), with an additional term representing the influence of a prior x:

$$y_{it} = p_{yy}y_{i(t-1)} + p_{yx}x_{i(t-g)} + u_y \tag{3}$$

where g represents the "causal interval" or time lag over which a prior x value influences a subsequent y value. In the case of $g = 1$ (y is influenced by the immediately prior x), p_{yx} becomes equivalent to Heise's path coefficient p_{41}.

One could also allow y to influence x (symbolized $y \rightarrow x$) by generating an x variable as in equation (1) with an additional term $p_{xy}y_{i(t-h)}$ representing the influence of a prior y value over a causa interval h. In the case of $h = 1$, p_{xy} becomes equivalent to Heise's path coefficient p_{32}. We shall call p_{yx} and p_{xy} the "causal coefficients."

After values for each variable have been generated over a large number of time periods, cross-correlations may be computed between x and y values separated by any measurement lag k: $r_{x_t y_{t+k}}$, where k can take any integral value . . . , -3, -2, -1, 0, $+1$, $+2$, $+3$, . . . , a positive k indicating that y is measured later than x, and a negative k the reverse. Autocorrelations within the x and y series respectively may also be computed for any measurement lag: $r_{x_t x_{t+k}}$ and $r_{y_t y_{t+k}}$. Heise's subscripts t and θ, standing for values at times 1 and 2 respectively, are equivalent in our notation to t and $t + 1$.

In the simple situation of one-way influence ($x \rightarrow y$ but not $y \rightarrow x$), p_{xy} of course equals 0. For this situation Lew has derived expressions for the theoretical auto- and cross-correlations as functions of parameters p_{xx}, p_{yy}, p_{yx}, g, and k (see Technical Note at the end of this paper).

ONE-WAY INFLUENCE

The data plotted in Figure 1 are based on two simple situations in which x was given a mild causal influence on y ($p_{yx} = +0.10$), causal interval g was four time units, and short-term stability coefficients for x and y were either moderate ($p_{xx} = p_{yy} = 0.70$) or very high ($p_{xx} = p_{yy} = 0.95$). To construct the curves in Figure 1 we used the theoretical values derived from expressions in the Technical Note at the end, rather than empirically simulated ones, which they closely approximated.

The two lighter curves plot cross-correlations between sets of x_{it} and $y_{i(t+k)}$ measured at various times separated by measurement lag k. At the left extreme of Figure 1, y precedes x by twenty-five time units, and at the right extreme x precedes y by the same amount.

The two heavier curves show path coefficients for $x \rightarrow y$ and $y \rightarrow x$, generated from the respective correlations. With empirical data, of course, one does not know whether one's measurement lag corresponds to the "true" causal interval; hence we arbitrarily took correlations corresponding to selected lags $k = 2, 5, 10, \ldots$ and computed the respective path coefficients by Heise's equations.[2]

An important feature of Figure 1 is that the path coefficients calculated in the right half (for $x \rightarrow y$ influence) are positive over many

---

[2] The computation of path coefficients used both the cross-correlations plotted in the figure and autocorrelations (not shown).

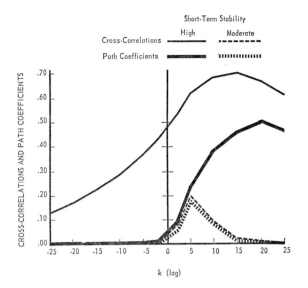

Figure 1. Theoretical cross-correlations between simulated x and y measures as a function of measurement lag, and corresponding path coefficients for $x \rightarrow y$ (right half) and $y \rightarrow x$ (left half). Solid lines correspond to $p_{xx} = p_{yy} = 0.95$, and broken lines to $p_{xx} = p_{yy} = 0.70$. In all curves the causal interval g is four time units, and x has a mild causal influence on y ($p_{yx} = +0.10$).

measurement lags, indicating correctly that x does influence y, that is, that the causal coefficient p_{yx} is positive. Path coefficients in the left half, by contrast, are all zero, indicating correctly the absence of any $y \rightarrow x$ influence, that is, that the causal coefficient p_{xy} is zero.

The path coefficients in the right half were by no means uniform, however, indicating that estimates of p_{yx} will depend on other parameters, such as the stability of each variable and the measurement lag. Several of these effects (which appear both in the cross-correlations and in the corresponding path coefficients) are interesting and not intuitively obvious: (1) The higher the short-term stability coefficients, the larger was the maximum cross-correlation and maximum path coefficient, even though the actual causal influence of x on y (p_{yx}) remained constant. (2) The higher the stability coefficients, the longer the cross-correlations and corresponding path coefficients persisted through time, over lags several times longer than the actual causal interval.[3] Thus high stability (of a short-term type) served to *magnify and perpetuate the observable*

[3] Although only two sets of data are shown, the relationships stated above were confirmed over additional values of stability coefficients.

effects of the causal influence. (3) The higher the stability coefficients, the greater was the *delay* between the point of actual causal impact (interval *g*) and the point at which a maximum cross-correlation (or path coefficient) was observed.[4] Thus when stability coefficients were extremely high (both equal to 0.95) the cross-correlations and path coefficients were maximum at a lag from ten to fifteen time periods later than the causal interval, and remained high for a considerable time thereafter.

ONE-WAY INFLUENCE WITH LONG-TERM STABILITY

In recursion equations (1) to (3), the autocorrelation between values of a variable measured at different times will decline toward an asymptote of zero as the measurement lag *k* increases. The theoretical autocorrelation in expression (1), over any lag *k*, will be: $\rho_{x_t x_{t+k}} = p_{xx}^k$.

With many real social data, however, it is inappropriate to assume a simple Markov process in which the value at time *t* depends only on immediately prior value at $t-1$. Rather there may exist for each individual some *long-term stability*, a tendency to persist at the same level through time—equivalent to individual differences in variables of intellectual ability, personality, or socioeconomic background. In such cases, the autocorrelation will not decline toward an asymptote of zero but toward some non-zero value, even over considerable lags.

In our simulation, long-term stability has been represented in the *x* variable by assigning to each individual a constant ζ_{ix} around which his observed values will fluctuate. The modified *x* variable is defined by the recursion equation:

$$x'_{it} = p_{xx}x'_{i(t-1)} + \tau_x\zeta_{ix} + u_x \tag{4}$$

where mean ζ_x across individuals is set equal to 0, and variance among ζ_{ix} can be set at any magnitude desired. To assure that the expected value for each individual remains constant through time (note that $E(x'_{it})$ should equal ζ_{ix}), a coefficient τ_x is set equal to $1 - p_{xx}$.

In a parallel fashion, variable y'_{it} is generated as a function of $p_{yy}y'_{i(t-1)}$ and $\tau_y\zeta_{iy}$. Causal influence by x' on y' is generated in the same way as in equation (3) by adding a term $p_{yx}x'_{i(t-g)}$.

The larger the variance among the ζ_{ix} or ζ_{iy} relative to the total variance of x'_{it} or y'_{it}, the greater is the amount of long-term stability, and the higher is the non-zero asymptote in the autocorrelation.

---

[4] Lew has demonstrated in Appendix C of the Pelz *et al.* (1968) report that there is zero delay if and only if $p_{yy}(1 + p_{xx}) \leq 1$.

The effect of such constants is to introduce another source of "outside disturbance" which, unlike u_{xt} or u_{yt}, is perfectly correlated for each individual over time.[5]

Effect on Cross-Correlations and Path Coefficients

In recursion equation (4) a high autocorrelation between adjacent values can be introduced either by a high p_{xx} coefficient or by a large ζ variance or both. However, the two sources of stability can be shown to differ strikingly in their effects. Strong short-term stability magnifies and perpetuates the cross-correlations, as illustrated in Figure 1. Strong long-term stability (large individual differences) has the opposite effect.

Figure 2 plots two sets of data having the same high short-term stability, the same moderate $x \rightarrow y$ influence, and the same causal interval. But in one set (represented by solid curves) the ζ variances are fixed at 70 per cent of respective total variances, while in the other set (represented by broken curves) the ζ variances are made 30 per cent of total variances. Again the lighter curves represent theoretical cross-correlations (the simulated values were similar), and the heavier curves the corresponding path coefficients.

As long-term stability increased, the cross-correlogram became— in a fashion not intuitively obvious—increasingly flat and also higher; that is, a high asymptotic cross-correlation appeared, even over long lags when the causal influence had disappeared.[6]

When path coefficients were calculated for the same two pairs of simulated variables, differing only in long-term stability, they were positive in the right half of Figure 2, indicating correctly that $x \rightarrow y$. In the left half they were lower but still positive, suggesting incorrectly a small $y \rightarrow x$ influence. The larger the long-term stability, the less clear was the difference between right and left halves.

EFFECTS OF RECIPROCAL INFLUENCE

To examine effects of reciprocal causation with positive feedback ($x \overset{+}{\rightarrow} y \overset{+}{\rightarrow} x$), a simulation was run with weak short-term stability ($p_{xx} = p_{yy} = 0.50$) and no long-term stability, in which x and y each

---

[5] Heise suggests that the individual constants could be treated as equivalent to implicit (unanalyzed) variables which themselves have perfect or near-perfect stability: $x'_{it} = p_{xx}x'_{i(t-1)} + p_{x\zeta}\zeta_{it} + u_{xt}$, where $\zeta_{it} = 1.0\zeta_{i(t-1)}$.

[6] Both simulated tests and the theoretical expression indicate that this effect arises only from ζ_x variance in the causal or determining variable and not from ζ_y variance in the resultant or dependent variable.

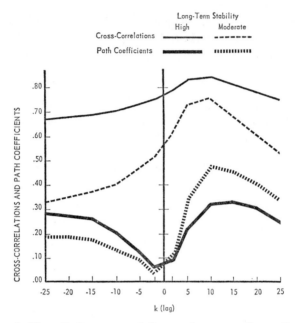

Figure 2. Theoretical cross-correlations and corresponding path coefficients when long-term stability is introduced. Solid lines: variance of ζ_x and ζ_y constants = 70 per cent of total x and y variance respectively. Broken lines: variance of ζ_x and ζ_y = 30 per cent of total x and y variance respectively. In all curves short-term stability was high ($p_{xx} = p_{yy} = 0.90$), $x \rightarrow y$ influence was moderate ($p_{yx} = +0.20$), and causal interval g equaled four time units.

exerted a strong influence on the other ($p_{yx} = p_{xy} = +0.40$), with causal intervals set at 3 and 5 respectively.[7]

The cross-correlations and corresponding path coefficients were found to be almost identical; hence only the latter are plotted by the solid curve in the upper part of Figure 3. Note that cross-correlations and path coefficients both correctly indicated the causal influence $x \overset{+}{\rightarrow} y$ and $y \overset{+}{\rightarrow} x$ only when the measurement lag corresponded to the actual causal intervals of 3 and 5 respectively. With longer lags the correlations and path coefficients both dropped, but did not wholly disappear.

In the next simulation, identical parameters were maintained but negative feedback was introduced: $x \overset{+}{\rightarrow} y$ but $y \overset{-}{\rightarrow} x$. Again correlations

---

[7] Since theoretical expressions for the situation of reciprocal influence are more complex and have not yet been derived, the simulated correlations were therefore utilized, although they are not plotted since the corresponding path coefficients were very similar.

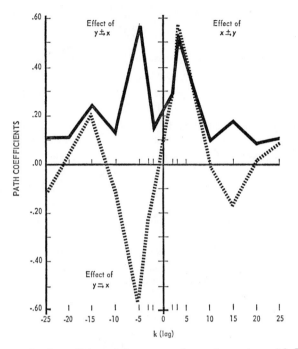

Figure 3. Path coefficients between x and y under reciprocal influence $x \rightarrow$ $y \rightarrow x$. Solid curve: positive feedback loop in which both influences are strong and positive ($p_{yx} = p_{xy} = +0.40$). Broken curve: negative feedback loop ($p_{yx} = +0.40$, $p_{xy} = -0.40$). In both curves the causal intervals are g equals three and five time units respectively; short-term stability is weak ($p_{xx} = p_{yy} = 0.50$).

and path coefficients were almost identical; the latter are plotted by the broken curve in the lower part of Figure 3.

Note the marked oscillation. As a result of the negative feedback loop, the positive influence ($x \overset{+}{\rightarrow} y$) produced a negative cross-correlation and path coefficient at $k = 15$, and the negative influence ($y \overset{-}{\rightarrow} x$) produced a positive cross-correlation and path coefficient at about $k = -15$.

Hence, given the negative feedback loops (reciprocal influences, one positive and the other negative), one runs the danger of inferring causal influence opposite in sign to the true influence if the measurement lag departs substantially from the causal interval.

CONCLUSION

A procedure proposed by Heise for estimating path coefficients in two-wave panel data was applied to simulated time series variables between which known causal connections had been introduced. Under several conditions of one-way and two-way influence, the path model gave meaningful results when the measurement lag approximated the actual causal interval. It also gave meaningful results when the measurement lag was substantially longer than the causal interval, provided that (a) the influence was one-way, and (b) the variables had high short-term stability from one time to the next as in a simple Markov chain. However, the presence of persisting individual differences ("long-term" stability) obscured the performance of the path coefficients.

In the presence of reciprocal effects, oscillations were observed in both the cross-correlations and corresponding path coefficients as measurement lag increased. These oscillations were especially marked with negative feedback loops (one influence positive, one negative). When measurement lag departed substantially from the true causal interval, the cross-correlation and path coefficient could be opposite in sign to the actual causal influence. When causal lag periods are unknown, one is wise to obtain more than two waves of observations and plot path coefficients as a function of measurement lag.

TECHNICAL NOTE

In appendices of the Pelz *et al.* (1968) interim report, Lew has derived expressions for the theoretical auto- and cross-correlations of the simulated data generated by recursion equations (1) to (4). Since simulation must begin at a finite time, the theoretical expressions are in a form which assumes that the systems have been operating a long time.

In terms of notation used earlier, the expressions are the following (respective equation and page numbers refer to those in the interim report).[8] In these, x_{it} or x'_{it} is the determining variable, and Y_{it} or Y'_{it} the dependent variable (as defined above in equations (3) and (4)). The autocorrelation of x' (expressed in slightly different notation to avoid double subscripts) is given by:

$$\rho(x'_{it}, x'_{i(t+k)}) = \frac{p_{xx}^k \sigma_x^2 + \mathrm{Var}(\zeta_{ix})}{\sigma_x^2 + \mathrm{Var}(\zeta_{ix})} \qquad \text{App. B.1 (2.4), page 91}$$

where σ_x^2 is the variance for each individual (constant across individuals) around his expected value, which equals his ζ_{ix}. In the absence of such

---

[8] In the present Technical Note, as well as in the interim report, the y variable is capitalized (Y_{it} and Y'_{it}) to indicate the presence of causal influence by x. A transcriptional error in (10) and (11) has been corrected here. In the appendices of the interim report, subscripts t and $t + k$ are replaced by s and t respectively, and the symbols p_{xx}, p_{yy}, and p_{yx} are replaced by ρ_x, ρ_y, and c respectively.

individual differences, the autocorrelation approaches an asymptote of zero as measurement lag k increases (*asymptote* here is used in a sense different from that above). In the presence of individual differences or long-term stability, as measurement lag increases the autocorrelation approaches an asymptote set by $\mathrm{Var}[(\zeta_{ix})/(\sigma_x^2) + \mathrm{Var}(\zeta_{ix})]$, that is, the proportion of ζ variance to total variance.

Autocorrelation of Y':

$$\rho(Y'_{it}, Y'_{i(t+k)}) = 1 - \frac{\mathrm{Var}(Y_t) - \mathrm{Cov}(Y_t, Y_{t+k})}{\mathrm{Var}(Y_t) + \dfrac{\mathrm{Var}(\theta_i)}{(1 - p_{yy})^2}} \qquad \text{App. B.2 (10), page 93}$$

Cross-correlation of $x'Y'$:

$$\rho(x'_{it}, Y'_{i(t+k)}) = \frac{\mathrm{Cov}(x_t, Y_{t+k})(1 - p_{yy}) + p_{yx}(\mathrm{Var}(\zeta_{ix}) + \tau_y \, \mathrm{Cov}(\zeta_{ix}, \zeta_{iy})}{\{[\mathrm{Var}(Y_t)(1 - p_{yy})^2 + \mathrm{Var}(\theta_i)][\sigma_x^2 - \mathrm{Var}(\zeta_{ix})]\}^{1/2}}$$

$$\text{App. B.2 (11), page 93}$$

where $\theta_i = \tau_y \zeta_{iy} + p_{yx}\zeta_{ix}$; $\mathrm{Cov}(\zeta_{ix}, \zeta_{iy})$ is fixed at any desired level; and other terms are defined by reference to the interim report to conserve space: $\mathrm{Var}(Y_t)$ in App. A.4 (15), p. 85; $\mathrm{Cov}(Y_t, Y_{t+k})$ in A.5 (18.1) and (18.2), p. 87; $\mathrm{Cov}(x_t, Y_{t+k})$ in App. A.6 (22.1) through (22.4), p. 90, for different conditions of p_{xx} and p_{yy}, g and k.

Arthur S. Goldberger has indicated (personal correspondence) how, by assuming an infinite past time series, in contrast to the finite starting point used in simulation as Lew has done, one can derive theoretical expressions for asymptotic autocorrelations of x and Y, and the cross-correlations xY, more directly than by the procedures Lew has adopted. The asymptotic results in Appendix A can be obtained by Goldberger's techniques.

REFERENCES

KENDALL, M. G. AND STUART, A.
  1966 *The Advanced Theory of Statistics*, Vol. 3. New York: Hafner.
PELZ, D. C., MAGLIVERAS, S., AND LEW, R. A.
  1968 "Correlational properties of simulated panel data with causal connections between two variables." Interim Report No. 1, Causal Analysis Project. Ann Arbor: Survey Research Center, University of Michigan.

3

PARTIALS, PARTITIONS, AND PATHS

Otis Dudley Duncan
UNIVERSITY OF MICHIGAN

In a good deal of recent sociological discussion, published and unpublished, one senses an implicit assumption that the objective of a piece of research is best served by a partitioning of the "explained variance" or by the calculation of a partial correlation. I wish to argue, to the contrary, that achieving an algebraically consistent partitioning or system of partialing is secondary in importance to setting up an appropriate representation (or "model") of the structure of the problem. Much confusion arises because of the protean character of regression and correlation statistics, which permits their algebraic manipulation into a large number of essentially equivalent but apparently distinct forms. Preoccupation with this algebra is not likely to generate anything new, for many capable statisticians have had a go at the subject during the twentieth century. Even worse, it is likely to distract one from the more urgent task of making sure that the regression setup itself is suited to the inferences and interpretations to be attempted. The viewpoint of this paper is that of the analyst seeking a rationally defensible and substantively interesting interpretation of a set of data. His objectives are distinct from those of the technician seeking an optimal prediction instrument, as is brought out in papers by Darlington (1968) and Gordon (1968).

Most of the issues that arise in trying to interpret partials or partitions are evident in a problem involving three explicit variables. Let us suppose that this problem can be represented appropriately by a recursive system of linear equations (Blalock, 1964, pp. 54–57). If our variables are denoted X_3, X_2, and X_1 (assigning subscripts in whatever way is convenient), we have to consider three cases:

Case 1: X_3 is prior to X_2 and X_1, but neither of the latter two is prior to the other. Stated otherwise, X_2 and X_1 depend on X_3, but X_2 does not depend on X_1 nor does X_1 depend on X_2.

Case 2: X_1 depends on X_2 and X_3, but neither of the latter depends on the other.

Case 3: X_1 depends on X_2 and X_3; and X_2 depends on X_3. This is the case of a causal chain. It should be noted that this model is not appropriate, for example, if there is reason to suspect that some fourth variable, X_4, is a common cause of X_3 and X_2. (Case 2 represents this situation.)

The three cases are diagrammed in Figure 1, following the conventions of path analysis.

Case 1 is the only one of the three in which the partial correlation as such provides an immediately interpretable figure. It is easily shown for this case that $p_{23} = r_{23}$, $p_{13} = r_{13}$, $p_{2v} = (1 - r_{23}^2)^{1/2}$, and $p_{1u} = (1 - r_{13}^2)^{1/2}$. From this it follows at once that $r_{12} = r_{13}r_{23} + p_{1u}p_{2v}r_{uv}$ and hence that $r_{uv} = r_{12 \cdot 3} = r_{21 \cdot 3}$. In this case, X_3 is taken to be a "common

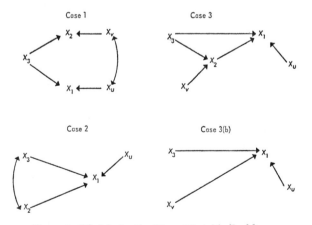

Figure 1. Models for the Three-Variable Problem.

cause" of X_2 and X_1. The null hypothesis is that this common cause completely accounts for the correlation r_{12}. On this hypothesis, $r_{uv} = r_{12 \cdot 3} = 0$ and $r_{12} = p_{23}p_{13} = r_{23}r_{13}$. In the event that the null hypothesis is rejected, so that $r_{uv} \neq 0$, the interpretation is that some other common cause is operating in addition to X_3. On the model for Case 1, any such other cause(s) is taken to be uncorrelated with X_3. If this assumption is inappropriate, a more elaborate model is required, taking us beyond the three-variable problem. Case 1 does not involve the multiple correlation, or its square, the coefficient of determination.

In Case 2, straightforward multiple regression calculations provide estimates of the path coefficients, which are, in this simple kind of system, identical with "beta weights" or partial regression coefficients in standard form (Walker and Lev, 1953, pp. 324–336). The problem—or, as I would insist, the pseudo-problem—with this model is how to divide up the whole of the "explained variance" between the two explanatory variables. Each generation of novices repeats the mistake of computing (correctly) $R^2_{1(23)} = p_{13}r_{13} + p_{12}r_{12}$ and then interpreting (incorrectly) the two terms on the right as the unique contributions, respectively, of X_3 and X_2 to the explanation of the variance in X_1. This does not work, for the simple reason that the product, say $p_{13}r_{13}$, can be negative, and it makes no sense to attribute to one of the variables alone a negative component of an intrinsically positive quantity. Such a negative component can only arise from the joint action of two independent variables and must, therefore, be attributed to them jointly.

When working with Case 2 it is instructive to consider the partitioning afforded by the formula $r_{11} = 1 = $ total variance of $X_1 = p_{12}^2 + p_{13}^2 + 2p_{12}p_{13}r_{23} + p_{1u}^2$, from which it follows that $R^2_{1(23)} = 1 - p_{1u}^2$. There are, then, three components of explained variance, one due to X_3, one due to X_2, and one due *jointly* to X_2 and X_3. Nothing is gained by the use of any formula that purports to achieve uniquely an allocation of the joint term (or a portion of it) to one or the other of the two explanatory variables. If the rationale for doing so is examined closely, it will turn out that the analyst is either using the model of Case 3 rather than Case 2 or invoking assumptions about other variables not included in the system (in which case the situation is no longer that of a three-variable problem). If it seems unsatisfactory to recognize a (typically large) joint component, then the only recourse is, indeed, to enlarge the system, so as to include, for example, an explanation of the correlation r_{23}. This will require reference to other variables, measured or unmeasured, and a rejection or elaboration of the model for Case 2.

This calculation is "instructive" (as stated above), therefore, not because it provides a resolution to the problem of partitioning but because it is likely to sensitize the analyst to the unsatisfactory state of his present understanding of the situation under study. It should be added immediately that the magnitude of the joint term, as calculated, is a property of the particular population in which the three variables are measured—as is indeed true of all simple and partial correlations, standardized regression coefficients, and proportions of variance explained (Wright, 1960; Blalock, 1967). In particular, one cannot infer from the size of the joint term what the change in the coefficient of determination would be if the variables were measured in a population wherein X_2 and X_3 are uncorrelated (Darlington, 1968, p. 170).

Case 3 is more interesting in that it presents genuine alternatives. Since the model is that of a causal chain, we may be interested in looking at it in either of two ways: tracing back from the effect to the most immediate cause, and then further back to more remote causes; or following forward from the initial cause, looking at intervening causes along the way. In either event, p_{13} and p_{12} have the same values as in Case 2, while $p_{23} = r_{23}$. There is no difference between the two models in terms of the numerical coefficients to be entered on the path diagram. However, the assertion of priority of X_3 with respect to X_2, together with the assumption that they share no common cause, opens up the two alternatives just mentioned, neither of which makes sense in the context of Case 2.

Working backward from effect to causes, the appropriate partitioning of variance is $R^2_{1(23)} = r^2_{12} + p^2_{13}(1 - r^2_{23})$. The first term, r^2_{12}, represents the *total* effect of X_2 including both its "unique" contribution to the variance of X_1 and such contribution as it transmits from X_3. The second term, $p^2_{13}(1 - r^2_{23})$, represents the *increment* to explained variance, secured by going back, of the most immediate cause to include, in addition, a more remote one. To the extent that remote causes are shown to be significant in such a calculation, the analyst will conclude that the "history" of the system is relevant. In a *simple* causal chain (as in a simple Markov chain) such history is irrelevant, so that the second term is zero even though $r_{13} \neq 0$.

The case of a simple causal chain, incidentally, nicely illustrates how a partial correlation may be not merely irrelevant to interpretation, but downright misleading. In a simple causal chain $p_{12} = r_{12}$, $p_{23} = r_{23}$, and $r_{13} = p_{12}p_{23} = r_{12}r_{23}$. Hence we find that $\beta_{12\cdot3} = (r_{12} - r_{13}r_{23})/(1 - r^2_{23}) = r_{12}$. This is the correct estimate of p_{12}. But the partial correlation $r_{12\cdot3} \neq r_{12}$ and the sense in which X_3 is "held constant" in its calculation is not relevant to the model. Partial correlations are sometimes defended on the ground that their values are often close to those of the beta weights, but this is not always true and is not a very cogent

defense anyway. Nor is it relevant that partial correlations are a ubiqui-
tous feature of multiple regression computer programs. The fact that
a statistic is easily obtained as a by-product of a computing routine does
not constrain the analyst to report it or to put an interpretation upon it.
In sum, in Case 3 (as in Case 2) the partial correlation provides no
useful interpretation that cannot be better conveyed another way.

The alternative perspective on Case 3 involves going forward
from the earliest cause to the effect. Thus the appropriate partitioning
is $R^2_{1(23)} = r^2_{13} + p^2_{12}(1 - r^2_{23})$. The first term, r^2_{13}, represents the *total*
effect of the most remote cause, X_3, on the dependent variable, while the
second term, $p^2_{12}(1 - r^2_{23})$, is the *increment* to the explanation secured by
including an intervening cause along with the initial one. This interpretation is clarified by noting that it is equivalent to $R^2_{1(23)} = r^2_{13} + r^2_{1v}$, since
$r_{1v} = p_{12}(1 - r^2_{23})^{1/2}$. This partitioning, therefore, has the effect of replac-
ing the intercorrelated independent (with respect to X_1) variables X_3
and X_2 with two uncorrelated independent variables X_3 and X_v whose
contributions to explained variance are additive without remainder. Of
course, X_v is not a directly measured variable but a construct, "X_2 freed
of the influence of X_3." This representation is shown in Figure 1 as
Case 3(b).

While either of the two interpretations of Case 3 is consistent,
legitimate, and informative, it makes no sense to attempt a calculation
in which both interpretations are made simultaneously. The insoluble
problem of achieving this (except in the limiting case of X_2 and X_3
being uncorrelated) is probably the one that so typically instigates the
confusion in the minds of users of multiple regression.

The general lesson from the comparison of the three cases is that
no interpretation whatever is possible, except on a definite assumption
as to the anatomy of the system. While it is possible to make all the
calculations reviewed, not to mention a number of others, from the
same statistics, only a particular subset of such calculations (partitions
or partials) will actually provide consistently interpretable results; and
the choice among possible subsets will not be a free one, once a com-
mitment as to the system's causal structure has been made. Fisher's
statement on partial correlation has too often been disregarded: "In
no case . . . can we judge whether or not it is profitable to eliminate
a certain variate unless we know, or are willing to assume, a qualitative
scheme of causation. For the purely descriptive purpose of specifying
a population in respect of a number of variates, either partial or total
[or multiple—O.D.D.] correlations are effective, and correlations of
either type may be of interest" (Fisher, 1946, p. 191). Further, "if . . .
we choose a group of social phenomena with no antecedent knowledge

of the causation or absence of causation among them, then the calculation of correlation coefficients, total or partial [or multiple—O.D.D.],
will not advance us a step towards evaluating the importance of the
causes at work" (Fisher, 1946, p. 190).

While the three-variable problem illustrates all the issues of
principle, applications can involve some tedious algebra and can afford
opportunities for confusion in more elaborate problems. In Figure 2
there are some diagrams for the four-variable problem, but it does not
seem worthwhile to write down all the formulas. The analyst who wishes
to feel secure in his interpretations should learn to write the formulas
from first principles. A few remarks will suggest the complications that
may arise.

Figure 2(a) shows the general case of the four-variable chain
model discussed by Blalock (1962–63). His discussion is limited to a

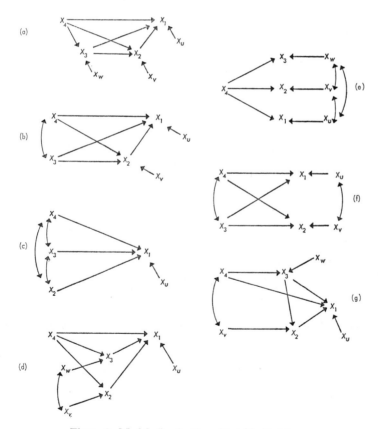

Figure 2. Models for the Four-Variable Problem.

specification of necessary and sufficient conditions for one or more of the path coefficients to be zero. While he chooses to state these conditions in terms of partial correlations, such partials have no useful role in interpreting numerical results obtained with this model. Much the more straightforward procedure, indeed, is to calculate the three regressions (X_3 on X_4; X_2 on X_3 and X_4; X_1 on X_2, X_3, and X_4) involved in this model and to test the estimated concrete regression or standardized path coefficients for significance. A partitioning of variance is obtained upon a straightforward extension of the approach already illustrated. Here, however, it may be easier to secure the desired partitioning making use of the definitions below:

Working backward, from effect to more and more remote causes,

Total effect of X_2:	r_{12}^2
Increment for X_3:	$R_{1(23)}^2 - r_{12}^2$
Increment for X_4:	$R_{1(234)}^2 - R_{1(23)}^2$
Sum, total variance explained	$R_{1(234)}^2$

Working forward,

Total effect of X_4:	r_{14}^2
Increment for X_3:	$R_{1(34)}^2 - r_{14}^2$
Increment for X_2:	$R_{1(234)}^2 - R_{1(34)}^2$
Sum, total variance explained	$R_{1(234)}^2$

Various formulas involving manipulations of the differences listed above have sometimes been offered under the label *multiple-partial correlation* or *multiple-partial coefficient of determination* (Cowden, 1952). If one wants to express increments to explained variance on a relative rather than an absolute basis, such formulas are logical enough. They contribute nothing to the interpretation. As for statistical inference, the significance of the increments to explained variance can be assessed with the calculation of the appropriate F-ratios (Cowden, 1952; Brownlee, 1960, p. 478), so that the multiple-partial approach contributes nothing to this problem either.

In Figure 2(b), the model is altered to the extent that no priority of X_3 with respect to X_4 or vice versa can be assumed. The foregoing partitioning can still be used, except that in working backward, the increments for X_3 and X_4 cannot be meaningfully separated, while in working forward the total effect of X_3 and X_4 jointly is taken as a single quantity, $R_{1(34)}^2$.

Figure 2(c), with no assumption as to ordering among the three variables taken to explain X_1, corresponds to a partitioning consisting of the sum of the three squared path coefficients and three joint terms. If, as is often true, the joint terms begin to assume a considerable size relative to the total variance explained, the analyst will do well to reconsider whether it really makes sense in his problem to try to separate the contributions of the three explanatory variables (Gordon, 1968). Possibly all three may be better regarded as "indicators" of some more general characteristic, although to represent this (or other possible interpretations) requires further complication of the model and acceptance of additional assumptions.

Figure 2(d) invites a partitioning in which the contributions of X_3 and X_2 are combined. The numerical value of this component will depend on whether the contributions to explained variance are being cumulated forward from the most remote cause (X_4) or back from the effect, assessing the two immediate causes first. Either point of view is legitimate and both are likely to be interesting. There is no possibility of a single set of numerical results that represents both simultaneously. It will be recognized that in Figure 2(d), r_{vw} is nothing other than the partial correlation $r_{23 \cdot 4}$. Whether the analyst is satisfied with an interpretation that leaves unexplained a substantial value of this coefficient is a question that must be answered before letting the model stand as a final result.

Similarly, Figures 2(e) and 2(f) represent the other ways in which partial correlations naturally arise in the four-variable case. Figure 2(e) merely signifies the coexistence of three first-order partial correlations, each of which may be tested against the hypothesis that X_4, as a common cause of the particular pair of dependent variables, explains the correlation between them (as in Case 1 of the three-variable problem). Figure 2(f) is, in effect, a definition of the second-order partial correlation, $r_{12 \cdot 34} = r_{uv}$. Here the relevant hypothesis is that X_4 and X_3 jointly act as common causes explaining the correlation r_{12}. There is no occasion for a partitioning of variance, nor is there in 2(e).

Finally, Figure 2(g) gives one example of what might be called a "pathological chain" model. The analyst is unwilling to assume that X_2 depends directly on X_4 yet the data do not permit him to accept the assumption of a simple causal chain, $X_4 \rightarrow X_3 \rightarrow X_2$, which implies that $r_{24} = r_{23}r_{34}$. This awkward state of affairs can be represented, formally, by a non-zero correlation r_{4v}. It is doubtful, however, that one would wish to leave the interpretation in this form if any plausible alternative were open. It merely stands for the conclusion that something has been omitted from the system that belongs there, such as a common cause of X_4 and X_2. If this cause cannot be identified and measured at the moment, the diagram calls attention to the priority to be given to its discovery. Under the circumstances, any partitioning of variance that yields an estimate of the net influence of X_4 on X_1 can only be suggestive.

Little has been said in this presentation about the numerical values of the path coefficients in the diagrams. The calculations in each case are straightforward (Duncan, 1966). These coefficients will often be of greater interest than the partitioning of variance, although the two viewpoints are closely related. Frequently the analyst will prefer to focus on the concrete regression coefficients as measures of the effects of interest. The contribution of path analysis, whether accomplished with (standardized) path coefficients or with (unstandardized) path regression coefficients (Wright, 1960), does not consist so much in rationalizing calculations of explained variance or in evaluating the "relative importance" of variables as in making explicit the formulation of assumptions that must precede any such calculations if they are to yield intelligible results. The real power of path analysis does not lie in its relationship to these calculations but in its use in studying the properties of systems more complicated than those of a straightforward recursive regression setup (Wright, 1931). In problems where this kind of system is an appropriate model, the calculation of explained variances is often an irrelevant or at best a secondary objective. As research workers increasingly attempt complex analysis involving explicit attention to unmeasured variables and measurement error (see, for example, Siegel and Hodge, 1968; Duncan, 1969) it will be easier to appreciate the force of this observation.

REFERENCES

BLALOCK, H. M., JR.
   1962–63   "Four-variable causal models and partial correlation." *American Journal of Sociology* 68 (September): 182–194, 510–512.
   1964   *Causal Inferences in Nonexperimental Research*. Chapel Hill: University of North Carolina Press.
   1967   "Path coefficients versus regression coefficients." *American Journal of Sociology* 72 (May): 675–676.
BROWNLEE, K. A.
   1960   *Statistical Theory and Methodology in Science and Engineering*. New York: Wiley.
COWDEN, D. J.
   1952   "The multiple-partial correlation coefficient." *Journal of the American Statistical Association* 47 (September): 442–456.
DARLINGTON, R. B.
   1968   "Multiple regression in psychological research and practice." *Psychological Bulletin* 69 (No. 3): 161–182.

DUNCAN, O. D.
    1966   "Path analysis: Sociological examples." *American Journal of Sociology*
           72 (July): 1–16.
    1969   "Contingencies in constructing causal models." Pp. 74–112 in E. F.
           Borgatta and G. W. Bohrnstedt (Eds.), *Sociological Methodology*
           1969. San Francisco: Jossey-Bass.
FISHER, R. A.
    1946   *Statistical Methods for Research Workers*, Tenth Edition. Edinburgh:
           Oliver and Boyd.
GORDON, R. A.
    1968   "Issues in multiple regression." *American Journal of Sociology* 73
           (March): 592–616.
SIEGEL, P. M. AND HODGE, R. W.
    1968   "A causal approach to the study of measurement error." Pp. 28–59
           in H. M. Blalock, Jr., and A. B. Blalock (Eds.), *Methodology in Social*
           Research. New York: McGraw-Hill.
WALKER, H. M. AND LEV, J.
    1953   *Statistical Inference*. New York: Holt, Rinehart, and Winston.
WRIGHT, S.
    1931   "Statistical methods in biology." *Journal of the American Statistical*
           Association 26 (March, supplement): 155–163.
    1960   "Path coefficients and path regressions: Alternative or complementary
           concepts?" *Biometrics* 16 (June): 189–202.

❧4❧

EVALUATING AXIOMATIC THEORIES

Kenneth D. Bailey
UNIVERSITY OF CALIFORNIA, LOS ANGELES

*The author is indebted to
Steven Riskin for his perceptive criticisms of an earlier draft of this paper.*

Recent developments in the construction of sociological theory reveal dissension among both constructors and evaluators. Deductive formulations have been stressed as the goal of sociological theorists, but virtually all attempts at deductive theory construction have been severely criticized, and seem, consequently, to have ceased. One writer concludes that "an explanation is a theory, and it takes the form of a deductive system" (Homans, 1964, p. 818). An obvious conclusion for would-be theory constructors is to master the nuances of deduction. To Zetterberg (1954; 1965), proper sociological theory consists of "systematic *lawlike* propositions about society that can be supported by evidence" (Zetterberg, 1965, p. 22, italics added). But exactly how does one deduce? Zetterberg (1954, p. 17) says, "At present we may, . . .

as far as sociology is concerned, be quite satisfied with the use of derivation rules implied in ordinary language." Or in propositional form:

POSTULATE I: *The greater the A, the greater the B.*
POSTULATE II: *The greater the B, the greater the C.*
THEOREM A: *The greater the A, the greater the C.*

According to Costner and Leik (1964, p. 820), Zetterberg's rules for deduction may be expressed as the "sign rule": "*The sign of the deduced relationship is the algebraic product of the signs of the postulated relationships*" (italics in the original).

The use of "derivation rules implied in ordinary language" has proven more bane than boon, however. In particular, sociologists have lacked the necessary "lawlike propositions." Deductive theories have been provided by Gibbs and Martin (1958; 1959; 1962; 1964), Schwirian and Prehn (1962), Gould and Schrag (1962), Catton (1961), Labovitz and Gibbs (1964), and Hage (1965). Their derivation procedures (among other points) have been criticized by Duncan (1963), Costner and Leik (1964), Chambliss and Steele (1966), and Blalock (1969). Prehn and Schwirian (1963) and Gibbs and Martin (1966) have replied to their critics. Costner and Leik (1964, p. 820) conclude that the deductions found in current axiomatic theories in sociology are not valid. According to them it is sufficient for users of the sign rule to state postulates in asymmetric causal form; make deductions only from postulates in which the common variable is prior to one or both of the other two variables included in two postulates; and assume a "closed system," that is, there is no connection (causal or "spurious") between the variables in the postulates except those stated or implied in the postulates. These sufficient conditions will be referred to henceforth as the *causal requirements*.

No doubt these statements represent useful clarification. However, their effect to date has been to damage sociologists' confidence in all of the criticized theories. This is particularly unfortunate because no deductions adhering to Costner and Leik's suggestions have appeared in the sociological literature. Perhaps Costner and Leik's requirements are unrealistic for the present state of sociology, and will thus serve only to discourage would-be constructors of sociological theory. If theorists feel that the assumptions of a "closed system" or of "asymmetrical causality" are not realistic, what should they do? The present paper examines the logical and empirical requirements of axiomatic theory. Criteria for evaluating actual axiomatic theories are provided. These criteria emphasize assessing theories in terms of what can realistically be expected from them.

LOGICAL REQUIREMENTS

Students of theory construction in the social sciences have recently placed much emphasis on the need to study separately the logical and empirical aspects of theories. Blalock (1968) has proposed the use of two "languages," a theoretical language and an empirical language. The former is used as a thinking language to construct a general theory containing abstract concepts. This general theory is used in conjunction with an auxiliary theory which contains operational definitions of the general terms and thus renders the formulation testable. The assessment of the effects of measurement error is facilitated by focusing upon the relationship between the concept and its operational definition (cf. Costner, 1969; Blalock, 1968).

Others who have stressed the distinction between the logical and empirical aspects of theories are Stinchcombe (1968) and Meehan (1968). Stinchcombe (1968, p. 16) states that the theorist first formulates a theoretical statement and then derives an empirical statement from it for testing purposes. However, Meehan (1968) charges that the "deductive paradigm" merges the logical and empirical aspects of theory through its dependence on the "empirical generalization." According to Meehan, the fact that social scientists are generally unable to establish empirical generalizations or laws suitable for deduction does not necessarily mean that the social sciences are inadequate. It may mean instead that the deductive paradigm is inadequate for the social sciences. Meehan proposes an alternative to the deductive paradigm. This is the system paradigm. A system describes a closed set of variables and the logical relationships governing their actions. As such, a system is a formal, logical structure. Explanation is achieved by describing an empirical situation, and then "loading" the variables in the system with empirical values from the real world. Probably most sociologists' primary objection to Meehan's proposal would be the fact that they feel the assumption of a closed system is too unrealistic. This assumption specifies that values of each variable in the set are completely determined by other variables in the set. The idea of attacking the logical and empirical problems of theory construction separately is definitely meritorious. Let us consider the logical requirements of axiomatic theory.

Deduction

Deduction is the process of logically deriving a statement from other statements. As Caws (1965, p. 118) puts it:

By a *deductive system* is meant any system of interrelated statements such that some of them follow deductively from others; by an *axiomatized deductive system* or *axiomatized system* is meant a deductive system in which every statement is either an *axiom* not following deductively from any other statement, or a *theorem* following deductively from one or more axioms; and by a *pure axiomatic system* or *calculus* is meant a system having the logical form of an axiomatic system, but making no reference to particular contents.

Or, in other words, if a theoretical system is said to be axiomatized, its axioms must not contradict each other, and no axiom must be deducible from other axioms. Also, the set of axioms must be necessary and sufficient for the deduction of all theorems (Popper, 1959). Axioms are assumed to be true and are not tested. Sociologists have also used the term *postulate* in place of *axiom*. A postulate is also a proposition that is assumed to be true and is not tested. Sociologists seem to use the terms *axiom* and *postulate* interchangeably, but probably the term *postulate* should be reserved for a "loaded" system in which empirical content has been specified. For example, empirical generalizations suitable for the derivation of theorems, but whose truth is assumed and is thus not tested, would be called postulates. Then the term *axiom* can be used to designate statements that are definitionally true, or statements in pure axiomatic systems where no particular content is designated, and thus where there is no question of establishing the statement as an empirical generalization. However, for the purpose of this paper it is not necessary to judge particular propositions as being either axioms or postulates. Rather, both terms are used to designate statements assumed to be true. Deductive theories generally rely upon either the statement calculus or the predicate calculus. The statement calculus deals with the relationships between statements. Statements are connected by the sentential connectives *and*, *or*, or *if–then* (implies), and *if and only if*. Predicate logic deals with the internal structure of the statement. This is the calculus of everyday language (Stoll, 1961, pp. 56–121). Deductive theories in sociology have mainly used the sentential calculus. In the sentential calculus, a logically valid deduction may be made from statements expressed as hypothetical "if–then" statements. All such statements assert some form of implication. But these statements need not be causal in the classical experimental sense. They may contain logical, definitional, decisional, or material implication (Copi, 1961, pp. 246–251). All of these types, however, have enough in common that they may be identically represented in symbolic terms. Thus for "if p then q" to hold, it must not be true that p is true while q is false.

Representing "if p then q" by $p \supset q$, and "negation" by $\sim$, it is true that

$$p \supset q$$
$$q$$
$$\therefore p$$

is clearly invalid. This is called the *fallacy of affirming the consequent* (Copi, 1961, pp. 257–258) and is what scientists do when they accept the truth of some postulates (p) by simply confirming the theorems (q) deduced from the postulates. But consider

$$p \supset q$$
$$\sim p$$
$$\therefore \sim q$$

This also is invalid and is called the *fallacy of denying the antecedent* (Copi, 1961, p. 261). Notice, though, that if p and q are necessary and sufficient conditions of each other, then

$$p \supset q$$
$$q$$
$$\therefore p$$

is no longer a fallacy.

The deductions illustrated follow the logic of classes. If symmetry is allowed (if p and q are necessary and sufficient conditions of each other), this logic assumes perfect relationships. Obviously few, if any, perfect relationships or general laws have been discovered in sociology. Thus, sociologists wishing to deduce must admit that deductions from such imperfect symmetrical relationships are logically invalid. If a theory is logically valid, a theorem cannot be false while the propositions from which it is deduced are true. Axioms which specify symmetrical relations can yield perfectly valid deductions if they can be stated in such a manner that they exhibit some form of implication. However, if the relationship expressed in correlational form is less than perfect, then logical implication is lacking, and deduction is dangerous. One can still make deductions which are reasonable, if not logically valid, if the values of his coefficients of correlation (rs) are assumed to be high enough. Specifically, as Costner and Leik (1964, p. 821) point out, the sign rule can be used to deduce the relationship between A and C only when $r_{AB}^2 + r_{BC}^2 > 1$.

But such specification of specific values of coefficients of correlation is obviously an empirical matter, and need not be considered in a discussion of logical requirements for axiomatic theories. The point to be emphasized is that as far as logical validity is concerned, *implication* is the key word. Whether a relationship is symmetrical or asymmetrical is not crucial for deduction (although, as shown above, symmetrical relationships enable one to avoid the common fallacy of affirming the consequent). If there are no logical proscriptions against making deductions from relationships stated in symmetrical form, then why did Costner and Leik state that relationships used as postulates should be both *asymmetrical* and *causal* in nature? The answer is apparently to be found by examining the empirical aspects of axiomatic theories.

EMPIRICAL REQUIREMENTS

Costner and Leik (1964, p. 820) say:

> The point to be elaborated in this paper is that although *deductions from such simple statements of relationship as are found in current axiomatic theories are not valid,* sociologists may find postulates of a somewhat different form useful in constructing deductive theories with perfectly valid deductions [italics added].

The bases for this blanket rejection of current axiomatic theories are never made clear by Costner and Leik. These theories cannot be rejected because of failure to meet the causal requirements. The causal requirements are only sufficient conditions for valid deductions (Costner and Leik, 1964, p. 831). Obviously, a theory cannot be rejected for failure to meet *sufficient* conditions; only if a theory fails to meet *necessary* conditions can it be rejected. The fact that certain conditions are sufficient but not necessary implies the existence of other sufficient conditions. Postulates stated in forms other than the "causal" form can be used by sociologists to make valid deductions.

It is true that many symmetrical relationships in sociology are not sufficiently large for theorists to have faith in deductions made from them. In such cases causality presents a tempting alternative. However, theorists are not in total agreement about the efficacy of the causal concept. Some sociological methodologists have recently discussed causality and methods for establishing it (cf. Blalock, 1964; Stinchcombe, 1968). But the concept is fraught with philosophical difficulties, and is the center of ancient controversies (cf. Bunge, 1959). According to Bunge (1959, p. 30), causation is best considered as one among several types of determinacy. Among others are statistical determinacy and teleological determinacy. Some other salient properties of causation are that it is essentially asymmetrical; it includes the idea of "process" or "production"; it is essentially a description of empirical relationships rather than a statement of logical connections.

The point to be stressed is that causality does not represent the whole of or the epitome of determinacy. The concept of interaction, involving symmetrical relationships, is another quite legitimate form of determinacy. As a description of the real world, interaction is in many ways a more realistic concept than causality. It seems quite likely that many relationships studied by sociologists are symmetrical. Many propositions written by sociologists exhibit a relationship of the following type: "The degree of urbanization in a society varies directly with the dispersion of objects of consumption" (Gibbs and Martin, 1962, p. 669). The relationship expressed is a form termed "cumulative" or "interdependent" by Zetterberg (1965, pp. 72–74) and Costner and Leik (1964, p. 834). The relationship is symmetrical. A certain value of each variable is in turn necessary for variation in the other to occur. This could only be expressed in causal terms as "reciprocal causation" or "mutual causation." However, while an increase in the dispersion of objects of consumption facilitates an increase in the degree of urbanization, and vice versa, it is by no means clear that one variable "produces" or "causes" change in the other. Further, the noncausal concept of interaction is more conductive to the study of multivariate systems, where many variables are interrelated in complex ways. In such a case it may seem a gross oversimplification to speak of asymmetrical causation. A number of writers seem to agree that interaction is in some ways preferable to causation as a description of empirical realities. As Lerner (1965, p. 7) states, if a relationship seems to be symmetrical, it is not necessary to speak of causation. Or as Bunge (1959, pp. 170–171) notes, the notion of asymmetry seems inappropriate for describing a world where "all known actions are accompanied or followed by reactions." But he adds that though the idea of asymmetry is often empirically unrealistic, it may be methodologically justified, as it is often the only view that is practical given the amount of information and the theoretical tools available.

What conclusions can be drawn about the efficacy of asymmetrical causal statements in axiomatic theories of sociology? There is little doubt that many relationships of interest to sociologists are symmetrical, and that an effect can have more than one cause. Thus, there is little doubt that statements of the type recommended by Costner and Leik (1964) are often empirically inadequate. However, although the concept of cause can be applied only to empirical relationships, it has implications for the logical aspects of deductive theory. That is, even though the principle of causation does not contain the notion of logical implication, it does order empirical phenomena in such a way that logical correlates of the causal statement may be specified. As Bunge (1959, p. 242) notes, statements of the form "if p, then q," which were said above to be suitable for deduction, are often said to be the formulation of causality. Although Bunge states that this formulation is incorrect, it is nevertheless true that causality represents (among other things) an attempt to structure reality in a manner so that it can be analyzed according to the logic of classes. The causality principle will always lack the necessity embodied in logical implication, but it provides a rough approximation to such implication.

The appeal of the causality principle for axiomatic theorists is now clear: it serves as a link between the perfect, ordered world of logic and the sometimes complex and unordered world of empirical reality. Empirical generalizations stated as causal laws are familiar sights in the natural sciences, and appear more suitable for deduction than symmetrical statements. Asymmetrical statements may also appear attractive to sociologists because the use of a number of statistical techniques such as path analysis is simplified if the system of variables may be assumed to be recursive.

But no matter how attractive causal relationships might be, symmetrical relationships cannot be dismissed in a cavalier manner. Costner and Leik's (1964, p. 820) contention that statements of relationship found in current axiomatic theories are too "simple" to allow valid deductions implies that *no* strong symmetrical relationships can be found in sociology. *Current axiomatic theories in sociology can be rejected only if it is shown that postulates expressed in correlational form represent correlations of low magnitude.* For testable propositions, this is a question of empirical demonstration that has not been forthcoming from critics. For untestable propositions it must be demonstrated that the assumption of a high magnitude of r is unreasonable. Thus, any blanket rejection of current axiomatic theories should not be accepted. Each theory deserves individual reconsideration.

The gist of the causal-symmetrical argument should be clear by now. Neither form is inherently superior to the other. Either form is all right if the necessary assumptions can be met. If it is unrealistic to assume high correlation, it may be equally unrealistic to assume that the causal requirements can be met. The wholesale substitution of symmetrical relationships with causal relationships is unrealistic and is not a panacea. Further, it seems feasible that in many cases where low correlations are found, direct evidence is available to indicate that statements of the form recommended by Costner and Leik are also inadequate for deduction. Postulates based on small correlations but which meet the causal requirements can be used to make valid deductions. Although valid, such deductions may prove to be of little worth to theorists. In particular, the assumption of uncorrelated error terms included in the causal requirements includes the assumption of linearity for the regression of B on A (where the postulate states that A "causes" B). In such a case r^2 can be interpreted as the proportion of variance in B that can be attributed to A (McNemar, 1963, p. 134). Also, r tells how well B can be predicted from A by a regression equation (McNemar, 1963, p. 134). In other words, r tells how accurately one can "explain" variation in the second postulated variable, and how well that variable can be predicted. Remember that the theorist's main goal is explanation. Thus, he has little interest in postulated relationships yielding rs of low magnitude. Further, if the proportion of variance in B attributable to A is low (and if measurement error is disregarded for heuristic purposes), there are obviously other "causes" of B. This implies that under the causal requirements the axiomatic theory under construction may constitute only a partial explanation of the phenomena under investigation. Other complementary deductive theories might have to be constructed to explain the remainder of the variance.

A further implication is that if a large proportion of the variance is unexplained, the probability that the causal requirements are not valid is increased. That is, in particular, if a number of causal variables remain unmeasured, the assumption of a closed system with uncorrelated error terms is dubious. It is also possible that the relationship is nonlinear.

To summarize, the assumption that the causal requirements have been met enables one to make valid predictions regardless of the magnitude of r involved. However, the lower the r, the less likely it is that the assumptions have been met.

The discussion has indicated that it is unrealistic and probably unprofitable to say that all postulates should be stated in asymmetrical causal form or that all postulates should be stated in symmetrical form. It seems that easy rules about which form to use are not available. Both the symmetrical and asymmetrical forms can meet the necessary logical requirements. But in the empirical world, some relationships appear to be essentially symmetrical and some asymmetrical. To pour both into one mold is grossly unrealistic. Rather the answer seems to lie in empirical investigation: the theorist should examine specific relationships to see whether they are symmetrical or asymmetrical. But a problem arises at this point. Many times the postulates or axioms are essentially untestable, and only the theorem is subject to test. In other cases the postulates may be tested. But if a set of postulates is itself testable, why would one wish to deduce theorems? Especially if the theory contained only a few postulates, most of the connections to be deduced would be clear by inspection. In this case, the actual process of deduction would have much less value, although the set of interrelated propositions constituting the theory would retain its explanatory value. But what if operational definitions are lacking for some variables in the set of postulates? Such theories can sometimes only be tested (if at all) by deducing one main theorem. This theorem is deduced via the chain form of deduction, and relates variables for which operational definitions exist. In such a case the sociologist has a clear choice: deduce or not test. Thus, the actual operation of deduction seems most useful for sociologists in exactly those cases where the higher order postulates cannot be tested. We are not saying that axiomatic theories as interrelated sets of propositions are most important in such cases, but only that the actual logical operation of deduction finds its greatest use here. Two different "types" of axiomatic theory may be identified.

EXPLANATORY AND SYNTHETIC DEDUCTIVE THEORIES

The first kind of deductive theory is constructed, according to Northrop (1947, p. 105) when the scientist can identify the primitive entities and relations with directly sensed entities and relations. In this case the scientist orders his concepts by inspection and directly tests the postulates themselves. (Northrop, 1947, p. 109) calls this type of theory *abstractively deductively formulated theory*. However, as has happened many times in physics, the problems being investigated by the scientist are not always capable of being solved by a direct appeal to observable entities and relations. One needs a *hypothetically inferred deductively formulated theory* (Northrop, 1947, p. 109). The abstractively formulated theory can be tested by testing the postulates directly, while the hypothetically formulated theory can be tested only by testing the theorem deduced from the postulates, because the postulates themselves are untestable. Which type one uses depends basically on whether the data he is dealing with are directly observable.

Coleman (1964, p. 9) also distinguishes between two general types of deductive theory. The first he calls explanatory theory. The term *explanatory theory* as used henceforth in this paper refers to Coleman's type of theory, and not to the explanatory power of the theory. These theories take empirical generalizations and set forth sets of postulates to explain the generalizations. The second type of theory Coleman calls synthetic theory. Synthetic theory construction consists of setting down sets of postulates "which are known to be true" by utilizing observed generalizations, and then generating deductions from the postulates. It should be clear that Coleman's synthetic theory is roughly the same as Northrop's abstractively deductively formulated theory, while his explanatory theory approximates hypothetically inferred deductively formulated theory.

Coleman points out that the role of the postulates A and the deductions B can be reversed in the two types. With explanatory theory, one starts with propositions concerning observed phenomena and then devises the set of underlying postulates. In synthetic theory, however, one may begin with the postulates and test them, while either testing or not testing the deductions. Coleman notes that most sciences rely primarily on one or the other type of deductive theory, depending on their subject matter. For example, psychology must deal with the outer man and so must devise logical constructs within the individual. Coleman (1964, p. 37) thinks that:

> Sociology, because of its very wide span of concern, from inside the individual to the organization of complete societies, must use both approaches to theory. It is difficult to predict which will be more important, but it appears that the former, explanatory theories, are more nearly the province of psychology, while it is the peculiar province of sociology to develop the synthetic theories.

For the purposes of this paper, the important distinction to be made is between the type of axiomatic theory in which the postulates are not testable, and the type in which the postulates are testable. The former will be called explanatory deductive theory, and the latter will be called synthetic deductive theory. Notice that the postulates of explanatory theory need not contain "hypothetical" concepts, but may remain untested because operational definitions are not available for all of the concepts.

Testing Explanatory Deductive Theories

Many sociological propositions cannot be tested, either because of measurement problems or because their variables are hypothetically derived. According to Popper (1959, p. 40), a formulation is not theory unless it is capable of being tested. A great advantage that explanatory deductive theory has over other types of theory is that sometimes a set of untestable postulates can be used to deduce a testable theorem. A set of n postulates can be used to deduce $n(n - 1)/2$ theorems. Quite often the theorist can deduce only one central testable theorem. Actually, some of the other possible deductions are made and are used to deduce the central theorem. The other deductions are left implicit as they are often untestable. This is called the chain rule, or chain pattern, of deduction

(Zetterberg, 1965, pp. 90–92). A good example of the chain rule is provided by Gibbs and Martin's (1958; 1959; 1964) theory of status integration and suicide. This procedure is eminently useful. It enables Gibbs and Martin to transform an untestable formulation into at least a partially testable theory. Consider their theory:

POSTULATE 1: *The suicide rate of a population varies inversely with the stability and durability of social relationships within that population.*

POSTULATE 2: *The stability and durability of social relationships within a population vary directly with the extent to which individuals in that population conform to the patterned and socially sanctioned demands and expectations placed upon them by others.*

POSTULATE 3: *The extent to which individuals in a population conform to patterned and socially sanctioned demands and expectations placed upon them by others varies inversely with the extent to which individuals in that population are confronted with role conflicts.*

POSTULATE 4: *The extent to which individuals in a population are confronted with role conflicts varies directly with the extent to which individuals occupy incompatible statuses in that population.*

POSTULATE 5: *The extent to which individuals occupy incompatible statuses in a population varies inversely with the degree of status integration in that population.*

GRAND THEOREM: *The suicide rate of a population varies inversely with the degree of status integration in that population.*

Notice that since the theory contains five postulates, $(5)(4)/2 = 10$ theorems could have been deduced. Instead, only one was presented. Why were not all possible deductions made? Or, for that matter, why were any made? Consider Postulate 1: a population's suicide rate varies inversely with the stability and durability of social relationships within that population. This relationship need not be asymmetrically causal. The relationship described in Postulate 1 might well be taken as cumulative or interdependent in form (cf. Zetterberg, 1965, pp. 72–74; Costner and Leik, 1964, p. 834). If so, it would be essentially symmetrical. A certain value of each variable would in turn be necessary for change in the other variable to occur. That is, a minimal suicide rate might be necessary for durability in social relations to increase. This same increase in durability might be necessary for the suicide rate to become lower. Such a relationship can be expressed in causal terms only as reciprocal causation or mutual causation. But what would sociological theorists really like to do with Postulate 1? We submit that the main goal of theorists studying suicide is to empirically establish a firm relationship (whatever the form) between suicide and some other variable. That is,

they would like to treat Postulate 1 as a hypothesis, examine it empirically, and establish it as an empirical generalization. If this could be
done so successfully that Postulate 1 were considered law, rejoicing
would be loud. Whether the relationship were actually symmetrical or
causal would be of secondary importance, and would be an empirical
matter that could be reserved for further investigation.

The important thing would be that the actual suicide rate of an
actual society could be deduced by combining data about the stability
and durability of its social relationships with the general law. Since the
deductive theory begins with Postulate 1, actual explanation of the law
itself (Postulate 1) would apparently not come from Postulates 2 to 5,
because Postulate 1 logically precedes them. Rather, explanation of
Postulate 1 would apparently come from an as yet undevised set of more
general laws. That this is not true is shown later.

Then the next question is, why did not Gibbs and Martin try to
establish the inverse relationship between suicide rate and "stability
and durability of social relationships" as a law by examining it in every
population for which data were available? Apparently because they
could not successfully measure stability and durability of social relationships. If they could measure this variable they would have no excuse.
They then chose the only available alternative. They deduced a relationship between suicide rate and a variable for which an operational
definition was available: degree of status integration. This variable can
be defined in terms of the frequency with which persons occupy measurable statuses such as occupations. It is thus much less ambiguous than
a measure of the stability and durability of social relationships.

What general rule, then, shall we provide for theorists who wish
to use the chain pattern of deduction to construct a theory similar in
form to Gibbs and Martin's suicide theory? Blalock (1969, p. 18)
provides two rules for theorists:

RULE 1: *Select as axioms those propositions that involve variables that are taken to be directly linked causally;
axioms should therefore be statements that imply direct
causal links among variables.*
RULE 2: *State theorems in terms of covariations and temporal
sequences, thereby making them testable provided adequate measures of all variables can be obtained.*

Should theorists follow Blalock's rules? Let us consider separately the
logical and empirical aspects of explanatory deductive theories such as
Gibbs and Martin's.

In speaking of Gibbs and Martin's suicide theory, Blalock (1969,
p. 16, italics added), says:

The theory would seem to imply that suicide rates should vary inversely with the relative frequency with which status combinations are occupied. *But given the fact that at each stage there will be numerous variables operating over and above those specified by the theory, it is by no means obvious that one can deduce even the sign or direction of the relationship between the two end variables.*

From a logical standpoint, this statement is subject to misinterpretation unless clarified. The contention that "outside" variables will disturb the postulated relationships overlooks the fact that the propositions referred to are postulates, and are thus assumed to be true regardless of any and all variables "operating over and above those specified by the theory." The only way that Gibbs and Martin can deduce the Grand Theorem is by utilizing the logic of classes. That is, by assuming that each postulate is a true and deterministic statement, whether causal or not. From a logical standpoint the postulates represent a loaded calculus, and could be represented in if-then form to reduce ambiguity (for example, Postulate 1: If a population has a high degree of stability and durability of social relationships, then it will have a low suicide rate). Thus, when Blalock says that "outside" variables will affect the deduction, he is forgetting what a "postulate" is. He is forgetting that a postulate is assumed to be true, regardless of other variables. From a logical standpoint a *ceteris paribus* clause is automatically included in the assumption. So from a logical standpoint, the relationship in each postulate is assumed to be true and deterministic, no more and no less. It is not required to be causal. On the contrary, causal relationships result in the fallacy of affirming the consequent if the Grand Theorem alone is empirically investigated.

If the relationship is considered to be causal, it must be reciprocally causal and not asymmetric. Postulates should be of this form: *An increase in A will result in an increase in B, an increase in B will result in an increase in A.* Both assumptions taken together are sufficient, along with the other two listed in the causal requirements. The assumption of symmetry (high correlation) is alone sufficient. In other words, the causal requirements are sufficient requirements only for synthetic theory. In particular, the assumption of asymmetrical causality is inappropriate for explanatory theory.

Empirical Aspects

Blalock's rules also deserve discussion from an empirical standpoint. If a symmetrical relationship is to be preferred from a logical standpoint, and if there is no empirical evidence for stipulating that a relationship is asymmetrical, why should one do so? It should be noted that Blalock does not demand asymmetry as do Costner and Leik, but states that relationships thought to involve reciprocal causation should be described in detail—a very good suggestion, since theorists should strive to reduce the ambiguity of their assumptions whenever possible. The problem with past theories has not necessarily been that theorists have made improper assumptions about the direction and sign of the relationship; instead, the problem has been that theorists have often failed to make the nature of their assumptions explicit to the reader. Such ambiguity obviously damages a theory's utility.

It appears, then, that Blalock's Rule 1 needs to be clarified, if not modified. For explanatory deductive theory only (but not for the synthetic deductive form): (1) Symmetrical relationships fulfill the logical requirements better than asymmetrical relationships because they allow one to avoid the fallacy of affirming the consequent. (2) Postulates should be stated in whichever form (symmetrical or asymmetrical) the theorist feels more perfectly describes the relation in the real world. (3) All assumptions should be stated as unambiguously as possible (as Blalock suggests), including not only a description of the degree and sign of the relationship, but also other pertinent information such as whether the relationship is linear or nonlinear. Information about the time lag is also relevant if feedback is postulated (Blalock, 1969, p. 18).

Testing Synthetic Deductive Theories

Perhaps synthetic and explanatory deductive theories can be contrasted by saying that in the explanatory form, questions about the proper form for stating postulates are largely academic, since the postulates are assumed to be true but are never tested. Such questions are not academic for synthetic theories. It should not be inferred that the explanatory deductive theory cannot be very useful for sociologists. It is definitely important in situations where the postulates are pre-established laws, or where important abstract or hypothetical variables are related in the postulates. However, in sociology, most of the postulates in most explanatory deductive theories are not established as laws. Further, the concepts involved are generally not hypothetical, but simply are not now measurable (for example, the stability and durability of social relationships).

A critic might complain at this stage that the concept of causality is being deemphasized in this paper, and that such deemphasis neglects the important fact that many problems of statistical model building are simplified if asymmetry can be assumed. Or as Blalock (1969, p. 25) says,

> It is a relatively simple matter to draw in a double-headed arrow indicating reciprocal causation. Likewise, one may insert arrows feeding back to the original "independent" variable . . . . But it is another matter to test these theories in a definite way.

It is obvious that this statement does not apply to an explanatory deductive theory like the Gibbs and Martin theory. As has been abundantly noted, the postulates in such a theory are not "tested." It may well be that testing an entire theory by gathering evidence for one Grand Theorem is not a definitive test, but it is better than no test at all, which one would face without the Grand Theorem.

But Blalock's point is certainly relevant in the case of synthetic theory, in which not only the theorems but also the axioms are empirically investigated. However, it is probably a misnomer to label such theories axiomatic, or to call any of the propositions axioms or postulates, unless such propositions can be established as laws. Rather, it is better to simply refer to such theory as a system of interrelated propositions, and to utilize the term *proposition* throughout, rather than *postulate, axiom,* or *theorem.* The only way that one can even make deductions in this case is by using Blalock's "thinking" language. One can act "as if" all of the original propositions were true, and deduce theorems that would then follow. However, when the theorist focuses his attention upon Blalock's auxiliary theory so as to test his formulation, he finds that he must find operational definitions for every variable, be it in an axiom or theorem. He must also provide evidence to support each proposition. The main point is that in synthetic axiomatic theories the distinction between those propositions that were deduced (the theorems) and those that were the basis of the deductions (the postulates) becomes blurred. All of these propositions may be stated as hypotheses. In synthetic theory, then, the manner in which the propositions are interrelated is of primary concern. The act of deduction is much less important than it is in the explanatory form. The explanatory form cannot be tested without deduction, but the synthetic form can.

Clearly the synthetic case is rather far removed from the explanatory. Clearly the synthetic form is where the concept of causality has practical utility. Thus, the form in which propositions are stated becomes much more important here. A synthetic theory can be transformed into a statistical model; an explanatory theory cannot. Equations can be written to relate the concepts in postulates of an explanatory theory. But since these concepts have no operational definitions, values for variables in the equations cannot be specified.

To illustrate the difference between explanatory and synthetic theory, let us treat Gibbs and Martin's theory of suicide as if it were a synthetic theory. This can be done by assuming that we can measure every variable in Postulates 1 through 5. Then by imagining what would follow if these statements were really postulates or laws and not merely hypotheses, we could "deduce" the nine remaining theorems that Gibbs and Martin left implicit. Reconsider the Gibbs and Martin theory with each proposition stated in a shortened form:

POSTULATE 1: *The suicide rate of a population* (S_1) *varies inversely with the stability and durability of social relationships* (X_1).

POSTULATE 2: *The stability and durability of social relationships* (X_1) *vary directly with conformity* (X_2).

THEOREM 1: *The suicide rate of a population* (S_1) *varies inversely with conformity* (X_2).

POSTULATE 3: *Conformity* (X_2) *varies inversely with role conflicts* (X_3).

THEOREM 2: *Suicide rate* (S_1) *varies directly with role conflicts* (X_3).

THEOREM 3: *Stability and durability of social relationships* (X_1) *vary inversely with role conflict* (X_3).

POSTULATE 4: *Role conflicts* (X_3) *vary directly with incompatible statuses* (X_4).

THEOREM 4: *Suicide rate* (S_1) *varies directly with incompatible statuses* (X_4).

THEOREM 5: *Stability and durability of social relationships* (X_1) *vary inversely with incompatible statuses* (X_4).

THEOREM 6: *Conformity* (X_2) *varies inversely with incompatible statuses* (X_4).

POSTULATE 5: *Incompatible statuses* (X_4) *vary inversely with status integration* (X_5).

THEOREM 7 (GRAND THEOREM): *Suicide rate* (S_1) *varies inversely with status integration* (X_5).

THEOREM 8: *Stability and durability of social relationships* (X_1) *vary directly with status integration* (X_5).

THEOREM 9: *Conformity* (X_2) *varies directly with status integration* (X_5).

THEOREM 10: *Role conflict* (X_3) *varies inversely with status integration* (X_5).

Since the axioms of synthetic theories can be tested, verbal synthetic theories can sometimes be translated directly into statistical models such as path analysis (Duncan, 1966). If one can assume that his model is a recursive system, the analysis is greatly simplified. The notion of asymmetrical causation is inherent in such a recursive system

(Blalock, 1969: p. 48). The assumption of asymmetrical causation can be a simplifying assumption which makes the analysis much easier to perform than if the system included a plethora of feedback loops. Thus, the assumption of asymmetrical causality is at least potentially useful to researchers who wish to translate verbal synthetic theories into statistical models.

But Blalock's rules do not seem to be designed for the translation of verbal synthetic theories into statistical models. Blalock's rule 1 tells us to select causal statements as axioms. Rule 2 says that theorems should be stated in covariance form to facilitate testability. These rules seem to imply that only the theorems can be tested. That is, these rules seem to be designed only for explanatory deductive theories. Further, Blalock says that these are rules for stating theories in verbal form. The reader should not conclude from this that theories stated in verbal form must be explanatory theories rather than synthetic theories. Both synthetic and explanatory theories can be stated verbally. However, only the theorems of explanatory theories can be tested. With synthetic theories the researcher can test either the postulates or the theorems. Thus, if the Gibbs-Martin theory were a synthetic theory, the researcher could test any of the five postulates and ten theorems presented above.

Blalock's rule 2 implies that stating propositions in terms of covariations and temporal sequences will facilitate testability. Critics of causality might take this to mean that since the postulates of synthetic theories can be tested, these postulates should be stated in terms of covariations and temporal sequences in order to facilitate testability. Such critics might feel that all five postulates and ten theorems in the Gibbs-Martin synthetic theory should be stated in terms of covariations and temporal sequences. This would be a violation of Blalock's rule 1.

It seems that strict rules dictating the correct form for stating postulates or axioms or theorems can bring about as many problems as they solve. Why, then, do methodologists such as Costner and Leik and Blalock set down such rules? Their reason is a sound one. They wish to reduce the high level of ambiguity that is present in most verbal theories in sociology. Many verbal theories tell the reader next to nothing about the nature of the relationship expressed. The reader does not know if the relationships are static or dynamic, linear or nonlinear. Probably the theorist does not know either. However, if such a high level of ambiguity exists, the theory cannot be transformed into a mathematical model. Verbal theories that are ridden with ambiguities are clearly deficient. Thus, many methodologists seem to reason that since the concept of cause is useful in simplifying the complexities of the real world, relationships should be stated in causal form. But as seen above, such rules can be as restricting as they are helpful. It is clearly necessary for verbal theories to be stated so that ambiguity is minimized. But to say that all postulates should be stated, for example, in asymmetrical causal form seems rather like saying farmers should plant only apples so that there would be less ambiguity about what was planted, and predictions about crop production would be simplified.

INTERNAL CONSISTENCY

We have been discussing theory testing as the actual process of gathering empirical evidence to compare with one or more postulates or theorems. Unformalized theories which are stated verbally and have not been tested in the above sense are sometimes said to be tested in quite another manner. That is, both explanatory theories and synthetic theories should meet Popper's requirements as given above. They should be internally consistent. In addition, theorists often either explicitly or implicitly suggest that the system represented by their theory will attain stability or equilibrium. Or at least these theorists would not suggest that the variables involved increase indefinitely so that their values approach infinity. Even without gathering data in the field, certain tests of a system's internal consistency can be made. For example, the system's ability to attain equilibrium can be tested. One method is to analyze the system as a series of simultaneous differential equations (cf. Blalock, 1969). Another way is to make assumptions such as "causality with a discrete time lag" and perform a computer simulation (cf. Markley, 1967). If a rather large number of variables are involved in the theory, it may not be obvious from inspection whether the system is of the proper form to attain stability, and tests for internal consistency may be necessary. In complex cases the use of differential equations may be very difficult, and the only practical alternative may well be to assume a series of asymmetrical causal connections. Without such assumptions a simulation of the system may be difficult. Again, though, to say that relationships should be stated in "causal" form is an oversimplification that may "cause" more problems than it solves.

CONCLUSION

The critics of various axiomatic theories in sociology have implied that such theories are deficient if their axioms are not stated in asymmetrical or causal form. Such categorical statements should not be accepted without clarification. It is true that many verbal theories in sociology are so ambiguously stated that the reader cannot even tell whether the relationships are thought to be static or dynamic, linear or nonlinear. Such ambiguity makes it very difficult to construct a formal model from the theory.

It is also true that the concept of asymmetrical causality is very useful. It reduces ambiguity and simplifies theories so that the use of statistical techniques such as path analysis is facilitated. While providing such simplification, the concept of cause hopefully provides an acceptable (although simplified) description of empirical realities. It would be a *non sequitur*, though, for readers of these critics to assume that axiomatic theories should be rejected by sociologists if their postulates are not stated in causal form. Rules and regulations make our lives simpler by decreasing the number of decisions we must make. But the rejection of diverse theories on the basis of general rules about causation is unfair to contemporary sociological theorists. Axiomatic theories in sociology have been constructed for a variety of very different purposes. Some theories are essentially logical exercises designed to derive a testable proposition. Other theories specify a set of variables interrelated in such a manner that the system supposedly attains equilibrium.

The use of general rules may obfuscate the differing logical and empirical requirements of such theories. These rules definitely blur the important distinctions between explanatory deductive theory and synthetic deductive theory. In the former, only the theorem deduced from the postulates is actually tested. The postulates themselves are not tested. If these postulates were truly "laws" (whatever their form), the theory would be valid. The question of causality would then be academic. However, explanatory theories in sociology may be theories of desperation, especially when dealing with macro variables like the stability and durability of social relationships in a population. Operational definitions for such variables may be lacking. Thus, the researcher cannot test hypotheses containing such variables. In such a case he may choose to deduce, via the chain rule, a theorem that includes only those variables for which operational definitions are available. Gibbs and Martin's theory of suicide is one such theory. It should be noted, though, that such theories are explanatory deductive theories only in the generic sense of containing postulates which cannot be tested. They are not explanatory theories in the sense that the postulates explain the theorem by providing a description of the causal processes leading to the relationship expressed in the theorem. The theory "explains" the theorem (that suicide rate is inversely related to the degree of status integration) only by describing the thought processes of Gibbs and Martin. It specifically does not explain the Grand Theorem by describing a causal chain beginning in Postulate 1 and culminating in the Grand Theorem. Rather the inverse is true. Consider Blalock's (1969, p. 20) statement that "if the theorist has spelled out a clear causal chain, as for example in the Gibbs-Martin formulation . . . ." The meaning of this statement is not clear. It seems rather obvious that the Gibbs-Martin theory as now stated is not an adequate description of a causal process. If one wanted to describe the genetic process by which the suicide rate is caused or produced in a society, he would have to invert the Gibbs-Martin theory and use what is now the Grand Theorem as Postulate 1. What is now Postulate 1 would become the Grand Theorem to be tested. That is, it would be much more appropriate to say that a high degree of status integration causes a low degree of role conflict, low role conflict causes high conformity, high conformity causes high stability and durability of relationships, and such stability causes a low suicide rate. The fact that this usage of the term *cause* may seem strained attests to the fact that *cause* is often an inaccurate description of the relationship between sociological variables. Sociologists stating a relationship between social class and fertility may hesitate to say that social class causes fertility, even though they are perfectly willing to say that smoking causes cancer. However, as the Gibbs and Martin theory now stands, the term *cause* is even more inappropriate. Who would say that a high degree of role conflict causes many individuals to occupy incompatible statuses (Postulate 4)? This relationship is apparently asymmetrical, but could be considered interdependent. In either case it is difficult to conceive of Postulate 4 as a link in a causal chain that begins with Postulate 1 and ends with Postulate 5.

Since symmetrical relationships are logically appropriate and may help one to avoid the fallacy of affirming the consequent, and since anyone who transforms Postulates 1 through 5 of Gibbs and Martin's theory into "causal" statements is writing gibberish, it seems clear that explanatory deduction theorists should adhere to no strict rules about cause, but should describe relationships that are as realistic as possible.

The synthetic type of deductive theory presents a different problem. Here sociologists have a better opportunity to represent the theory in a statistical model. In this case asymmetry is a great aid in simplifying the problems inherent in such a task. Again, though, the categorical statement of rules is arbitrary and unwise. It precludes flexibility and unfairly impugns existing theories.

Finally, it must be said that no theory will completely satisfy all the requirements listed above. Just as there are no perfect theories, there is certainly not perfect agreement among theorists as to what constitutes a good theory. So, in the last analysis, even evaluation of a theory by means of the criteria above depends to a certain extent upon the prejudices and preferences of the evaluator. And certainly theories are accepted or rejected for reasons wholly different from the ones listed above. Still, if sociological theorists will keep the above points in mind, and if they strive first and foremost to construct theories which are both testable and which "explain" something by answering a specific question, then their efforts should be well received by evaluators. Sociologists do not require perfection of their essays or descriptive studies. Neither should they reject all imperfect theory. Such rejection could be fatal to sociology if it discouraged would-be constructors of social theory. Surely the tentative acceptance of a deduction whose validity is undetermined is no worse than the acceptance of vague and untestable statements as "theory." Surely imperfect theory is better than no theory at all.

REFERENCES

BLALOCK, H. M., JR.
  1964 *Causal Inferences in Nonexperimental Research*. Chapel Hill: University of North Carolina Press.
  1968 "The measurement problem: A gap between the languages of theory and research." Pp. 5–27 in H. M. Blalock, Jr., and A. B. Blalock (Eds.), *Methodology in Social Research*. New York: McGraw-Hill.
  1969 *Theory Construction*. Englewood Cliffs, N.J.: Prentice-Hall.

BUNGE, M.
  1959 *Causality: The Place of the Causal Principle in Modern Science*. Cambridge: Harvard University Press.

CATTON, W. R.
  1961 "The functions and dysfunctions of ethnocentrism: A theory." *Social Problems* 8 (Winter): 201–211.

CAWS, P.
  1965 *The Philosophy of Science: A Systematic Account*. Princeton, N.J.: Van Nostrand.

CHAMBLISS, W. J. AND STEELE, M. F.
  1966 "Status integration and suicide: An assessment." *American Sociological Review*, 31 (August): 524–532.

COLEMAN, J. S.
  1964 *Introduction to Mathematical Sociology*. New York: Free Press.

COPI, I. M.
  1961 *Introduction to Logic*. New York: Macmillan.

COSTNER, H. L.
  1969 "Theory, deduction, and rules of correspondence." *American Journal of Sociology* 75 (September): 245–263.

COSTNER, H. L. AND LEIK, R. K.
  1964 "Deductions from 'axiomatic theory.'" *American Sociological Review* 29 (December): 819–835.

DUNCAN, O. D.
    1963   "Axioms or correlations?" *American Sociological Review* 28 (June): 452.
    1966   "Path analysis: Sociological examples." *American Journal of Sociology*
           72 (July): 1-16.
FRANK, P. G.
    1956   "The variety of reasons for the acceptance of scientific theories." Pp.
           3-18 in P. G. Frank (ed.), *The Validation of Scientific Theories*. Boston:
           Beacon Press.
GIBBS, J. P. AND MARTIN, W. T.
    1958   "A theory of status integration and its relationship to suicide." *American
           Sociological Review* 23 (April): 140-147.
    1959   "Status integration and suicide in Ceylon." *American Journal of Soci-
           ology* 64 (May): 585-591.
    1962   "Urbanization, technology, and the division of labor: International pat-
           terns." *American Sociological Review* 27 (October): 667-677.
    1964   *Status Integration and Suicide*. Eugene: University of Oregon.
    1966   "On assessing the theory of status integration and suicide." *American
           Sociological Review* 31 (August): 533-541.
GOULD, L. C. AND SCHRAG, C.
    1962   "Theory construction and prediction in juvenile delinquency." *Proceed-
           ings of the Social Statistics Section of the American Statistical Association*,
           68-73.
HAGE, J.
    1965   "An axiomatic theory of organizations." *Administrative Science Quarterly*
           10 (December): 289-320.
HOMANS, G. C.
    1964   "Bringing men back in." *American Sociological Review* 29 (December):
           809-818.
LABOVITZ, S. AND GIBBS, J. P.
    1964   "Urbanization, technology, and the division of labor: Further evidence."
           Pacific Sociological Review 7 (Spring): 3-9.
LERNER, D.
    1965   "On cause and effect." Pp. 1-10 in D. Lerner (Ed.), *Cause and Effect*.
           New York: Free Press.
MCNEMAR, Q.
    1963   *Psychological Statistics*. New York: Wiley.
MARKLEY, O. W.
    1967   "A simulation of the SIVA model of organizational behavior." *American
           Journal of Sociology* 73 (November): 339-347.
MEEHAN, E. J.
    1968   *Explanation in Social Science: A System Paradigm*. Homewood, Ill.:
           Dorsey Press.
NORTHROP, F. S. C.
    1947   *The Logic of the Sciences and the Humanities*. New York: Macmillan.
POPPER, K. R.
    1959   *The Logic of Scientific Discovery*. New York: Basic Books.
PREHN, J. W. AND SCHWIRIAN, K. P.
    1963   "Reply to Duncan." *American Sociological Review* 28 (June): 452-453.

SCHWIRIAN, K. P. AND PREHN, J. W.
  1962 "An axiomatic theory of urbanization." *American Sociological Review*
        27 (December): 812–825.
STINCHCOMBE, A. L.
  1968 *Constructing Social Theories.* New York: Harcourt, Brace, and World.
STOLL, R. R.
  1961 *Sets, Logic, and Axiomatic Theories.* San Francisco: Freeman.
ZETTERBERG, H. L.
  1954 *On Theory and Verification in Sociology.* Stockholm: Almquist and Wiksell.
  1965 *On Theory and Verification in Sociology.* Totowa, N.J.: Bedminster Press.

PART TWO

MEASUREMENT, RELIABILITY, AND VALIDITY

5

STATISTICAL ESTIMATION WITH RANDOM MEASUREMENT ERROR

H. M. Blalock

UNIVERSITY OF NORTH CAROLINA

Caryll S. Wells

CARLETON UNIVERSITY

Lewis F. Carter

UNIVERSITY OF CALIFORNIA, RIVERSIDE

*We are indebted to the
National Science Foundation for partial support of this research and to
Arthur S. Goldberger and Powhattan J. Wooldridge for making extensive
comments on an earlier version.*

As sociological research becomes increasingly oriented toward
providing definitive information designed to test alternative theories or
to yield accurate estimates of fundamental parameters, we shall find it
absolutely essential to improve our measurement procedures. This will,

of course, require much more attention to the data collection stage of the research process, but once the data have been gathered there still remains the problem of finding ways to analyze imperfect data either to reduce the effects of measurement error or to obtain estimates of these effects so that corrections can be made. In the present paper we discuss several alternative statistical procedures for handling purely random measurement errors and provide some data that suggest the advantages and disadvantages of each approach.

It is well known that least-squares estimating procedures yield biased estimates in the case of purely random measurement errors in independent variables and that this bias is in the direction of attenuating both correlation and slope coefficients. It is sometimes thought that this bias automatically leads to conservative conclusions, in the sense that whenever one finds relationships between imperfectly measured variables, he can be assured that if the measurement error has been strictly random then the true relationships must be even stronger than the obtained relationships. But while this is the case for bivariate relationships, differential measurement errors can lead to incorrect inferences in the multivariate case. For example, one may infer a partly spurious relationship between two variables when it is actually totally spurious. Or he may conclude that there is statistical interaction when an additive model would be more appropriate. And in the case of intercorrelated independent variables, he may arrive at incorrect weights of their relative contributions to a dependent variable.[1] In short, the existence of random (or nonrandom) measurement errors becomes a serious problem for inference in any study that is designed to go beyond merely locating correlates of a particular dependent variable.

In order to introduce the problem we first discuss the nature of the bias in ordinary least-squares procedures. We then present data to show that a relatively simple grouping approach suggested by Wald (1940) and Bartlett (1949) has approximately the same biases as ordinary least squares. Finally, we consider two alternative procedures that appear to be based on similar principles, and that seem to provide similar estimates. We shall then be in a position to contrast the relative merits of the various alternative estimating procedures. We assume throughout that there is no systematic measurement error. We also assume that there is only a single measure of each variable, although in

---

[1] For a more detailed discussion of these and other kinds of distortions produced by random measurement error see Blalock (1965), Gordon (1968), and Bohrnstedt (1969).

some instances it may be possible (and preferable) to utilize multiple indicator approaches to provide supplementary estimates.[2]

ORDINARY LEAST SQUARES

One of the basic assumptions underlying the use of ordinary least-squares estimators is that "independent" variables in any given structural (or regression) equation must be uncorrelated in the *population* with the error term in that equation. This assumption is rather simple to state mathematically, but its practical implications are somewhat more difficult to pin down. Consider the simple structural equation

$$X_1 = \alpha_1 + \beta_{12}X_2 + \epsilon_1 \tag{1}$$

and the ordinary least-squares estimating equation

$$X_1 = a_1 + b_{12}X_2 + u_1 \tag{2}$$

where we wish to estimate α_1 with a_1, β_{12} with b_{12}, and the unknown error term ϵ_1 with the residual component u_1.[3] It can be shown that b_{12} will be an unbiased estimator of β_{12} provided that there is no specification error (that is, that equation (1) is in fact the true equation linking X_1 and X_2), and that the population covariance between X_2 and the error term ϵ_1 is zero. It is usually assumed that the expected value of ϵ_1 is also zero, though if it is any other value this will merely affect the estimate of the constant term. In order to make the customary F and t tests, it is also necessary, strictly speaking, to assume a normal distribution for the error term. The homoscedasticity assumption (equal variances of the error term for all levels of X_2) seems somewhat more crucial in connection with tests and confidence bands, but moderate departures from homoscedasticity can be tolerated reasonably well. The crucial assumption, however, is that the error term of the structural equation be uncorrelated with the independent variable.[4]

The model can readily be extended to any number of independent variables without complication provided that this crucial assumption is

---

[2] For an approach to estimation through the use of multiple indicators see Costner (1969) and Siegel and Hodge (1968).

[3] The beta in equation (1), as well as elsewhere, is not to be confused with the standardized beta weight. It is the unstandardized regression coefficient for the population, or what has been termed a structural parameter.

[4] Strictly speaking, lack of correlation between an independent variable and a disturbance term is sufficient only for asymptotic (large-sample) unbiasedness but not for exact unbiasedness. Independence suffices but is unnecessarily strong. A compromise notion of "mean independence" is developed in Goldberger (1968).

actually met. But if these additional independent variables are themselves highly intercorrelated, then any minor deviation from this particular assumption can lead to major complications in the estimating procedure. This point has been well documented by Gordon (1968). This assumption is also of critical importance in systems of equations involving variables that are reciprocally interrelated causally. For example, if it were true that X_1 were a cause of X_2, as well as X_2 being a cause of X_1, then it would be necessary to write down a second equation in which X_2 is taken as the dependent variable. It can then be shown that it will be impossible to meet the assumption that X_2 and ϵ_1 are uncorrelated, as required by ordinary least squares.[5] In such cases of reciprocal causation, ordinary least-squares estimating procedures are therefore necessarily biased (except in trivial cases where some of the coefficients are set equal to zero), and alternative estimating procedures should be used (Christ, 1966; Goldberger, 1964; Johnston, 1963).

Any random measurement errors in the independent variables will produce attenuating biases in the ordinary least-squares estimates, the degree of bias being dependent on the relative magnitudes of the measurement error variance as compared with the variance in the independent variable concerned. Where there are several independent variables, this in effect means that there will be differential attenuations that will imply trouble whenever one wishes to sort out the component effects of each independent variable. In general, the higher the intercorrelations among the independent variables, the greater the distortions produced by differential measurement error.

In this paper we shall not deal with the multivariate case, although the extensions are in most instances straightforward. Considering the bivariate model of equation (1), let us suppose that the independent variable has been imperfectly measured by $X_2' = X_2 + e_2$, where e_2 is a random variable and therefore independent of X_2. The measurement error component e_2 must be kept conceptually distinct from the error components ϵ_1 and u_1 that appear in equations (1) and (2) respectively. We are thinking of e_2 as representing measurement error, whereas ϵ_1 is thought of as a residual term produced by (causal) variables that have been omitted from the equation. The term u_1 represents the empirically obtained residuals about the least-squares equation (2) used to estimate the parameters in equation (1). If there were also measurement error in the dependent variable X_1, this might be represented by a similar error term e_1, but it turns out that such measurement error in a dependent variable can be absorbed into the

---

[5] This is true because if X_2 were a function of X_1, which in turn is a function of ϵ_1, then X_2 would ordinarily be correlated with ϵ_1.

error ϵ_1 without any complications, provided that this measurement error is truly random.

If we now substitute the measured value X_2' in equation (1) we get the following result:

$$X_1 = \alpha_1 + \beta_{12}X_2 + \epsilon_1 = \alpha_1 + \beta_{12}(X_2' - e_2) + \epsilon_1$$
$$= \alpha_1 + \beta_{12}X_2' + (\epsilon_1 - \beta_{12}e_2)$$

where the new error term $(\epsilon_1 - \beta_{12}e_2)$ is obviously correlated with the imperfectly measured independent variable X_2'. This is true because X_2' is a function of e_2, which now appears as a component of the error term.[6] Thus if we use the least-squares equation

$$X_1 = a_1' + b_{12}'X_2' + u_1'$$

we can expect to obtain a biased estimate of β_{12}.

If the measurement errors in the independent variable X_2 are truly random, then they will be statistically independent and therefore the population covariance between X_2 and e_2 will be zero, and we will have the result that

$$\sigma_{X_2'}^2 = \sigma_{X_2}^2 + \sigma_{e_2}^2 \tag{3}$$

The reason for the downward bias in the slope estimate of β_{12} is that the least-squares formula for b_{12} involves the ratio of the sample covariance between X_1 and X_2, which is not systematically affected by random measurement errors in either variable, to the sample variance in the measured value of X_2, namely $\hat{\sigma}_{X_2'}^2$, which will generally be larger than the sample variance of the true value of X_2. For large random samples it can be shown (Johnston, 1963, p. 150) that the least-squares estimate b_{12}' based on the measured value X_2' is related to the parameter β_{12} according to the approximate formula:

$$E(b_{12}') = \frac{\beta_{12}}{1 + \sigma_{e_2}^2/\sigma_{X_2}^2} = \beta_{12}\frac{\sigma_{X_2}^2}{\sigma_{X_2}^2 + \sigma_{e_2}^2} \tag{4}$$

The so-called classical approaches to correcting for this attenuation depend on the very strong assumption that we have independent means of estimating the absolute magnitude of the measurement error variance $\sigma_{e_2}^2$ or the ratio $\sigma_{e_2}^2/\sigma_{X_2}^2$. Obviously, if either of these quantities could be known a priori, it would be possible to apply the proper correction factor to b_{12}', but in most sociological research we lack this crucial information. Therefore these classical approaches would not seem to

---

[6] This follows because $E[X_2'(\epsilon_1 - \beta_{12}e_2)] - E(X_2'\epsilon_1) - \beta_{12}E(X_2'e_2) = -\beta_{12}E(X_2'e_2) \neq 0$.

have much practical value at the present time and are not discussed further in this paper (see Johnston, 1963, pp. 150–162).

Whenever the scientist is in a position to make repeated measurements on the same individual, whose properties can be assumed to remain fixed over the period of measurement, it becomes possible to obtain estimates of the measurement error variance.[7] Furthermore, much of the measurement error may be canceled out by the simple device of using the mean score of the several observations, rather than resorting to corrections for attenuation of the sort that are commonly used whenever only two measurements per individual have been obtained. The fundamental problem facing the social scientist is that repeated measurements on the same individual may be practically impossible, or it may not be plausible to assume that the true value is in fact remaining constant from one measurement to the next. However, if it were possible to cancel out random errors by grouping together *similar* individuals (with nearly identical true values) and using their mean score to represent the group, then we would in effect have a functional equivalent to the procedure of taking repeated measurements on the *same* individual.

Two of the three alternatives to least-squares estimates that will be discussed in the remainder of this paper are based on this principle of attempting to group together similar individuals so as to take out random error. In comparing each of these alternatives with least-squares estimation, we shall see, however, that this simple principle is not easy to apply in practice, because the true scores for the independent variable X_2 will not be known. The next procedure we discuss involves grouping individuals according to the *measured* values of the independent variable, whereas one of the two procedures in the following section involves grouping them according to scores on some variable assumed to be a cause of the independent variable.

ESTIMATING ERROR VARIANCE

The magnitude of measurement error in the independent variable may be taken as measured by the error variance $\sigma_{e_2}^2$ where the true values of X_1 and X_2 are related by the equation:

[7] We are grateful to P. J. Wooldridge for pointing out that repeated measurements on the same individual make it possible to obtain estimates of only that portion of the measurement error variance due to sources that vary over the time period for the individual. Sources that may vary from individual to individual within the sample may be entirely neglected by using repeated measurements. Possibly, then, there might be certain advantages of procedures that cancel out errors by grouping together similar individuals, provided a way could be found to justify the assumption that they are, in fact, similar with respect to the independent variable(s) under consideration.

$$X_1 = \alpha_1 + \beta_{12}X_2 + \epsilon_1$$

and the measured values of these variables

$$X_1' = X_1 + e_1$$
$$X_2' = X_2 + e_2$$

where e_1 and e_2 are random measurement errors. Thus the measured values are estimated from sample data by the equation:

$$X_1' = a' + b_{12}'X_2' + u_1'$$

Wald (1940) has shown that we can also obtain a consistent estimate (with a negligible large-sample bias) of the error variance $\sigma_{e_2}^2$ from the observed (sample) variances $\hat{\sigma}_{X_2'}^2$ and an unbiased estimate of β_{12} plus the least-squares estimator b_{12}'.[8] This may be done with the following equation:

$$\hat{\sigma}_{e_2}^2 = \hat{\sigma}_{X_2'}^2 \left[\frac{\hat{\beta}_{12}}{b_{12}'} - 1 \right] \tag{5}$$

where $\hat{\beta}_{12}$ is an unbiased estimate of β_{12}. As can readily be seen, this equation gives a measurement error variance estimate that is based on the variance for the observed values X_2' and a function of the attenuation in the least-squares estimate.

Wald (1940) and Bartlett (1949) have shown that under certain conditions, we can calculate the requisite unbiased slope estimators from the observed distributions. Their techniques, outlined below, are quite similar.

Wald's estimator, b_W, is given by the following formula, where it will simplify notation to refer to Y as the dependent variable and X as the independent variable. Thus, to avoid multiple subscripting and superscripting, Y has been substituted for X_1 and X has been substituted for X_2. N is the number of observations. $M = N/2$ and $N/2$ is an integer. The term y_i is the elements of Y and x_i is the elements of X. The prime notation refers to *observed* values. The a and b refer to means for *groups* a and b discussed below:

$$b_W = \frac{\bar{Y}_a' - \bar{Y}_b'}{\bar{X}_a' - \bar{X}_b'} = \frac{(y_1' + y_2' + \cdots + y_M') - (y_{M+1}' + \cdots + y_N')}{(x_1' + x_2' + \cdots + x_M') - (x_{M+1}' + \cdots + x_N')} \tag{6}$$

Bartlett's estimator, b_B, is given by the following formula, where Y is the dependent variable, X is the independent variable, N is the number of observations, $I = N/3$, $J = 2N/3$, and $N/3$ is an integer:

---

[8] We have taken the argument found in Johnston (1963, p. 150) and solved for the error variance.

82   H. M. BLALOCK, CARYLL S. WELLS, AND LEWIS F. CARTER

$$b_B = \frac{\bar{Y}'_a - \bar{Y}'_c}{\bar{X}'_a - \bar{X}'_c} = \frac{(y'_1 + y'_2 + \cdots + y'_I) - (y'_J + \cdots + y'_N)}{(x'_1 + x'_2 + \cdots + x'_I) - (x'_J + \cdots + x'_N)} \quad (7)$$

Both estimation techniques require that observations first be ordered in increasing magnitude on X'. Basically, the techniques consist of ordering the observations on the independent variable, and then separating the observations into groups, G_a and G_b. Means are calculated for each group on X' and Y'. The ratio of the difference in the Y' means and the difference in the X' means for the two groups are taken as an unbiased slope estimator. The only difference in the two techniques is that Wald divides the distribution into two equal groups G_a and G_b whereas Bartlett divides the distribution into three equal groups G_a, G_b, and G_c, uses the first and third group as G_a and G_c, and excludes the middle third of the distribution. There are minor differences in the operating characteristics of these two techniques, but these need not be discussed here for reasons which will become apparent below.

Neither technique, in fact, gives unbiased slope estimates for data of the quality usually seen in social science. This is because both techniques involve the assumption that the grouping is unrelated to the error term, e_2, in the equation $X'_2 = X_2 + e_2$, which becomes, with our simplified notation, $X' = X + e_2$. It is obvious that since the grouping is done for scores ordered on the *observed* values X', the grouping cannot be independent of e_2 save in situations where the e_{2i} are very small. [Strictly, the groupings will be independent of the error terms if and only if $\max e_{2i} < \frac{1}{2} \min |x_i - x_j|$, $(i \neq j)$. This requires that the measurement error be very small. Strictly, for distributions of income, measured in whole dollars, error would have to be less than fifty cents. In practical terms, errors of fifty dollars or more could probably not be tolerated by the techniques, for most purposes. Of course, there is no way to verify that this assumption is true from the observed scores.]

In isolating the effects of this critical assumption in these techniques, we constructed data which conformed to all of the assumptions of the techniques save this, in practice, untestable one. The assumptions of the techniques may be summarized as follows (Wald, 1940, pp. 286–287 and 294–297): (1) The true values of the independent and dependent variables must be related by a single linear function, (2) the measurement error terms must be uncorrelated with each other, (3) the measurement error terms must be uncorrelated with the true values, (4) the measurement error terms must have the same distribution, (5) the groupings must be independent of the error terms.

In practice one never knows both "measured" and "true" values for naturally occurring data. Thus, the reasonableness of the Wald assumptions is not verifiable for such data. An assessment of these estimation techniques requires that we first make inferences about "true" values and measurement error from "measured" values. Next, and most importantly, we must be able to verify those inferences by comparison with "true" values which are known independently of the techniques. Simulation is the only really practical solution. We can construct artificial data with known properties.

The effects of different kinds of measurement error for those data can be simulated producing synthetic data like those we should observe if the "true" values were as constructed and the measurement error were as applied. In this study we have used only random normal measurement error, as that clearly conforms to the assumptions of Wald. Inferences from the "measured" to the "true" values can thus be evaluated. Details of this simulation may be found in Carter and Blalock (1970). A description of the resulting data follows.

The Data. To meet the first four of Wald's assumptions, several data sets were constructed. A distribution of sixty true X values were drawn from a set of normally distributed random numbers with mean equal to 0 and standard deviation equal to 1.[9] Wald dealt with true Ys which were exact functions of true Xs, though the measurement error problem is the same with imperfect functions. Following Wald and in accordance with his assumption 1 (above), true Y values were constructed by the equation:

[9] These are expected values for the mean and standard deviation. The actual values varied normally around these for the samples used. Parent distributions and error terms were generated by first getting a set of uniformly distributed pseudorandom numbers by the "power-residue" method discussed in *Random Number Generation and Testing* (IBM manual #C20-8011). The distributions were normalized by the transformation

$$S_i = \frac{\sum_{j=1}^{k} V_j - (k/2)}{k/12}$$

where: V_j is a uniformly distributed random number between 0 and 1, k is the number of V_js to be used for each S_i, S_i is a variable the distribution of which will approach a true normal distribution asymptotically as $k \to \infty$. The term k was chosen as 12 and the transformation simplifies to:

$$S_i = \sum_{j=1}^{12} V_j - 6.0$$

This is an application of a special case of the central limit theorem. See also Hamming (1962), pp. 34 and 389.

$$y_i = 0 + 1x_i$$

Two distributions of error terms e_{1i} and e_{2i} were generated. These distributions were each normally distributed random numbers with mean equal to 0 and standard deviation equal to 1. This satisfies Wald's assumptions 2, 3, and 4 (above). Checks were employed at this point testing the independence assumptions (2 and 3) and the isomorphism assumption (4). The results of these tests, which were totally satisfactory, are reported in footnote 1 of Carter and Blalock (1970).

Observed values for Y and X were constructed by the following equations:

$$y_i' = y_i + ce_{1i}$$
$$x_i' = x_i + de_{2i}$$

where c and d are constants which were manipulated to simulate the effects of measurement errors of varying magnitudes. In one analysis, c was given a value of 0.1 to simulate rather accurate measurement on the dependent variable with $\sigma_y^2 = 1$ and $\sigma_{ce_1}^2 = 0.01$.[10] In another analysis, c was given a value of 2 to simulate a very poorly measured dependent variable with $\sigma_y^2 = 1$ and $\sigma_{ce_1}^2 = 4$. Under each set of conditions, d was allowed to take on the values 0.1, 0.5, and 2, successively. Thus, for accurately measured and inaccurately measured dependent variables, analyses were run simulating independent variables measured in an accurate, a mediocre, and a very inaccurate fashion.[11] These analyses were replicated one hundred times with independent samples of true values, measured values, and error terms. For each of these one hundred replications the sample size was sixty.

Results. It should be kept in mind that the observed and measured variables as well as the error term distributions satisfy the first four Wald-Bartlett assumptions. However, as in all empirical research where only the measured values are obtainable, the groupings are based on an ordering of the measured x_i'. Thus, except in the case of miniscule

---

[10] Though we are dealing conceptually with error terms e_1 and e_2, the data analyzed involved error terms ce_1 and de_2. Each empirical distribution ce_1 or de_2 may be treated as a conceptual equivalent of e_1 and e_2, though tests using successive values of c and d are, of course, not independent.

[11] Of course, the measurement error in the dependent variable does not bias the least-squares estimator, b_{yx}. However, it does make that estimator more variable. More importantly, measurement error is introduced into the dependent variable as well as the independent variable because the problem becomes a misleadingly simple one when one of the variables is known to be perfectly measured. The opportunity for such a simplifying assumption seldom presents itself in social science.

measurement errors, they are not wholly independent of the measurement errors, e_{2i}. The effect of this nonindependence is quite serious, the bias in slope estimates being almost as extreme for the grouping techniques as for the least-squares technique.[12] For one hundred replications, the Wald and Bartlett techniques give estimates which are generally slightly *more* attenuated than those based on the least-squares technique. Means of these slope estimates are shown in Table 1.

TABLE 1
Slope Estimates for Normally Distributed Parent Distributions
with True Slope $\beta_{12} = 1.0$[a]

Expected Value of Error Variance in Dependent Variable	Expected Value of Error Variance in Independent Variable	Least-Squares Slope Estimate	Slope Estimates from Grouping Techniques Wald	Bartlett
0.01	0.01	0.9923 (0.0193)	0.9920 (0.0247)	0.9920 (0.0221)
0.01	0.25	0.8029 (0.0553)	0.8042 (0.0663)	0.8040 (0.0583)
0.01	4.00	0.1939 (0.0554)	0.1898 (0.0672)	0.1928 (0.0622)
4.00	0.01	1.0013 (0.2674)	0.9944 (0.3413)	1.0058 (0.3112)
4.00	0.25	0.7916 (0.2615)	0.7744 (0.3087)	0.7909 (0.2840)
4.00	4.00	0.1769 (0.1355)	0.1623 (0.1748)	0.1740 (0.1507)

[a] Means of one hundred replications are presented, using each slope estimation technique under each set of error conditions. In each case, the expected values for the true variances are $\sigma_Y^2 = \sigma_X^2 = 1.0$. Standard errors, estimated from these one hundred replications, are presented in parentheses. For each replication, $N = 60$.

[12] In the discussion and tables relevant to these findings, we have presented some information which could have been obtained without the simulation. The bias in the least-squares estimator can be obtained analytically with ease. Its inclusion here serves two purposes. It provides an independent check on the simulation programs themselves and it facilitates the reader's comparisons with the biases produced in the Wald and Bartlett estimators.

The findings where errors in the dependent variable are large are in most respects like those where the errors in the dependent variable are small. This is known analytically. These findings are also presented as an aid to the reader and to provide an independent check on the simulation procedures. The reader should also note the extreme differences in the variability (sampling fluctuation) of the estimation procedures under conditions of accurately and inaccurately measured dependent variables.

For the condition of minimal error in Y, the Wald technique gives estimates which are closer to the true value than the least-squares estimates for forty-two of the replications and slightly less close for fifty-eight of the replications. For one of the six error conditions, both grouping techniques give somewhat closer estimates than least squares. Even so, the estimates are poor under this condition, least squares giving $b = 0.8029$, Wald giving $b = 0.8042$, and Bartlett giving $b = 0.8040$, when the true slope is 1.00. Finally, the least-squares estimate has smaller estimated standard errors than do the estimates from the other techniques. Other replications, not reported here, show that with X and Y distributions which are not normally distributed, the grouping techniques actually perform much worse than does the least-squares technique. These analyses, involving rectangular and log-normal distributions, like much social data, show that Wald-Bartlett estimates are less satisfactory than least-squares estimates under certain conditions.[13]

Obviously, one would be quite misled if he were to take Wald-Bartlett estimates as giving unbiased estimates of β_{12} for most social data. Taking the slope estimates of these grouping techniques as unbiased, as suggested by Wald, would have especially serious consequences for an investigator who wished to assess the accuracy of his measurements. Table 2 summarizes the error variance estimates derived from the one hundred replications with the normally distributed X and Y values. Compare the means for the actual error variances (column 3) with the means for the error variance estimates we would get using the true slope of 1.0 (column 6). It is apparent that a knowledge of the true slope and the measured X' and Y' values permits moderately accurate estimates of the error variances. However, taking the Wald and Bartlett slope estimates (columns 4 and 5) as unbiased results in gross underestimation of error variance. The underestimation is so extreme that in most cases we get negative error variance estimates.

It should be obvious from the foregoing analysis that the Wald-Bartlett techniques have little utility for sociology. In general, they do not provide unbiased slope estimates for data of the quality usually found in sociology. Even where the techniques provide less biased

---

[13] We also examined several other variations of the Wald-Bartlett procedures for each of these replications. For example, in one modification the X' values were grouped into four groupings of equal number of cases, with the middle two groupings excluded. The results were essentially the same as those presented in Tables 1 and 2. Conceivably, we might have obtained better results either by using widely scattered scores or by excluding all but the extreme scores on X'.

TABLE 2
Error Variance Estimates from Four Grouping Techniques Compared with
True Error Variance and an Estimate Based on the True Slope

Expected Value of Error Variance in Dependent Variable	Expected Value of Error Variance in Independent Variable	Actual Value of Error Variance in Independent Variable	Estimates of Error Variance in Independent Variable Using Slope Estimation Source Indicated		
			Wald	Bartlett	Unbiased Slope[a]
0.01	0.01	0.0101	−0.0007[b]	−0.0006	0.0079
0.01	0.25	0.2531	0.0006	0.0015	0.2449
0.01	4.00	4.0502	−0.4211	−0.2190	4.0194
4.00	0.01	0.0101	−0.0843	−0.0261	−0.0013[c]
4.00	0.25	0.2531	−0.0684	−0.0021	0.2572
4.00	4.00	4.0502	−8.8833	−0.5611	4.1121

[a] These error variance estimates are for a β_{YX} of 1.00.

[b] The negative error variance estimates result when the slope estimate, assumed to be nearer the true value than least squares, is in fact farther away.

[c] This negative error variance estimate results because the least-squares slope estimate is larger than the true slope.

estimates than least squares, those estimates are themselves seriously attenuated. Consequently, all error variance estimates are biased downward. This is attributable to the violation of the sensitive assumption that the grouping must be unrelated to the error terms. If the error variance is in fact small, the techniques give fairly accurate estimates of it. However, if the error variance is large, the estimates of that variance are seriously biased, indicating, erroneously, that the variance is small. The most serious aspect of this finding is that these techniques *always* lead to the conclusion that error variance is small and measurements are accurate, whether that conclusion is justified or not.

INSTRUMENTAL VARIABLES AND GROUPINGS BY EXOGENOUS VARIABLES

If the Wald-Bartlett approach were workable in instances where measurement errors cannot be assumed negligible, this would indeed be fortunate. We would have a technique that does not require strong *a priori* assumptions and that is almost guaranteed to take out purely random measurement errors in any reasonably sized sample. In retrospect, it is perhaps naive to hope to find a simple procedure that can take care of random errors so easily. The two procedures we consider in the present section are of a very different variety. They depend on *a priori* assumptions regarding the causal structure of the system in which a particular equation is embedded. We shall see that both procedures work very well when these assumptions are in fact true, but that they are dependent on the correctness of the required *a priori* assumptions. This is also true with respect to least-squares estimates, and the degree of bias depends on the values of the parameters of the equation systems. The bias using least squares differs from that for these alternative procedures, however, and it will be necessary for the investigator to make enlightened guesses as to which procedure will yield the smallest biases in any given instance.

The fundamental problem we encounter in making a comparison between least-squares estimates and those based on these alternative approaches is that in any given situation there is a combination of measurement errors and what are termed *specification errors*, or errors in the equations themselves. For example, both the alternative procedures presently under discussion depend on our locating a third variable (or several such variables) which is a direct or indirect cause of the "independent" variable X_2 but which does not appear in the equation for X_1. (It should be noted that we have here returned to our initial notation.) In other words, this third variable cannot be a cause of X_1 except through X_2 as an intervening variable. In the case of the first of these alternative procedures, the "instrumental-variables" approach, it is possible to obtain a formula for the expected large-sample bias if this assumption is violated. But in the case of the second alternative, which involves a grouping procedure, we have to rely entirely on Monte Carlo experiments to obtain estimates of the bias. Let us first consider the instrumental-variables approach since its rationale is much more clearly understood.

The Instrumental-Variables Approach. In order to see the nature of this approach in its full generality, it will be necessary to broaden our discussion to a consideration of simultaneous-equation approaches to estimation. Let us consider a set of mutually interdependent variables X_i, which will be referred to as endogenous variables. Added to this set will be a number of exogenous variables Z_j which are assumed not to depend on any of the endogenous X_i, although the exogenous variables may be intercorrelated for unknown reasons. The Z_j are the "givens" that cannot be explained by the theory under concern, though some other theory may of course be developed which takes the Z_j as endogenous. We then write a separate equation for each of the endogenous variables in terms of a certain subset of both the remaining endogenous variables and the exogenous variables. Restricting our attention to linear systems, and retaining a notation consistent with our previous equations, we can write such a system of equations as follows:

$$X_1 = \alpha_1 + \beta_{12}X_2 + \beta_{13}X_3 + \cdots + \beta_{1k}X_k + \gamma_{11}Z_1$$
$$+ \gamma_{12}Z_2 + \cdots + \gamma_{1m}Z_m + \epsilon_1$$
$$X_2 = \alpha_2 + \beta_{21}X_1 + \beta_{23}X_3 + \cdots + \beta_{2k}X_k + \gamma_{21}Z_1$$
$$+ \gamma_{22}Z_2 + \cdots + \gamma_{2m}Z_m + \epsilon_2$$

$$\cdot$$
$$\cdot \quad (8)$$
$$\cdot$$

$$X_k = \alpha_k + \beta_{k1}X_1 + \beta_{k2}X_2 + \cdots + \beta_{k,k-1}X_{k-1} + \gamma_{k1}Z_1$$
$$+ \gamma_{k2}Z_2 + \cdots + \gamma_{km}Z_m + \epsilon_k$$

We have of course been dealing with a very simple special case of this general system consisting of a single equation in which X_1 is dependent only on X_2 and where it was possible (though perhaps not realistic) to assume that X_2 is uncorrelated with the error term ϵ_1. As we have already noted, whenever we allow for reciprocal causal relationships among the endogenous X_i, it is no longer possible to meet this assumption unless we modify the equation system by explicitly allowing for lagged relationships. Even in such a lagged model, it is seldom realistic to assume no intercorrelations between the X_i and the error terms for equations in which these X_i appear as "independent" variables. (See Christ, 1966, pp. 482–487; Fisher, 1966, pp. 168–175.)

It is possible, however, to assume that the exogenous Z_j are uncorrelated with the error terms. This assumption amounts to saying that any factors that affect the X_i but that have been omitted from the equation system are *not* causally connected to the exogenous variables. In fact, we may take this to be a defining characteristic of what we mean by an exogenous variable (Fisher, 1966, p. 16). If, for example, any omitted variable that is a cause of X_1 is also a cause of one of the Z_j, then this particular Z_j is not truly exogenous and should be brought into the system as an endogenous variable, thus necessitating the addition of a further equation. Obviously, then, whenever we commit ourselves to the distinction between endogenous and exogenous variables we are forced to make a *priori* assumptions to the effect that a certain subset of variables are not dependent on the others.

It would be desirable not to have to make such a *priori* assumptions. But it can be shown that unless this can be done the system will contain too many unknowns for solution. This will mean that there will be an infinite number of different sets of parameter values, all of which will be consistent with the same set of data. When this occurs, the system is said to be underidentified. Sometimes a particular equation may contain too many unknowns, whereas others may not. Therefore it is useful to examine each equation in turn. It can be shown that given only the assumption that the Z_j's cannot be correlated with the ϵ_i, a necessary (but not sufficient) condition for identification of the parameters in any given equation is that there must be at least $k - 1$ variables left out of the equation, where k represents the number of equations or endogenous variables.[14] In effect, this means that not all variables can directly cause any endogenous variable whose equation is to be identified. We must make the *a priori* assumption that certain of the possible β_{ij} and γ_{ij} are set equal to zero (or have some other known value).

If precisely $k - 1$ variables have been left out of an equation, we say that this equation is exactly identified, whereas if more than $k - 1$ variables have been omitted we say that it is overidentified. In either case it will be possible to obtain estimates of the parameters, but in the overidentified case there will be an excess of information over the number of unknowns, and there will be no unique solution. In this case there are a number of simultaneous-equation estimating techniques that yield different results, and it appears at present to be an open question as to which is generally superior (Johnston, 1963, Chapter Ten). If *all* equations are exactly identified, these alternative procedures become mathematically equivalent. In the case of any particular equation that is exactly identified, the method of instrumental variables under present consideration is equivalent to the method of indirect least squares, which can be shown to yield consistent estimators (that is, estimators with negligible large-sample biases). In the context of our present discussion, the instrumental-variables approach can also be used to obtain consistent estimators even in the presence of random measurement errors in the independent variable(s).

In order to keep our exposition as simple as possible let us consider the two-equation system

$$X_1 = \alpha_1 + \beta_{12}X_2 + \gamma_{11}Z_1 + \epsilon_1 \tag{9}$$
$$X_2 = \alpha_2 + \gamma_{21}Z_1 + \epsilon_2 \tag{10}$$

where the exogenous variable Z_1, assumed uncorrelated with ϵ_1, constitutes an instrumental variable, the role of which will presently be explained, and where we again assume that X_2 has been imperfectly measured by $X_2' = X_2 + e_2$, where e_2 is uncorrelated with X_1, X_2, and Z_1. We first examine the situation in which $\gamma_{11} = 0$ and where equation (9) therefore reduces to equation (1) as previously discussed. In this case Z_1 does not appear at all in the equation for X_1 but is taken as a cause of X_2. Actually, we do not need to know the value of the coefficient

---

[14] As noted by Fisher (1966, pp. 28ff.), this necessary condition may be stated somewhat more generally. There must be at least $k - 1$ independent restrictions on the parameters of the equation in question.

γ_{21} linking Z_1 to X_2, but we see that its value enters into the expression for the bias produced in the instrumental-variables approach when γ_{11} takes on particular non-zero values, that is, when Z_1 in fact appears in the equation for X_1.

In less abstract terms, we are searching for exogenous variables that do not directly affect X_1, that are uncorrelated with the error term ϵ_1, and that are reasonably direct causes of X_2. Fisher (1965) has noted that the latter two criteria may, in practice, be difficult to satisfy simultaneously, so that some sort of compromise may have to be reached. We might add that the first and third criteria may also be difficult to satisfy simultaneously; variables that directly affect X_2 may also directly affect X_1, but this is merely conjecture on our part.[15] Let us temporarily assume, however, that the above three criteria are in fact met, and thus that we have found a variable that does not appear in the equation for X_1 but that is an important cause of X_2.

In this simple two-variable case the instrumental-variable estimator b_{12}^* of β_{12} is formed by taking the ratio of the covariances of Z_1 with X_1 and X_2' respectively.[16] Thus

$$b_{12}^* = \frac{\Sigma x_1 z_1}{\Sigma x_2' z_1} \tag{11}$$

where the lower-case letters here refer to deviations around the respective means. Since b_{12}^* is a ratio of *covariances*, which are not systematically affected by random measurement errors in any of the variables, this estimator turns out to be a consistent estimator of β_{12}.[17] But this argument

---

[15] Liu (1960) has argued that since, in reality, there will inevitably be specification error whenever we introduce simplifying assumptions such as that $\gamma_{11} = 0$, all models will be underidentified and therefore estimation will be hopeless. Fisher (1961), however, shows that to the degree that such simplifying assumptions are approximately correct, the resulting biases will be negligible. As we shall see below, the bias of the instrumental-variables estimator in this very simple model is proportional to the ratio of γ_{11} to γ_{21}.

[16] We are indebted to Arthur S. Goldberger for pointing out that both the Wald-Bartlett methods and our grouping procedure can be considered special cases of an instrumental-variables approach. For an extensive treatment of the interrelationship among various approaches, and for a very complete bibliography, see Madansky (1959). For additional simulation experiments see Cragg (1966).

[17] This can be seen by noting that

$$b_{12}^* = \frac{\Sigma(\beta_{12}x_2 + \epsilon_1)z_1}{\Sigma x_2' z_1} = \beta_{12} + \frac{-\beta_{12}\Sigma e_2 z_1 + \Sigma \epsilon_1 z_1}{\Sigma x_2' z_1}$$

But we are assuming that $E(e_2 z_1) = E(\epsilon_1 z_1) = 0$, and therefore in the case of large samples the bias of b_{12}^* will be negligible. Strictly speaking, the instrumental-variables estimator is not unbiased, but it is consistent, which implies negligible biases for large samples.

depends on the assumption that $\gamma_{11} = 0$. If this assumption is not met, then we shall see that the instrumental-variable estimator will generally have a greater bias than the least-squares estimator *if* there is in fact no measurement error in X_2. In the presence of both specification error ($\gamma_{11} \neq 0$) and measurement error the relative biases may be difficult to estimate except by making enlightened guesses.

Before dealing with this more complex case, and before discussing our empirical results, let us consider still another estimating procedure based on a grouping argument.

Grouping by Z_1. The following ad hoc procedure was suggested by one of the authors before he was acquainted with the instrumental-variables approach.[18] Suppose we have a variable Z_1 which is a direct cause of X_2 but not X_1. If Z_1 is unrelated to the source of measurement error in X_2, as is true whenever measurement error is purely random, then if individuals are ranked according to their scores on Z_1 (even if this variable is itself measured with random error), and if they are grouped by levels of Z_1, then they ought to be roughly similar within groupings according to their scores on X_2. If we then use the mean X_2 scores for each grouping, we ought to take out the random measurement error component. The larger the size of each grouping, the smaller the variance of the measurement error component in accord with the law of large numbers. The variance in the mean values of X_2 should also be reduced, but by nowhere near as much as the variance of the measurement error component. This should be true because if we group individuals according to the similarity of their Z_1 scores, then to the degree that X_2 and Z_1 are highly correlated, the X_2 scores should also be similar within groupings.

If we work with the mean X_2 and X_1 scores for the groupings, and utilize ordinary least-squares estimators, we should take out most of the attenuation in the slope estimate. In terms of the formula

$$E(b'_{12}) = \frac{\beta_{12}}{1 + \sigma^2_{e_2}/\sigma^2_{X_2}}$$

we will have reduced $\sigma^2_{e_2}$ to a small fraction of $\sigma^2_{X_2}$, with the magnitude of this fraction approaching zero as (1) the correlation between Z_1 and X_2 approaches unity, and as (2) the size of the group increases. With large samples that permit large groupings, a very close approximation should be attainable provided the required assumptions are actually met. Crucial to this procedure, as to the instrumental-variables approach, is the assumption that Z_1 does not appear in the equation for X_1.

[18] See Blalock (1964). For an interesting discussion of almost identical grouping procedures in the econometrics literature see Eisner (1958) and Houthakker (1958).

This grouping procedure involves the same kind of rationale as is involved in the repeated measurements approach and the Wald-Bartlett method, but it requires the *a priori* assumption that the grouping variable Z_1 can be legitimately used to group together individuals who are similar with respect to true X_2 scores, without at the same time distorting the true relationship between X_1 and X_2 as measured by β_{12}. Since it involves basically the same assumptions as the instrumental-variables approach, and uses Z_1 in much the same way, we might expect intuitively that the estimate it produces will behave in much the same way. As we shall see, this appears to be the case. Its mathematical properties seem much more difficult to specify exactly, however, and we have had to rely on the Monte Carlo data to appraise its behavior.

Empirical Results, No Specification Error ($\gamma_{11} = 0$). We constructed a basic set of data consisting of variables that were independently distributed, each having a normal frequency distribution with unit variance. From these basic data we selected random samples of size 500, replicating each condition (described below) four times. The parameter to be estimated, β_{12}, was arbitrarily set at 2.0, which constitutes the standard with which our various estimates should be compared.

In the set of data under present consideration we set γ_{11} equal to 0, so that Z_1 did not appear in the equation for X_1. For convenience, $\alpha_1 = \alpha_2 = 0$, so that the constant terms need be of no concern to us. The coefficient γ_{21} relating X_2 to Z_1 was set at 1.0, but we used four different levels of measurement error in X_2: no measurement error ($X'_2 = X_2$), moderate measurement error ($r_{x_2' x_2} = 0.8$), large measurement error ($r_{x_2' x_2} = 0.55$), and exceptionally large error ($r_{x_2' x_2} = 0.2$). The last level of measurement error is of course much greater than would ordinarily be found in practice, but our aim was to investigate the behavior of the estimators under extreme random errors. Ideally, it would have been desirable to vary the sample size and to use more replications in order to estimate standard errors of the estimators, but the number of possible combinations of data sets would have become too large for our limited resources.

Thus the Monte Carlo data conformed to the following specifications:

$$X_1 = 2X_2 + \epsilon_1 \qquad \beta_{12} = 2.0$$
$$X_2 = Z_1 + \epsilon_2 \qquad \gamma_{11} = 0$$
$$X'_2 = X_2 + k\epsilon_2 \qquad \gamma_{21} = 1.0$$

where Z_1, ϵ_1, ϵ_2, and ϵ_2 were independently normally distributed with zero means and unit variances, and where k was given the values of

TABLE 3

Comparison of Estimated Biases in Least-Squares, Instrumental-Variables, and Grouping Methods, with Random Measurement Error in X_2, $\beta_{12} = 2.0$, and no Specification Error[a]

Measurement Error in X_2	Estimate of β_{12} by: Least Squares	Instrumental Variables	Grouping Method Groups of Size 50	Groups of Size 20	Groups of Size 10
None	2.01	2.02	2.04	2.03	2.06
$(X_2' = X_2)$	2.05	2.05	1.97	2.05	1.97
	2.04	2.06	2.05	2.04	2.02
	1.94	1.96	1.93	1.97	2.04
Means	2.01	2.02	2.00	2.02	2.02
Moderate	1.33	2.08	2.05	1.96	1.90
$(X_2' = X_2 + e)$	1.32	2.13	2.05	1.96	1.85
	1.30	2.09	2.08	1.98	1.84
	1.29	1.99	2.11	1.91	1.91
Means	1.31	2.07	2.07	1.95	1.88
Large	0.36	2.18	1.89	1.48	0.97
$(X_2' = X_2 + 3e)$	0.35	2.27	1.86	1.31	1.18
	0.32	2.33	1.87	1.49	0.98
	0.33	1.96	1.65	1.39	0.97
Means	0.34	2.19	1.82	1.42	1.02
Very Large	0.04	2.76	0.70	0.39	0.24
$(X_2' = X_2 + 10e)$	0.03	1.84	0.78	0.37	0.21
	0.04	2.98	0.85	0.21	0.13
	0.04	1.92	1.00	0.35	0.11
Means	0.04	2.37	0.83	0.33	0.17

[a] For each replication, $N = 500$.

0, 1, 3, and 10 in order to vary the magnitude of the random measurement error component.

The results are given in Table 3. Each major cell of the table contains the results of the four separate replications of each condition, plus the mean of each of the sets. Some idea of the variation from one replication to the next may be gained by comparing the slope estimates across replications, but the overall picture can be grasped more satisfactorily by examining the means given at the bottom of each set of four figures.

Looking down the first column, we see that the attenuation of the least-squares slope estimate is very pronounced, and that in the cases where $k = 3$ and $k = 10$ the measurement error variance is so large relative to the variance in X_2 that the degree of attenuation is such as to produce almost useless results. In contrast, the means for column 2 remain relatively stable around the true value of 2.0. In comparing the least-squares and instrumental-variables estimates, we see that the sampling variability of the least-squares estimates is much less than that of the instrumental-variables estimates whenever measurement error becomes pronounced. In general, it appears that least squares gives estimates with smaller standard errors than do the alternative simultaneous-equation estimators, including the method of instrumental variables (Johnston, 1963, Chapter Ten). But this is no consolation whenever the bias becomes extremely large. In comparing alternative estimating procedures it is obviously preferable to use their mean square errors, taking squared deviations around the true parameter value (here 2.0), rather than their standard errors. If this were done the instrumental-variables estimators would obviously seem superior whenever random measurement error is pronounced.

Three different sizes of groupings by Z_1 were used, and the results can be compared by reading across the last three columns. As expected, the larger the size of the grouping, the less the attenuation. Grouping the scores into ten groups of fifty cases works remarkably well except in the case of the bottom set of figures, where measurement error is extremely pronounced. The grouping into twenty-five groups of twenty produces much better results than ordinary least squares, but less satisfactory ones than does the instrumental-variables approach. The attentuation in the case of fifty groups of ten each is much more pronounced, however. It seems clear that it is preferable to utilize a relatively small number of large groups, rather than the opposite.[19]

There is some suggestion in these results that the sampling errors obtained by the grouping method may be less than those for the instrumental-variables approach, and that for relatively large measurement error variances and extremely large samples, the grouping procedure may even be preferable to that of instrumental variables. Further research with larger samples would be necessary to establish this as fact, however. In view of the attenuation evidenced even in the third column,

---

[19] We are indebted to an anonymous reviewer for pointing out that if one is willing to assume that the obtained groups (each of size N) have a fixed value of the grouping variable Z_1, then the following will hold approximately:

$$\frac{\sigma^2_{\bar{X}_2}}{\sigma^2_{\bar{X}_2'}} = \frac{\sigma^2_Z + \sigma^2_{\epsilon_2}/N}{\sigma^2_Z + \sigma^2_{\epsilon_2}/N + k^2\sigma^2_e/N}$$

Given our specifications of the parameters, the right-hand side becomes $(N + 1)/(N + 1 + k^2)$, which of course approaches unity as N increases. However, for a fixed total sample size, the larger the size of each grouping the less tenable the assumption that each grouping is homogeneous with respect to Z.

where each group contained fifty cases, it would appear that the instrumental-variables approach is superior for two important reasons: there is no reason to expect a systematic bias even in small samples and the mathematical properties of the procedure are much better understood. In particular, the instrumental-variables approach can be extended to much more complex models, whereas the reasoning behind the grouping approach is more ad hoc and therefore more difficult to generalize systematically.

Specification Error ($\gamma_{11} \neq 0$). Although the instrumental-variables approach is obviously superior to that of ordinary least squares when the required assumptions are met, it may turn out to be very inferior whenever specification error is involved. In fact, econometricians have pointed out that whenever several different instrumental variables are used, the results often differ considerably. In effect, there will *always* be a certain amount of specification error in any model, and results using different instrumental variables will be dependent on these errors. Least-squares procedures will also be sensitive to specification errors, and therefore the question of the relative advantages of the procedures depends on the *degree* to which they are distorted by specification errors.

There are of course various kinds of specification errors, some of which can be evaluated in terms of the empirical data. Obviously, if the relationship between X_1 and the measured value of X_2 turned out to be highly nonlinear, then the linear model represented by equations (9) and (10) would have to be modified. We shall deal with only one very important kind of specification error in the present context, namely the possibility that Z_1 appears in the equation for X_1. In causal terms we allow for the possibility that Z_1 affects X_1 either directly or through some path other than through X_2.

If we introduce specification error by allowing for the possibility that $\gamma_{11} \neq 0$, then the coefficients in equation (9) cannot be identified, and therefore estimated, without further assumptions. In the particular equations under consideration, the assumption that $E(\epsilon_1\epsilon_2) = 0$ makes the system recursive, so that if there is no measurement error ordinary least squares can be used to provide unbiased estimates. In effect, this assumption requires that the aggregate effects of omitted variables in equation (9) are uncorrelated with those for equation (10). In the more general equation system (8), it is not necessary to set $k - 1$ coefficients equal to zero; it is merely essential that they have known values (for example, $\gamma_{11} = 1.0$). Therefore, in studying biases introduced by specification errors we may construct data with fixed, non-zero values for some of the parameters and then see what effects this would have on estimating procedures based on the (erroneous) assumption that these parameters have values of zero. In particular, we shall construct data for which γ_{11} of equation (9) is not zero, and we shall then see the consequences this has for least-squares and instrumental-variables estimators based on the assumption that $\gamma_{11} = 0$.

If we could assume no random measurement error in X_2 we could test for the possibility that $\gamma_{11} \neq 0$ by simply forming the estimating equation

$$X_1 = a_1 + b_{12}X_2 + c_{11}Z_1 + u_1$$

and seeing whether the coefficient c_{11} departed significantly from zero. If it did not, we could not reject the assumption that $\gamma_{11} = 0$. But we must remember that we are presently allowing for the possibility of random measurement error in X_2, so that we would have to replace X_2 by X_2'. In this case c_{11} becomes a biased estimator of γ_{11} (biased away from zero), and we cannot easily infer the numerical value of γ_{11}. And if we also allow for random measurement error in Z_1, the situation will be all the more ambiguous empirically. This illustrates the important point that allowing for random measurement error introduces too many unknowns into the system and forces one to make a *priori* assumptions of one kind or another.

In this situation, we obviously cannot assess the relative merits of the alternative estimating procedures by using real data with unknown measurement errors. We must rely on mathematical derivations of expected biases or on Monte Carlo procedures. Here we shall rely on both, except in the case of our grouping procedure. Returning to the model of equations (9) and (10), where $\gamma_{11} \neq 0$, it can be shown that in the recursive model the approximate large-sample biases (for random samples) are as follows:[20]

[20] The proof for the least-squares result can be outlined as follows. Representing all variables in deviation form:

$$b_{12} = \frac{\Sigma x_1 x_2}{\Sigma x_2^2} = \frac{\Sigma x_2(\beta_{12}x_2 + \gamma_{11}z_1 + \epsilon_1)}{\Sigma x_2^2} = \frac{\beta_{12}\Sigma x_2^2 + \gamma_{11}\Sigma x_2 z_1 + \Sigma x_2 \epsilon_1}{\Sigma x_2^2}$$

$$= \beta_{12} + \gamma_{11}\left(\frac{\Sigma x_2 z_1}{\Sigma x_2^2}\right) + \frac{\Sigma x_2 \epsilon_1}{\Sigma x_2^2}$$

But since $x_2 = \gamma_{21}z_1 + \epsilon_2$ we can multiply through by z_1 and sum over the sample observations, obtaining

$$\Sigma x_2 z_1 = \gamma_{21}\Sigma z_1^2 + \Sigma z_1 \epsilon_2$$

and therefore

$$\frac{\Sigma x_2 z_1}{\Sigma x_2^2} = \gamma_{21}\frac{\Sigma z_1^2}{\Sigma x_2^2} + \frac{\Sigma z_1 \epsilon_2}{\Sigma x_2^2}$$

Instrumental variables: γ_{11}/γ_{21}
Ordinary least squares: $(\gamma_{11}/\gamma_{21})[1 - \sigma_{\epsilon_2}^2/\sigma_{X_2}^2]$

Let us first look at the simpler expression for the approximate large-sample bias in the case of instrumental variables. This bias is proportional to γ_{11}, the direct effect of the instrumental variable Z_1 on X_1, and inversely proportional to γ_{21}, which measures the direct effect of Z_1 on X_2. This result is consistent with common sense and says that the greater the effect of the instrumental variable on the independent variable X_2 *relative* to its direct contribution to the dependent variable X_1, the less the bias. In other words, the approach depends on our locating important causes of X_2 that do not enter into the equation for X_1 in a major way.

Looking next at the least-squares bias, we first note that there is a bias that is proportional to γ_{11}/γ_{21} but that this bias is less than that of the instrumental-variables estimate because of the factor $(1 - \sigma_{\epsilon_2}^2/\sigma_{X_2}^2)$. It should come as no surprise that specification error of this type produces a bias in the least-squares estimate, since we must remember that the estimate b_{12} is obtained by ignoring Z_1. Thus if we omit a variable (such as Z_1) from the equation, and if this variable happens to be related to X_2, then least squares produces a biased estimate. But of course the omission of Z_1 from the equation when, in fact, $\gamma_{11} \neq 0$ means that the error term ϵ_1 (which contains the effects of Z_1) will be correlated with X_2, contrary to the assumptions required by least squares.

The differential in the relative biases, however, depends on the ratio of the variances $\sigma_{\epsilon_2}^2$ and $\sigma_{X_2}^2$ from the equation $X_2 = \alpha_2 + \gamma_{21}Z_1 + \epsilon_2$. The larger the error variance $\sigma_{\epsilon_2}^2$ relative to the variation in X_2 produced by Z_1, the closer the ratio $\sigma_{\epsilon_2}^2/\sigma_{X_2}^2$ approaches unity, and therefore the

---

Taking expected values, assuming that we are dealing with very large samples, and noting that $E(x_2\epsilon_1) = E(z_1\epsilon_2) = 0$ by assumption, we obtain the result that

$$E(b_{12}) \simeq \beta_{12} + \gamma_{11}(\gamma_{21}\sigma_{z_1}^2/\sigma_{x_2}^2)$$

Utilizing the population relationship that $\sigma_{x_2}^2 = \gamma_{21}^2\sigma_{z_1}^2 + \sigma_{\epsilon_2}^2$ we note that

$$\gamma_{21}\sigma_{z_1}^2/\sigma_{x_2}^2 = \frac{1}{\gamma_{21}}(1 - \sigma_{\epsilon_2}^2/\sigma_{x_2}^2)$$

and thus

$$E(b_{12}) \simeq \beta_{12} + \frac{\gamma_{11}}{\gamma_{21}}(1 - \sigma_{\epsilon_2}^2/\sigma_{x_2}^2)$$

The result for the approximate bias of the instrumental-variables estimation can be similarly obtained.

less the bias in the least-squares estimate. In other words, the lower the correlation between Z_1 and X_2, holding constant γ_{11} and γ_{21}, the less the least-squares bias. It should be noted that the ratio $\sigma_{\epsilon_2}^2/\sigma_{X_2}^2$ will always be less than unity because, for a random disturbance term, $\sigma_{X_2}^2 = \gamma_{21}^2\sigma_{Z_1}^2 + \sigma_{\epsilon_2}^2$. This equation of course implies that the ratio of the least-squares bias to the instrumental-variables bias approaches unity to the degree that (1) the variation in Z_1 increases (relative to the variation in ϵ_2) and (2) γ_{21}^2 is large. Thus we wish to find not only an instrumental variable that has a strong effect on X_2 but also one that varies considerably within the population under study.

We have not been able to derive an exact expression for the expected bias of the grouping procedure except to show that this bias should be *less than* γ_{11}/γ_{21} and that it should approach this ratio as an upper limit to the degree that the grouping procedure is effective in taking out the random measurement error. In the data reported below, we have confined ourselves to groupings of fifty cases, for which the reductions in measurement errors were substantial except where measure-

TABLE 4

Comparison of Biases in Least-Squares, Instrumental-Variables, and Grouping Methods, Given Specification Error ($\gamma_{11} = 2.0$)

Bias

Parameter Values	Least Squares	Instrumental Variables	Grouping (ten groups of fifty cases)	Mean of Instrumental Variables and Grouping
$X_2 = 2Z_1 + \epsilon_2$	0.76	0.97	0.97	
$(r_{X_2Z_1}^2 = 0.80)$	0.84	1.04	1.03	1.002
	$\underline{0.80}$ $(0.80)^a$	$\underline{1.005}$ $(1.00)^b$	$\underline{1.00}$	$(1.00)^b$
$X_2 = 3Z_1 + \epsilon_2$	0.58	0.66	0.66	0.672
$(r_{X_2Z_1}^2 = 0.90)$	0.62	0.69	0.68	$(0.667)^b$
	$\underline{0.60}$ $(0.60)^a$	$\underline{0.675}$ $(0.667)^b$	$\underline{0.67}$	
$X_2 = Z_1 + 2\epsilon_2$	0.35	2.08	1.89	2.185
$(r_{X_2Z_1}^2 = 0.20)$	0.36	2.56	2.21	$(2.00)^b$
	$\underline{0.355}$ $(0.40)^a$	$\underline{2.32}$ $(2.00)^b$	$\underline{2.05}$	
$X_2 = 2Z_1 + 4\epsilon_2$	0.17	1.03	0.90	1.075
$(r_{X_2Z_1}^2 = 0.20)$	0.18	1.27	1.10	$(1.00)^b$
	$\underline{0.175}$ $(0.20)^a$	$\underline{1.15}$ $(1.00)^b$	$\underline{1.00}$	
$X_2 = Z_1 + 4\epsilon_2$	0.09	2.17	1.43	2.205
$(r_{X_2Z_1}^2 = 0.06)$	0.08	3.52	1.70	$(2.00)^b$
	$\underline{0.085}$ $(0.118)^a$	$\underline{2.845}$ $(2.00)^b$	$\underline{1.565}$	

[a] Expected large-sample bias $= (\gamma_{11}/\gamma_{21})(1 - \sigma_{\epsilon_2}^2/\sigma_{X_2}^2)$.

[b] Expected large-sample bias $= \gamma_{11}/\gamma_{21}$.

ment error variance was extreme ($k = 10$). Therefore we expect that the estimated biases for the grouping procedure should approximate those for the instrumental-variables estimate.

The data given in Table 4 all involve rather large specification errors ($\gamma_{11} = 2.0$) relative to the effects of Z_1 on the "independent" variable X_2. These latter effects were constructed at three different levels ($\gamma_{21} = 1, 2,$ and 3). The coefficient in front of the error term ϵ_2 was also assigned several different values (namely 1, 2, and 4) so as to vary the correlation between X_2 and Z_1. In the case of the data displayed in Table 4, there is no random measurement error in X_2. We are therefore studying the biases produced by specification error ($\gamma_{11} \neq 0$) when there is, in reality, no measurement error. Additional data were also obtained for combinations of specification and measurement error, with results being essentially a combination of those for Tables 3 and 4. Given the large number of combinations of parameter values, we obtained only two replications (of size 500) for each combination, since the empirical results turned out so close to the biases as computed by formula. The means for each pair of replications are given below the lines, as in Table 3, and the computed expected values for the least-squares and instrumental-variables estimators are given to the side in parentheses.

In the case of the top two data sets, for which Z_1 and X_2 are highly correlated, we see that the biases of least squares and instrumental variables are not too different. The close correspondence between all sample estimates and the computed biases would also lead us to infer very small sampling errors for all three estimating techniques. Of course we have not been able to supply computed values in the case of the grouping approach, but we have argued that with relatively large groupings and relatively small measurement errors the grouping and instrumental-variables estimators should be very similar.[21] For this reason, we have averaged together the instrumental-variables and grouping estimates in the final column so as to give a single comparison between the actual and computed biases. As can be seen, the two sets of figures are remarkably close in the case of the top two sets of data.

When we examine the bottom three data sets, where the correlation between X_2 and Z_1 is very weak, we see that the least-squares estimates are considerably closer to the true value than are either the instrumental-variables or grouping estimators. As expected, there ap-

[21] Other data, which we have not included, indicate that for combinations of random measurement error *and* specification error, the numerical values of the estimates based on the grouping procedure are intermediate between those for the least-squares and instrumental-variables procedures.

pears to be considerably greater sampling instability in the case of the instrumental-variables estimator, with intermediate instability in the case of the grouping technique. There can be no doubt, however, that the least-squares estimator is far superior, in terms of both estimated bias and sampling error. Of course it must be kept in mind that the data were constructed to amplify any differences that might exist among the three estimators. In the case of the third and fifth sets of data, the coefficient γ_{11} representing the specification error was taken as twice the magnitude of γ_{21} representing the magnitude of the effect of Z_1 on X_2.

In general, then, we would prefer the instrumental-variables estimators to the degree that we feel justified in assuming that (1) the ratio γ_{11}/γ_{21} is small (specification error is minimal); (2) the correlation between the instrumental variable Z_1 and the true value of X_2 is high; and (3) the assumed measurement error variance $\sigma_{e_2}^2$ is relatively large as compared with $\sigma_{X_2}^2$. Least-squares estimators would be preferred under the opposite conditions. It should be kept in mind that we are in addition assuming that the instrumental variable Z_1 is independent of the disturbance term ϵ_1 in the equation for X_1. While the basic principles involved in this simple case appear to generalize readily to more complex models, a good deal of further research will be necessary to spell out the implications of the numerous possible kinds of specification errors and nonrandom measurement errors.[22]

In view of the difficulty of obtaining realistic estimates of the parameters necessary in choosing between the least-squares and instrumental-variables alternatives, we strongly favor combining these approaches with those involving the use of multiple indicators. Whenever a multiple-indicator approach yields results that are similar to those of the instrumental-variables or the least-squares estimators (applied to single indicators), then one would appear to have supplementary evidence in favor of either the one or the other estimator. In view of the subtle methodological problems involved, however, it will be necessary to investigate rather thoroughly the implications of combining several distinct approaches in this manner.

[22] It should be noted that we have been conceiving of the measured value of X as dependent upon the true value. We have not explored situations where the measured value is taken as a cause of X, as for example in an experiment in which one performs a manipulation (for example, withholding food for a certain number of hours) in order to induce a certain state (for example, hunger or frustration) which is indirectly measured in terms of the manipulation. In such an instance, the instrumental variable Z would not necessarily be related to the measured value X' as assumed in our models.

REFERENCES

BARTLETT, M. S.
    1949 "Fitting a straight line when both variables are subject to error." *Biometrics* 5 (June): 207–212.

BLALOCK, H. M.
    1964 *Causal Inferences in Nonexperimental Research.* Chapel Hill: University of North Carolina Press.
    1965 "Some implications of random measurement error for causal inferences." *American Journal of Sociology* 71 (July): 37–47.

BOHRNSTEDT, G. W.
    1969 "Observations on the measurement of change." In E. F. Borgatta and G. W. Bohrnstedt (Eds.), *Sociological Methodology 1969.* San Francisco: Jossey-Bass.

CARTER, L. F. AND BLALOCK, H. M.
    1970 "Underestimation of error variance when employing Wald-Bartlett slope estimation techniques: A Monte Carlo simulation." *Journal of the Royal Statistical Society, Series C* 19 (Part 1), (forthcoming).

CHRIST, C.
    1966 *Econometric Models and Methods.* New York: Wiley.

COSTNER, H. L.
    1969 "Theory, deduction and rules of correspondence." *American Journal of Sociology* 75 (September): 245–263.

CRAGG, J. G.
    1966 "On the sensitivity of simultaneous-equations estimators to the stochastic assumptions of the models." *Journal of the American Statistical Association* 61 (March): 136–151.

EISNER, R.
    1958 "The permanent income hypothesis: Comment." *American Economic Review* 48 (December): 972–990.

FISHER, F. M.
    1961 "On the cost of approximate specification in simultaneous equation estimation." *Econometrica* 29 (April): 139–170.
    1965 "The choice of instrumental variables in the estimation of economy-wide econometric models." *International Economic Review* 6 (September): 245–274.
    1966 *The Identification Problem in Econometrics.* New York: McGraw-Hill.

GOLDBERGER, A. S.
    1964 *Econometric Theory.* New York: Wiley.
    1968 *Topics in Regression Analysis.* New York: Macmillan.

GORDON, R.
    1968 "Issues in multiple regression." *Americal Journal of Sociology* 73 (March): 592–616.

HAMMING, R. W.
    1962 *Numerical Methods for Scientists and Engineers.* New York: McGraw-Hill.

HOUTHAKKER, H. S.
    1958 "The permanent income hypothesis." *American Economic Review* 48 (June): 396–404.

JOHNSTON, J.
    1963 *Econometric Methods.* New York: McGraw-Hill.

LIU, T. C.
  1960 "Underidentification, structural estimation, and forecasting." *Econometrica* 28 (October): 855–865.
MADANSKY, A.
  1959 "The fitting of straight lines when both variables are subject to error." *Journal of the American Statistical Association* 54 (March): 173–205.
SIEGEL, P. M. AND HODGE, R. W.
  1968 "A causal approach to the study of measurement error." In H. M. Blalock and A. B. Blalock (Eds.), *Methodology in Social Research*. New York: McGraw-Hill.
WALD, A.
  1940 "The fitting of straight lines if both variables are subject to error." *Annals of Mathematical Statistics* 2: 284–300.

VALIDITY, INVALIDITY,
AND RELIABILITY

David R. Heise
QUEENS COLLEGE

George W. Bohrnstedt
UNIVERSITY OF MINNESOTA

*Principal support for the work
in this paper came from the Office of Education (OE 5-10-292), for which
the authors are grateful. They also would like to thank Arthur S. Goldberger
for valuable discussions on an earlier version of this paper.*

Sociologists almost always rely on fallible measuring instruments
in attempting to estimate parameters. Recent work by Heise (1969) has
shown how parametric estimates can be made with fallible data when
one has three waves of panel data. However, when one has only cross-
sectional data, he must obtain multiple measurements on the same underlying "true" variable and use the correlations among the fallible measurements to make estimates of the parameters. Two different approaches

with multiple indicators have been taken. In the first, one usually begins with a set of items or indicators assumed to have one or more underlying causes and factor analyzes the set of items to determine the relationships of the items to the underlying factors or causes. Then the items which are the "purest" indicators (based on the factor loadings) are built into some kind of linear composite (for example, an index or summated rating scale). The reliability of the composite can be estimated using one of the internal consistency methods (Lord and Novick, 1968, pp. 134–137; Bohrnstedt, 1969), and given a reliability coefficient, one can correct the obtained correlations or regression coefficients for attenuation due to unreliability. This approach to parametric estimation with fallible data has its historical roots in educational psychology and has been widely adopted by sociologists and social psychologists in recent years.

More recently, Costner (1969) and Blalock (1969) have presented a second approach to the problem—an approach which grows largely out of the "errors in variables" problem in economics (Johnston, 1963, Chapter Six) and path analysis (Duncan, 1966). In this approach one makes assumptions about the causal structure relating the items to the underlying variables, and the underlying variables to each other, and then, using the correlation among the indicators, obtains estimates of the various paths.

At this time it would be premature to argue which approach is likely to be the more fruitful. However, since the former is in wide use, it would seem appropriate to explore it more carefully than it has been. In this paper three issues are considered. First, what is the validity of the composite one has created? Stated differently, what is the correlation between the composite one has constructed and the underlying variable which is assumed to have generated the correlations among the indicators in the composite? The validity formula that is derived in this paper has been obtained previously by Cattell and Radcliffe (1962) using a different approach. However, their work has remained obscure. Second, the concept of invalidity is introduced. It is possible (and often the case, one can assume) that the indicators built into a composite show variation due to causes (factors) other than the one they are intended to measure. The greater the amount of this unwanted variation, the greater the invalidity of one's composite. Finally, the relationship between factor analysis and the reliability of a composite score is shown, and a formula is introduced for obtaining a reliability coefficient from factor analysis results.

In the derivations it is assumed that the reader is familiar with the basic procedures of path analysis (see Wright, 1934; Duncan, 1966;

Land, 1969), factor analysis (see Harman, 1967), and matrix algebra. Readers not interested in the derivations will find key formulas in the section titled, "Rescaling the Formulas," and examples of their use in the section, "Some Examples."

DERIVATIONS

Underlying the building of composites from factor analysis and the derivations below are a number of assumptions about how n items or indicator variables are related to one another: (1) relationships among the items are assumed to be linear; (2) the total variance in items is a function of m orthogonal latent variables, of the n disturbances that uniquely affect the items, and of n measurement errors; (3) the disturbances of the items are assumed uncorrelated with each other, with the latent variables, and with the measurement errors; similarly, measurement errors are assumed uncorrelated with each other or with latent variables; (4) the items themselves are assumed to be locally independent (Lord and Novick, 1968, pp. 360–362); that is, items are assumed to be causally unrelated to each other except by their mutual dependence on latent traits; (5) the observed factor structure accurately represents the structure of the latent traits.

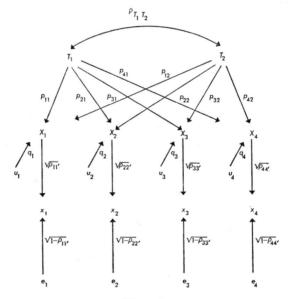

Figure 1

In the path diagram in Figure 1, T_1 and T_2 represent two latent variables or traits and $\rho_{T_1 T_2}$ represents the correlation between the traits; however, in derivations below, we will be assuming $\rho_{T_1 T_2} = 0$. The ps indicate the influence of the traits on four items measured without error, labeled X_i. The ps can be thought of as validity coefficients relating the items measured without error to the latent traits. The us represent unique sources of variance for the items measured without error; and the qs indicate the degree of influence from unique sources. The degree of relationship between the items measured without error and the empirical items with measurement errors, x_i, is $\sqrt{\rho_{ii'}}$ (Lord and Novick, 1968, p. 61) where $\rho_{ii'}$ represents the reliability of the item. The extent to which observed responses are a function of errors is defined as a residual, $\sqrt{1 - \rho_{ii'}}$. The lack of additional paths reflects various previously stated assumptions. We have shown only two latent traits and four items so as to simplify the presentation.

Following the rules of path analysis (Duncan, 1966), the diagram can be simplified somewhat as shown in Figure 2. In turn, this diagram can be translated into one employing customary factor analytic quantities as shown in Figure 3. Here, f_{ik} is the factor loading for the ith item on the kth factor and also the validity coefficient for that empirical item, the h_i^2 is the communality for that item, and the v_i represent the com-

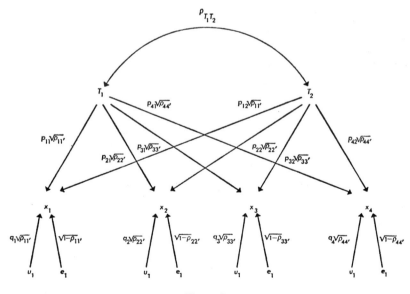

Figure 2

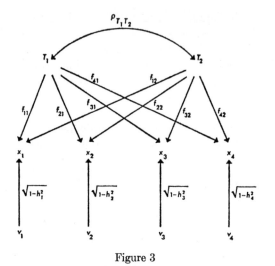

Figure 3

bined effects of u_i and e_i. The translation between Figures 2 and 3 involves the following identity in the model:

$$f_{ik} = p_{ik} \sqrt{\rho_{ii'}} \tag{1}$$

That is, the factor loading of item i on factor k equals the validity of the item measured without error times the square root of the item's reliability.

A path diagram also can be drawn to indicate how a composite score to measure T_1 is related to its component items (Figure 4). Here

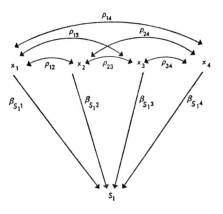

Figure 4

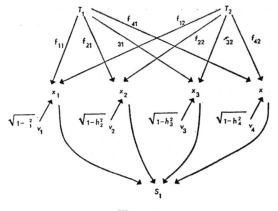

Figure 5

the ρ_{ij} represent inter-item correlations, and the $\beta_{S_1 i}$ are path coefficients indicating how much each item affects the total score, S_1. It is important to notice that no disturbance term is drawn to S_1 since the variance of the composite score obviously is completely determined by the items.

Finally, since the latent-trait model assumes that the inter-item correlations are entirely a function of the latent traits, Figures 3 and 4 can be combined, as in Figure 5, to indicate how a composite score is linked to latent traits. Figure 5 is the key diagram for analysis in this paper. In the next section, it will be shown that the $\beta_{S_1 i}$ are a function of the f_{ik} and of the observed inter-item correlations so all of the parameters of the model are defined in terms of statistics obtained in the course of a factor analysis. And, using the path diagram, it is possible to define the correlation between a latent trait and the composite score. For example, assuming the underlying factors are orthogonal, by the rules of path analysis, the correlation between latent trait T_1 and the score S_1 is:

$$\rho_{T_1 S_1} = (f_{11}\beta_{S_{11}}) + (f_{21}\beta_{S_{12}}) + (f_{31}\beta_{S_{13}}) + (f_{41}\beta_{S_{14}}) \qquad (2)$$

The correlation between a composite S_1 and the variable it is meant to measure, T_1, is the validity of the composite. So, the path model leads to the definition of a validity index for the composite score. Note that in Figure 5 a second unwanted factor, T_2, also is responsible for some of the covariation among the four indicators. The procedure outlined above will later be extended to obtain indices of invalidity for such a situation. Then, reliability coefficients will also be developed from a similar procedure.

For convenience in the derivations, it is assumed that item scores are standardized, that is, have means equal to zero and standard deviations equal to unity, although formulas are eventually rescaled into the original metric of the items.

We begin by defining the matrix of inter-item correlations among items x_i, $i = 1, 2, \ldots , n$:

$$\mathbf{R} = \begin{pmatrix} 1 & \rho_{12} & \cdots & \rho_{1n} \\ \rho_{21} & 1 & \cdots & \rho_{2n} \\ \cdots & \cdots & \cdots & \cdots \\ \rho_{n1} & \rho_{n2} & \cdots & 1 \end{pmatrix} \qquad (3)$$

Correlations among the items are assumed to be generated by mutual dependencies on factors T_k, $k = 1, 2, \ldots , m$, where m $<$ n. Throughout the derivations, the factors are assumed to be orthogonal, so both the factor pattern and the factor structure are defined in terms of a single matrix in which an element f_{ik} is the factor loading of item i on factor k. The matrix of factor loadings is:

$$\mathbf{F} = \begin{pmatrix} f_{11} & f_{12} & \cdots & f_{1m} \\ f_{21} & f_{22} & \cdots & f_{2m} \\ \cdots & \cdots & \cdots & \cdots \\ f_{n1} & f_{n2} & \cdots & f_{nm} \end{pmatrix} \qquad (4)$$

The loadings of items on factor k will be represented as a vector:

$$\mathbf{f}_k = \begin{pmatrix} f_{1k} \\ f_{2k} \\ \cdot \\ \cdot \\ \cdot \\ f_{kn} \end{pmatrix} \qquad (5)$$

A composite score to measure factor T_k is generated by summing items in accordance with an appropriate weighting scheme. That is:

$$S_{kg} = \sum_{i=1}^{n} w_{ik} x_{ig} \qquad (6)$$

where S_{kg} is the score to measure factor T_k for observation g, x_{ig} is observation gs score on item i, and w_{ik} is the weight assigned to item i in order to measure factor T_k. The set of weights which measure one factor will be represented as a vector:

$$\mathbf{w}_k = \begin{pmatrix} w_{1k} \\ w_{2k} \\ \cdot \\ \cdot \\ \cdot \\ w_{nk} \end{pmatrix} \qquad (7)$$

Validity

Our first objective is to define the correlation between a given factor, T_k, and its corresponding score, S_k. Referring to Figure 5 and applying the rules of path analysis, it is seen that the correlation between factor T_1 and score S_1 is:

$$\rho_{T_1 S_1} = f_{11}\beta_{S_{11}} + f_{21}\beta_{S_{12}} + \cdots + f_{n1}\beta_{S_{1n}} \qquad (8)$$

Let the path coefficients linking items to a given score, S_k, be represented as a vector.

$$\mathbf{b}_k = \begin{pmatrix} \beta_{S_k 1} \\ \beta_{S_k 2} \\ \cdot \\ \cdot \\ \cdot \\ \beta_{S_k n} \end{pmatrix} \qquad (9)$$

Now, equation (8) can be rewritten:

$$\rho_{T_1 S_1} = \mathbf{f}_1' \mathbf{b}_1 \qquad (10)$$

Or, in general, the correlation between trait T_k and its corresponding score S_k is:

$$\rho_{T_k S_k} = \mathbf{f}_k' \mathbf{b}_k \qquad (11)$$

where $\mathbf{b}_k$ is the set of path coefficients or standardized regression weights for predicting S_k from the items, and these are defined as follows:

$$\mathbf{b}_k = \mathbf{R}^{-1} \mathbf{r}_{S_k} \qquad (12)$$

where $\mathbf{r}_{S_k}$ is the vector of item-to-total score correlations (Walker and Lev, 1953, p. 332). That is,

$$\mathbf{r}_{S_k} = \begin{pmatrix} \rho_{1 S_k} \\ \rho_{2 S_k} \\ \cdot \\ \cdot \\ \cdot \\ \rho_{n S_k} \end{pmatrix} \qquad (13)$$

Now consider an element ρ_{aS_k} from $\mathbf{r}_{S_k}$, where a refers to the ath item. Since the items are in standardized form, we can write from equation (6)

$$\rho_{aS_k} = E(S_k x_a)/\sigma_{S_k} = \frac{E\left(\sum_{i=1}^{n} w_{ik} x_i x_a\right)}{\sigma_{S_k}} \tag{14}$$

The variance of S_k is

$$\sigma_{S_k}^2 = E\left[\left(\sum_{i=1}^{n} w_{ik} x_i\right)^2\right] = E\left(\sum_{i=1}^{n}\sum_{j=1}^{n} w_{ik} w_{jk} x_i x_j\right) \tag{15}$$

Substituting the square root of equation (15) in equation (14) gives:

$$\rho_{aS_k} = \frac{E\left(\sum_{i=1}^{n} w_{ik} x_i x_a\right)}{\sqrt{E\left(\sum_{i=1}^{n}\sum_{j=1}^{n} w_{ik} w_{jk} x_i x_j\right)}} \tag{16}$$

or

$$\rho_{aS_k} = \frac{\sum_{i=1}^{n} w_{ik}\rho_{ai}}{\sqrt{\sum_{i=1}^{n}\sum_{j=1}^{n} w_{ik} w_{jk}\rho_{ij}}} \tag{17}$$

since $E(x_i x_j) = \rho_{ij}$ for standardized variables. Again, equation (17) shows the solution for one element in equation (13). The general solution for all n items can be expressed in matrix form as:

$$\mathbf{r}_{S_k} = \frac{\mathbf{R}\mathbf{w}_k}{\sqrt{\mathbf{w}_k'\mathbf{R}\mathbf{w}_k}} \tag{18}$$

The denominator in equation (18) is a scaler quantity equal simply to the square root of the sum of the weighted entries in the matrix of inter-item correlations.

Now, substituting equation (18) in equation (12), we obtain

$$\mathbf{b}_k = \frac{\mathbf{R}^{-1}(\mathbf{R}\mathbf{w}_k)}{\sqrt{\mathbf{w}_k'\mathbf{R}\mathbf{w}_k}} = \frac{\mathbf{w}_k}{\sqrt{\mathbf{w}_k'\mathbf{R}\mathbf{w}_k}} \tag{19}$$

and substituting equation (19) in equation (11), we find:

$$\rho_{T_k S_k} = \frac{\mathbf{f}_k'\mathbf{w}_k}{\sqrt{\mathbf{w}_k'\mathbf{R}\mathbf{w}_k}} \tag{20}$$

or, in summation terms:

$$\rho_{T_k S_k} = \frac{\sum_{i=1}^{n} w_{ik} f_{ik}}{\sqrt{\sum_{i=1}^{n} \sum_{j=1}^{n} w_{ik} w_{jk} \rho_{ij}}} \tag{21}$$

The term $\rho_{T_k S_k}$, as defined by the computing formulas (21), is a validity index specifying the correlation between the trait T_k and its corresponding score, S_k, and $\rho_{T_k S_k}^2$ indicates the proportion of variance in S_k that is associated with T_k. The use of this formula is shown in the section, "Some Examples."

Invalidity

The correlation between a score, S_k, and some trait, q, that S_k is *not* supposed to measure is given by a variation of equation (20):

$$\rho_{T_q S_k} = \frac{\mathbf{f}_q' \mathbf{w}_k}{\mathbf{w}_k' \mathbf{R} \mathbf{w}_k} \tag{22}$$

and this quantity squared indicates the proportion of variance in S_k that is due to the unwanted trait, T_q. Hence,

$$\rho_{T_q S_k}^2 = \frac{(\mathbf{f}_q' \mathbf{w}_k)^2}{\mathbf{w}_k' \mathbf{R} \mathbf{w}_k} = \frac{\mathbf{w}_k' \mathbf{f}_q \mathbf{f}_q' \mathbf{w}_k}{\mathbf{w}_k' \mathbf{R} \mathbf{w}_k} \tag{23}$$

When there are several unwanted traits being measured by S_k, the total proportion of variance in S_k that is due to all the unwanted traits, represented below by $\Psi_{S_k}^2$, is simply the sum of these coefficients squared since the traits are assumed to be orthogonal. That is:

$$\Psi_{S_k}^2 = \sum_{\substack{q=1 \\ q \neq k}}^{m} \left(\frac{\mathbf{w}_k' \mathbf{f}_q \mathbf{f}_q' \mathbf{w}_k}{\mathbf{w}_k' \mathbf{R} \mathbf{w}_k} \right) \tag{24}$$

Equation (24) can be rewritten as follows:

$$\Psi_{S_k}^2 = \frac{\mathbf{w}_k' \mathbf{F} \mathbf{F}' \mathbf{w}_k}{\mathbf{w}_k' \mathbf{R} \mathbf{w}_k} - \frac{\mathbf{w}_k' \mathbf{f}_k \mathbf{f}_k' \mathbf{w}_k}{\mathbf{w}_k' \mathbf{R} \mathbf{w}_k'} \tag{25}$$

The second term in equation (25) is simply the validity squared. Now, assuming that $\mathbf{F}\mathbf{F}' = \mathbf{R} - \mathbf{I} + \mathbf{H}^2$, where $\mathbf{I}$ is the identity matrix and $\mathbf{H}^2$ is the diagonal matrix of communalities, equation (25) can be rewritten:

$$\Psi^2_{S_k} = 1 - \rho^2_{T_k S_k} + \frac{\mathbf{w}'_k \mathbf{H}^2 \mathbf{w}_k - \mathbf{w}'_k \mathbf{w}_k}{\mathbf{w}'_k \mathbf{R} \mathbf{w}_k} \tag{26}$$

In summation terms, equation (26) becomes:

$$\Psi^2_{S_k} = 1 - \rho^2_{T_k S_k} + \frac{\displaystyle\sum_{i=1}^{n} w^2_{ik} h^2_i - \sum_{i=1}^{n} w^2_{ik}}{\displaystyle\sum_{i=1}^{n} \sum_{j=1}^{n} w_{ik} w_{jk} \rho_{ij}} \tag{27}$$

where $\Psi^2_{S_k}$ is a measure of invalidity. It indicates the proportion of variance in S_k that is associated with latent variables other than the one of interest. Its actual use shall also be shown in the section, "Some Examples."

RELIABILITY

The reliability of a measure is defined as the correlation between two equivalent forms of a test (Lord and Novick, 1968, p. 58). Figure 6 presents a path diagram for a simplified case to indicate what this means in terms of the latent trait model. Figure 6 is like Figure 5 except, for simplicity, it deals with a single latent trait, and it shows the construction of two equivalent scores, S and S', based on different but equivalent items, x_i and x'_i, $i = 1, 2, \ldots, n$. The key point to notice in Figure 6 is that the correlation between the two equivalent scores depends only on their mutual dependence on T_1.

Actually, it is not necessary to work out all the separate paths linking S and S' since we already have an expression for the validity

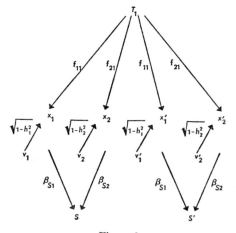

Figure 6

coefficient for each test, and this coefficient is equivalent to a standardized regression coefficient or path coefficient indicating the degree of influence of T on S or S'. Therefore,

$$\rho_{SS'} = \rho_{TS}\rho_{TS'} \tag{28}$$

However, since items in one test are equivalent to those in the other, $\rho_{TS} = \rho_{TS'}$ and:

$$\rho_{SS'} = \rho_{TS}^2 \tag{29}$$

However, formula (29) is not a general formula since it presumes a single factor. In the multi-factor case $\rho_{SS'}$ would be obtained by summing the correlations between S and S' due to the different latent variables. That is (changing notations to correspond to the multiple factor situation):

$$\rho_{SS'} = \rho_{T_1S}^2 + \rho_{T_2S}^2 + \cdots + \rho_{T_mS}^2 \tag{30}$$

From equation (23) it follows that:

$$\rho_{SS'} = \sum_{k=1}^{m} \left(\frac{\mathbf{w}'\mathbf{f}_k\mathbf{f}_k'\mathbf{w}}{\mathbf{w}'\mathbf{R}\mathbf{w}} \right) \tag{31}$$

which is simply:

$$\rho_{SS'} = \frac{\mathbf{w}'\mathbf{R}\mathbf{w} + \mathbf{w}'\mathbf{H}^2\mathbf{w} - \mathbf{w}'\mathbf{I}\mathbf{w}}{\mathbf{w}'\mathbf{R}\mathbf{w}} \tag{32}$$

assuming $\mathbf{FF'} = \mathbf{R} - \mathbf{I} + \mathbf{H}^2$. We have chosen to call formula (32) Ω. Rewritten in summation notation and rearranging terms, the reliability of composite k is:

$$\Omega = \rho_{S_kS'_k} = 1 - \frac{\sum_{i=1}^{n} w_{ik}^2 - \sum_{i=1}^{n} w_{ik}^2 h_i^2}{\sum_{i=1}^{n} \sum_{j=1}^{n} w_{ik}w_{jk}\rho_{ij}} \tag{33}$$

Rescaling the Formulas

Traditionally, reliability formulas have been expressed in the original metric of the items. To accomplish this in our formulas, we merely substitute σ for w, where σ is a vector of the n item standard deviations. Doing this, equation (21), the measure of validity, becomes

$$\rho_{T_k S_k} = \frac{\sum_{i=1}^{n} \sigma_i f_{ik}}{\sqrt{\sum_{i=1}^{n} \sum_{j=1}^{n} \mathrm{Cov}(x_i, x_j)}} \tag{34}$$

where it is understood that $\mathrm{Cov}(x_i, x_i) = \sigma_i^2$. Similarly, equation (27), the invalidity measure, becomes:

$$\Psi_{S_k}^2 = 1 - \rho_{T_k S_k}^2 + \frac{\sum_{i=1}^{n} \sigma_i^2 h_i^2 - \sum_{i=1}^{n} \sigma_i^2}{\sum_{i=1}^{n} \sum_{j=1}^{n} \mathrm{Cov}(x_i, x_j)} \tag{35}$$

And, equation (33), the reliability measure, is changed to:

$$\Omega = 1 - \frac{\sum_{i=1}^{n} \sigma_i^2 - \sum_{i=1}^{n} \sigma_i^2 h_i^2}{\sum_{i=1}^{n} \sum_{j=1}^{n} \mathrm{Cov}(x_i, x_j)} \tag{36}$$

Note from equation (35) and (36) that $\Psi_{S_k}^2$ can be simplified to:

$$\Psi_{S_k}^2 = \Omega - \rho_{T_k S_k}^2 \tag{37}$$

Comparison of α and Ω

Novick and Lewis (1967) have demonstrated that in general α, the most popular interval consistency measure (Cronbach, 1951), is not equal to the reliability of a composite score, but instead is a lower bound to it. It is not the only lower bound reliability estimate, but since it is the most popular, it will be compared to Ω in this section.

Cronbach defined α as:

$$\alpha = \frac{n}{n-1} \left[1 - \frac{\sum_{i=1}^{n} \sigma_i^2}{\sum_{i=1}^{n} \sum_{j=1}^{n} \mathrm{Cov}(x_i, x_j)} \right] \tag{38}$$

Novick and Lewis (1967) prove that if the items are τ-equivalent, that is, true scores on one item differ from true scores on another item by no more than a constant, then α is an exact estimate of the reliability. When one's items are essentially τ-equivalent, α and Ω will equal each other. Under this condition all the inter-item correlations are equal, and the item variances are equal, as shown in Lord and Novick (1968, p. 90). Hence,

$$\alpha = \rho_{xx'} = \frac{n\rho}{1 + (n - 1)\rho} \tag{39}$$

where ρ is an inter-item correlation. Now, under this condition,

$$\begin{aligned}
\Omega &= 1 - \frac{n\sigma^2 - n\sigma^2\rho}{n\sigma^2 + n(n - 1)\sigma^2\rho} \\
&= 1 - \frac{(1 - \rho)}{1 + (n - 1)\rho} \\
&= \frac{n\rho}{1 + (n - 1)\rho} \\
&= \alpha
\end{aligned} \tag{40}$$

Thus, under the condition of essential τ-equivalence, α and Ω are equal, but otherwise Ω will generally be larger than α since when the h_i^2 are known, Ω is exactly equal to the reliability of a composite.

Weighting Selected Items

Frequently, when building a composite score, one assigns zero weights to those items which have low loadings on a given factor. In this case one can simply collect the items with non-zero weights and apply directly formulas (34), (35), and (36) to the reduced set of items. One is likely to apply this procedure when there are multiple factors and one wishes to include each item in but a single score. Then the low loadings of each item on the other factors are simply ignored. Of course, the values of the f_{ik} and the h_i^2 used are those obtained in the factor analysis of all items. This procedure shall be followed when the use of the formulas is shown with actual data.

If one chooses to apply weights other than the standard deviations to his items, one can use the following formulas. The validity formula (34) is changed to:

$$\rho_{T_k S_k} = \frac{\sum_{i=1}^{n} w_{ik}\sigma_i f_{ik}}{\sqrt{\sum_{i=1}^{n} \sum_{j=1}^{n} w_{ik}w_{jk} \operatorname{Cov}(x_i, x_j)}} \tag{41}$$

The invalidity formula (35) is changed to

$$\Psi_{S_k}^2 = 1 - \rho_{T_k S_k}^2 + \frac{\displaystyle\sum_{i=1}^{n} w_{ik}^2 \sigma_i^2 h_i^2 - \sum_{i=1}^{n} w_{ik}^2 \sigma_i^2}{\displaystyle\sum_{i=1}^{n}\sum_{j=1}^{n} w_{ik} w_{jk} \operatorname{Cov}(x_i, x_j)} \tag{42}$$

and the reliability formula (36) is changed to

$$\Omega = 1 - \frac{\displaystyle\sum_{i=1}^{n} w_{ik}^2 \sigma_i^2 - \sum_{i=1}^{n} w_{ik}^2 \sigma_i^2 h_i^2}{\displaystyle\sum_{i=1}^{n}\sum_{j=1}^{n} w_{ik} w_{jk} \operatorname{Cov}(x_i, x_j)} \tag{43}$$

where w_{ik} is the weight applied to the ith indicator to measure the kth factor.

Some Examples

The data for the following examples came from an unpublished study of the values of college students. Two of the values to be measured were called *religiosity* and *fatalism*. Items were constructed to measure these two domains and then several factor analyses were done on a sample of 500 males to establish the validity of the items. The six items from which the religiosity scale was to be built and the five items for the

TABLE 1
Items Included in the Religiosity and Fatalism Composites[a]

Religiosity
1. Everyone should believe in and practice some religion.
2. The best way to foster the moral development of civilization is through organized religion.
3. There should be stricter observance of the Sabbath, the religious day of rest.
4. The world moves in an evolutionary process of unfolding rather than through divine guidance.[b]
5. There is an almighty God who watches over us.
6. There is a life after death.

Fatalism
7. The world seems to move as though to reveal the destinies of men—men do not shape the world.
8. People should live for today and let tomorrow take care of itself.
9. Since most things are inevitable, people should relax and enjoy themselves.
10. People can actually do very little to change their lives.
11. A person really has very little control over his own fate.

    [a] Response categories were "strongly disagree," "probably disagree," "probably agree," and "definitely agree."

    [b] Weighted negatively in composite to align the item in meaning with others in the composite.

measure of fatalism are shown in Table 1. The respondents were asked to show degree of agreement with each of the items on a four-point scale ranging from "strongly disagree" to "strongly agree."

Several methods for estimating factor loadings exist, and since these methods do not all yield exactly the same factor structure, the estimates of Ω, ρ_{TS}, and Ψ^2 will differ from one method to another. Also, one might expect somewhat different estimates of the three statistics depending upon whether one factors the two sets of items together rather than separately. In order to investigate what differences might occur in the statistics using an empirical example, the following procedures were followed. The data were factored using four different methods: a principal factor solution (Harman, 1967, Chapter Eight); two maximum likelihood solutions (Harman, 1967, Chapter Ten)—one where the squares of the multiple correlations (smc) are used as communality estimates and a second where the smcs are the first values used and then iteration procedures are applied until the communality estimates from one iteration do not diverge significantly from those on the previous iteration; and, finally, the alpha procedure (Kaiser and Caffrey, 1965) which also estimated the communalities by iteration after beginning with the smcs. Readers interested in the technical differences between these methods of estimating the loadings are directed to the sources indicated.

Each set of items was factored separately using the above four factoring methods, and then the two sets of items were pooled and again analyzed using the four factoring methods.

Scores were created by giving the items zero or unit weights. The covariances among the eleven items composing the two scores are shown in Table 2. These will be used in later computations.

In Table 3 we show the factor analysis of just one of the factoring methods—the maximum likelihood solution without iteration. The results of this factor analysis are typical of those of the other three methods in the following ways. First, almost without exception, when the two sets of items were factored *separately*, two factors emerged indicating that a score constructed from that set would contain some invalid variance. The single exception was the alpha factoring of the religiosity items which formed a single factor. Second, when the two sets were factored *jointly* by the four methods, three or more factors emerged, not two, again indicating some invalidity. Three, when the factors were rotated using the varimax criterion (Kaiser, 1958), the solutions made far less substantive sense than did the unrotated solutions. Hence, all the results shown here are based on unrotated factors (that is, the principal factor solution).

DAVID R. HEISE AND GEORGE W. BOHRNSTEDT

TABLE 2
Covariances Among the Items in the Religiosity and Fatalism Composites

	1	2	3	4	5	6	7	8	9	10	11
			Religiosity						Fatalism		
1	*0.928*	0.429	0.438	0.383	0.428	0.479	0.114	0.025	0.046	−0.025	0.046
2	0.429	*0.698*	0.370	0.299	0.340	0.382	0.112	−0.016	0.018	0.005	0.015
3	0.438	0.370	*0.795*	0.354	0.358	0.435	0.139	0.003	0.003	0.003	0.004
4	0.383	0.299	0.354	*0.894*	0.396	0.519	0.010	0.005	0.000	0.000	0.004
5	0.428	0.340	0.358	0.396	*0.671*	0.561	0.009	−0.002	0.024	−0.019	0.004
6	0.479	0.382	0.435	0.519	0.561	*0.994*	0.109	0.019	−0.012	0.019	0.049
7	0.114	0.112	0.139	0.010	0.009	0.109	*0.636*	0.169	0.147	0.110	0.170
8	0.025	−0.016	0.003	0.005	−0.002	0.019	0.169	*0.784*	0.223	0.101	0.120
9	0.046	0.018	0.003	0.000	0.024	−0.012	0.147	0.223	*0.660*	0.118	0.134
10	−0.025	0.005	0.003	0.000	−0.019	0.019	0.110	0.101	0.118	*0.541*	0.245
11	0.046	0.015	0.004	0.004	0.004	0.049	0.170	0.120	0.134	0.245	*0.635*

TABLE 3

Factor Analyses of the Religiosity and Fatalism Items[a] Using the Maximum Likelihood Solution Without Iteration

Items	Factored Separately			Factored Jointly				
	Factors			Factors				
	I	II	h^2	I	II	III	IV	h_i^2
1	0.693	−0.169	0.509	0.694	−0.023	−0.167	−0.036	0.511
2	0.651	−0.208	0.467	0.652	−0.034	−0.189	−0.109	0.473
3	0.660	−0.153	0.459	0.663	−0.029	−0.135	−0.070	0.464
4	0.639	0.125	0.424	0.638	−0.023	−0.115	−0.076	0.427
5	0.784	0.107	0.625	0.782	−0.062	0.096	0.044	0.627
6	0.773	0.164	0.624	0.771	−0.050	0.169	0.042	0.628
7	0.444	0.085	0.205	0.229	0.423	−0.096	0.039	0.242
8	0.415	0.237	0.228	0.047	0.415	−0.071	0.242	0.238
9	0.447	0.191	0.237	0.053	0.446	−0.121	0.162	0.242
10	0.506	−0.203	0.297	0.026	0.512	0.128	−0.177	0.311
11	0.547	−0.184	0.333	0.100	0.536	0.128	−0.141	0.334

[a] N = 500 college freshman males.

DAVID R. HEISE AND GEORGE W. BOHRNSTEDT

TABLE 4

An Example of How to Compute Estimates of Ω, ρ_{TS}, and Ψ^2 from the
Factor Analysis of the Religiosity Items Shown in Table 3

Item	(1) h_i^2	(2) σ_i^2	(3) $h_i^2\sigma_i^2$	(4) f_i	(5) σ_i	(6) $f_i\sigma_i$
1	0.509	0.928	0.472	0.693	0.963	0.667
2	0.467	0.698	0.326	0.651	0.836	0.544
3	0.459	0.795	0.365	0.660	0.892	0.589
4	0.424	0.894	0.379	0.639	0.946	0.604
5	0.625	0.671	0.419	0.784	0.819	0.642
6	0.624	0.994	0.620	0.773	0.997	0.771
Sums		4.980	2.581			3.817

$$\Omega = 1 - \frac{\sum_{i=1}^{n}\sigma_i^2 - \sum_{i=1}^{n}\sigma_i^2 h_i^2}{\sum_{i=1}^{n}\sum_{j=1}^{n}\mathrm{Cov}(x_i, x_j)} = 1 - \frac{(4.980 - 2.581)}{17.322} = 0.8615$$

$$\rho_{TS} = \frac{\sum_{i=1}^{n}\sigma_i f_{ik}}{\sqrt{\sum_{i=1}^{n}\sum_{j=1}^{n}\mathrm{Cov}(x_i, x_j)}} = \frac{3.817}{\sqrt{17.322}} = 0.9171$$

$$\Psi^2 = \Omega - \rho_{TS}^2 = 0.8615 - (0.9171)^2 = 0.0204$$

Table 4 shows an example of how to compute estimates of Ω, ρ_{TS}, and Ψ^2 using the results from Table 3 of the maximum likelihood factor analysis of the separate set of religiosity items. Note that column 3 is the product of columns 1 and 2. The sum of column 2 and column 3 is used in computing the numerator of the second term of the expression for Ω—formula (36). The denominator of that term is simply equal to the sum of all the entries in the covariance matrix for the religiosity items (upper left hand quadrant of Table 2). The numerator of ρ_{TS}— formula (34) is the sum of the entries in column 6, which in turn are products of columns 4 and 5. The entries in column 5 are, of course, just the square roots of the entries in column 2. The denominator of ρ_{TS} is just the square root of the sum of the terms in the covariance matrix, which was obtained in computing Ω. Finally, Ψ^2 is simply the difference between Ω and ρ_{TS}^2.

Thus, using this factoring method one would estimate the reliability to be 0.8615 and the validity 0.9171. Roughly 2 per cent of the variance in the score would be invalid, owing to the second factor.

Table 5 presents the statistics obtained from all the different methods of analysis. It is clear that estimates do depend somewhat upon the method of factoring, and whether one factors the item sets separately or together. Two findings deserve comment. In every case, no matter what factoring method was used, Ω estimates exceeded Cronbach's α (the values of α for the two scores are shown at the bottom of Table 5), as one would expect since α is a lower bound to the reliability. Second, when one factors all sets of items together, the reliabilities of the composites generally increase, as expected (the single exception was for the fatalism score, alpha factoring). However, note that the validity decreases and the invalidity increases at the same time the reliability increases. This suggests that the reliability of a composite sometimes can be increased by adding items from other domains of content, but only at the expense of validity.

Since there is no one best factoring method, it cannot be argued on a mathematical basis that any one of the estimates above is better than the other. At the same time it is to be noted that all of the procedures that were tried here gave estimates that were in the same range.

DISCUSSION

Some verbal elaboration of the concepts as used in this paper are in order. First, validity is defined as the correlation between a measure and the true underlying variable. A high validity coefficient does not imply that one has measured that which he set out to measure. It means only that whatever the items are measuring, the composite constructed is highly correlated to it. Other types of validity assessment also are needed as pointed out in the "Technical Recommendations" of the American Psychological Association (1966). Second, one ordinarily thinks of validity as equaling the square root of the reliability, but this is not necessarily the case in practice. The validity of a composite can be considerably less than the square root of the reliability when the composite's variance is due to several underlying factors instead of to a single factor. It may seem paradoxical that one can increase reliability by adding items from a domain of content other than that being measured. However, reliability deals only with whether individuals would have the same relative standing on measurement. Thus, a measure can be highly reliable but invalid. As shown in equation (37), the measure of invalidity is simply the difference between the reliability and the validity squared. Obviously, if this difference is zero, the validity will equal the square root of the reliability. A very small amount of algebraic manipulation of formula (37) makes it clear that the reliability of a

TABLE 5
Estimates of Ω, ρ_{TS}, and Ψ^2 When Items Are Factored Separately and Jointly Using Four Different Methods

Factoring Method	Ω Factored		ρ_{TS} Factored		Ψ^2 Factored	
	Separately	Jointly	Separately	Jointly	Separately	Jointly
A. *Religiosity*						
Principal Components	0.8616	0.8628	0.9171	0.9149	0.0205	0.0258
Maximum Likelihood	0.8615	0.8626	0.9171	0.9171	0.0204	0.0215
Maximum Likelihood—Iterate	0.8726	0.8735	0.9330	0.9324	0.0021	0.0041
Alpha—Iterate	0.8570	0.8577	0.9255	0.9010	0.0004	0.0459
B. *Fatalism*						
Principal Components	0.6177	0.6243	0.7528	0.7360	0.0510	0.0826
Maximum Likelihood	0.6177	0.6247	0.7520	0.7432	0.0522	0.0723
Maximum Likelihood—Iterate	0.6560	0.6625	0.8009	0.7937	0.0146	0.0325
Alpha—Iterate	0.6669	0.6611	0.8156	0.7559	0.0017	0.0897

$\alpha_r = 0.8550$ for religiosity composite.

$\alpha_f = 0.6068$ for fatalism composite.

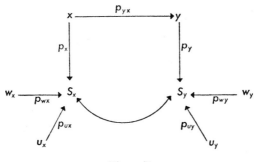

Figure 7

composite is the sum of both valid and invalid variance. This fact has important consequences for correcting estimates for attenuation due to errors in measurement.

Assuming one finds more than a single factor underlying a set of items, he cannot simply correct obtained coefficients for unreliability using standard attenuation formulas because the invalid variance in one's score yields too high a reliability estimate. Instead, one is advised to use a path analytic approach such as indicated for the two-variable case in Figure 7. Here it is assumed that x causes y and one wants to estimate the path between x and y, that is, p_{yx}. One cannot measure x and y directly but instead builds scores, S_x and S_y. If one factor analyzed the two sets of items and found more than a single factor underlying each set, the causal representation of the effects on S_x and S_y would be that shown in Figure 7. There is reliable variance in S_x due not only to x, but also to some other common factor(s) labeled w_x. Similarly for S_y, some variance is due to w_y. As was seen above, Ω, the reliability estimate, is due to *all* common factors. Thus, simply to estimate p_{yx} by dividing ρ_{xy} by the square root of the product of the two reliability estimates would give an estimate of p_{yx}, which is too small. The proper approach would be to note that

$$\rho_{xy} = p_x p_{yx} p_y \quad \text{and hence} \quad p_{yx} = \rho_{xy}/(p_x p_y)$$

But, $p_x = \rho_{S_x x}$ and $p_y = \rho_{S_y y}$—these paths simply equal the validity coefficient for S_x and S_y. Hence, one corrects for attenuation in p_{xy} not by dividing by the square root of the product of the Ωs, but instead by dividing by the product of the two validity coefficients.

For example, suppose one found that $\rho_{xy} = 0.4$, $\Omega_x = 0.8$, $\rho_{S_{xx}} = 0.85$, $\Omega_y = 0.9$, and $\rho_{S_{yy}} = 0.92$. Using the usual correction for attenuation procedures, one would estimate that $p_{yx} = 0.4/\sqrt{(0.9)(0.8)} = 0.47$. However, the correct estimate would be $p_{yx} = 0.4/(0.85)(0.92) = 0.51$.

The extension to the multivariate case is straightforward and, hence, is not discussed here.

The equations defining validity, invalidity, and reliability involve factor analysis, so two standard problems in factor analysis must be kept in mind when applying the formulas.

Factor rotation is a central concern since there are an infinite number of rotations which will satisfy any set of data (Harman, 1967, p. 24). It has been assumed here that where more than a single factor exists a unique rotation exists where the factors are aligned with latent traits, and, therefore, that factor loadings indicate the degree to which latent traits influence item scores. If the factors are markedly misaligned with latent traits, the factor loadings will not be interpretable this way, and the validity and invalidity measures will be in error. Also, the equations were derived under the assumption of orthogonal factors. Actually, the validity, invalidity, and reliability formulas all can be applied in cases of oblique factor structures, providing that pattern coefficients (as opposed to structure coefficients) are used when validity is calculated and when the formula calls for f_{ik}. Interpretation of Ω is not affected by nonorthogonality. However, the validity and invalidity coefficients do shift in meaning. When traits are correlated, the validity coefficient simply specifies the correlation of the score with the desired trait, and one must allow that some part of this correlation may be due to the influence of other traits that are correlated with the one of interest. The invalidity coefficient only specifies the proportion of reliable variance that is not correlated with the desired trait; it does not necessarily indicate how much variance is determined by unwanted traits. Indices for dealing more suitably with oblique factor scores are discussed by Cattell and Radcliffe (1962).

The second major problem involves the *communalities*, or the values entered into the diagonal of the correlation matrix before factoring. Communalities have two effects on results of factor analyses: (1) they determine the number of factors extracted, and (2) they affect the size of factor loadings. Although our formulas depend upon knowing the communalities, there is no way to determine them exactly—they must be estimated. Obviously, then, one's choice of communality estimates affects the size of the validity, invalidity, and reliability coefficients presented here. There are several procedures for estimating communalities including the highest inter-item correlation a given item has with the other items, the squared multiple correlation of an item with the remaining $n - 1$ items, and iteration procedures which usually begin with the squared multiple correlations and through refactorings improve the estimates upward. As is well known, the first of these estimates (highest correlation) has no mathematical basis for use and should be avoided. Of the other two methods mentioned above, both provide reliability estimates which exceed α in all cases with actual data that have been tried. Use of the squared multiple correlation typically leads to a minor increment while the iteration procedures usually provide an Ω which is clearly higher than α.

The term Ω frequently will be less than the test-retest correlation for a composite score since the latter is a function not only of latent traits but also of stabilities in the specific sources of variance for each item. Cattell and Radcliffe (1964) have presented a formula similar to formula (36) which substitutes test-retest correlations for items in place of h_1^2, and their formula estimates the test-retest correlation for composite score.

Three other issues need to be mentioned. First—generally speaking—the more items that are included in a factor analysis, the higher will be the estimated communalities, since in a large analysis a greater number of small factors will be discovered that affect just couplets or triplets of items. Such minor factors, if they are true representatives of latent traits affecting a few items, ideally should be allowed to contribute to the values of h^2 because they do indicate reliable sources of item variance, and one wants this reflected in Ω (which is a function of the h^2 values). Hence, as a general rule, one wants to factor as many items together as possible. Unfortunately, the general rule is complicated by two other considerations. First, some rotation procedures (like varimax) are sensitive to the number of factors extracted so that large analyses with mechanical rotation will not always yield the desired latent trait structure that would occur in a smaller, more parsimonious study. Thus, a large analysis may create the need to rotate manually or to use one of the less popular rotation procedures (like quartimax) that is less sensitive to added factors. Second, there is a danger that small factors do not really represent true latent traits but develop merely as a function of sampling fluctuations, and this danger is enhanced when one analyzes many items relative to the number of observations. So, for a given sample size (N), there is a limit on how many items should be factored simultaneously; one rule of thumb specifies this limit as no more than $N/10$ (Nunnally, 1967, p. 257).

Second, formulas (35) and (36) for invalidity and reliability assume that $\mathbf{FF'} = \mathbf{R} - \mathbf{I} + \mathbf{H}^2$, that is, that the solution used to estimate factors will reproduce the observed correlation matrix (Harman, 1967, p. 63). None of the methods of estimating the h_{ik} will ever exactly satisfy this assumption (Harman, 1967, p. 24), and, to the degree that this assumption is not met, results from formulas (35) and (36) will be in error. However, when all major factors are extracted, most factoring methods will reasonably reproduce the correlation matrix, allowing that some residuals are to be expected because of sampling variations.

Finally, the formulas presented here are defined in terms of population statistics, and when these formulas are applied to sample statistics, the resulting indices would be subject to some sampling error. Since the sampling distributions of the indices are not known, the use of large samples is suggested.

REFERENCES

AMERICAN PSYCHOLOGICAL ASSOCIATION
1966 *Standards for Educational and Psychological Tests and Manuals.* Washington: American Psychological Association.
BLALOCK, H. M., JR.
1969 "Multiple indicators and the causal approach to measurement error." *The American Journal of Sociology* 75 (September): 264–272.
BOHRNSTEDT, G. W.
1969 "A quick method for determining the reliability and validity of multiple-item scales." *American Sociological Review* 34 (August): 542–548.
CATTELL, R. B. AND RADCLIFFE, J.
1962 "Reliability and validity of simple and extended weighted and buffered unifactor scales." *British Journal of Statistical Psychology* 15: 113–128.
COSTNER, H. L.
1969 "Theory, deduction, and rules of correspondence." *The American Journal of Sociology* 75 (September): 245–263.
CRONBACH, L. J.
1951 "Coefficient alpha and the internal structure of tests." *Psychometrika* 16: 297–334.
DUNCAN, O. D.
1966 "Path analysis: Sociological examples." *The American Journal of Sociology* 72(1): 1–16.
HARMAN, H. H.
1967 *Modern Factor Analysis.* Chicago: University of Chicago Press.
HEISE, D. R.
1969 "Separating reliability and stability in test-retest correlations." *American Sociological Review* 34 (February): 93–101.
JOHNSTON, J.
1963 *Econometric Methods.* New York: McGraw-Hill.
KAISER, H. F.
1958 "The varimax criterion for analytic rotation in factor analysis." *Psychometrika* 23: 187–200.
KAISER, H. F. AND CAFFREY, J.
1965 "Alpha factor analysis." *Psychometrika* 30: 1–14.
LAND, K. C.
1969 "Principles of path analysis." Pp. 3–37 in E. F. Borgatta and G. W. Bohrnstedt (Eds.), *Sociological Methodology 1969.* San Francisco: Jossey-Bass.

LORD, F. N. AND NOVICK, M. R.
  1968 *Statistical Theories of Mental Test Scores.* Reading: Addison-Wesley.

NOVICK, M. R. AND LEWIS, C.
  1967 "Coefficient alpha and the reliability of composite measurements."
        Psychometrika 32: 1–13.

NUNNALLY, J. C.
  1967 *Psychometric Theory.* New York: McGraw-Hill.

WALKER, H. M. AND LEV, J.
  1953 *Statistical Inference.* New York: Holt, Rinehart, and Winston.

WRIGHT, S.
  1934 "The method of path coefficients." *Annals of Mathematical Statistics* 5:
        161–215.

7

EFFECT OF RELIABILITY
AND VALIDITY ON POWER
OF STATISTICAL TESTS

T. Anne Cleary
UNIVERSITY OF WISCONSIN

Robert L. Linn
EDUCATIONAL TESTING SERVICE

G. William Walster
UNIVERSITY OF WISCONSIN

Editors' note: Reading Chapter Fourteen first may facilitate reading certain sections of this chapter.

It is well known to most behavioral scientists that the power of a statistical test depends on such factors as the magnitude of the difference between the true situation and the hypothesis being tested, the Type I error rate, and the sample size. In order to have the power that he wishes against particular alternatives, the experimenter will select an appropriate Type I error rate and sample size (see Walster and Cleary, 1970). But, if the magnitude of the alternatives is expressed in terms of true underlying variability, power also depends on the reliability and validity of the dependent measure.

All too frequently, reliability and validity are ignored in the design of experiments. In most statistics texts used by the behavioral scientists, observations are treated as if they were errorless or "true" measurements, and attention is focused on sampling error rather than measurement error. On the other hand, the test theory literature has focused primarily, and sometimes exclusively, on measurement error. In test theory, observations are considered fallible and repeated measures of the same object are assumed to vary about the "true" value.

A few authors have considered the two types of errors simultaneously. Sutcliffe (1958) studied the effect of error of measurement in the random-effects analysis of variance. He showed that, with other things being equal, the power of an F-test against a particular alternative decreases as measurement error is introduced. Overall and Dalal (1965) discussed the problem of choosing a research design which maximizes power relative to cost. They concluded that, no matter how unreliable the measurement, it is better to use more subjects and obtain a single measurement per subject than to obtain several measures on each of fewer subjects. As Overall and Dalal point out, this conclusion is based on the assumption that there is a fixed cost per measurement unit and that this cost is the same whether the units are obtained for the same subject or different subjects. Frequently, however, the costs are not the same for all measurement units. In such cases, increased power may be more efficiently obtained by increasing test length and thus improving reliability and validity.

It should be noted that the application of statistical tests to fallible measures is not necessarily incorrect or inappropriate: the assumptions of the statistical tests may be satisfied by the observed scores. However, if the hypotheses are formulated in terms of true scores and tested with observed scores, the noncentrality parameter and, therefore, the power can be quite different from that expected with true scores.

In this paper we consider the effect of both reliability and validity on the power of the fixed-effects, analysis-of-variance F-test. It will be shown not only that unreliability decreases power against a particular alternative, but that simultaneous consideration of reliability and validity is both more realistic and more devastating.

TEST THEORY

Let us review the test theory that we require in our study of the effect of reliability and validity on power. In classical test theory, it is assumed that the observed score, X_i, for individual i, is equal to a true score, T_i, plus an error score, E_i:

$$X_i = T_i + E_i \tag{1}$$

where T_i and E_i are independently and normally distributed with expectations, μ_T and zero respectively, and variances, σ_T^2 and σ_E^2. Thus X_i are distributed independently and normally with expectation μ_T and variance $\sigma_T^2 + \sigma_E^2$. The reliability of the observed scores is defined as the ratio of the variance of the true scores to the variance of the observed scores:

$$\rho_{XX'} = \frac{\sigma_T^2}{\sigma_T^2 + \sigma_E^2} \tag{2}$$

The validity of X is defined as a correlation between X and another measure of interest, say Z. The validity of the measure X might then be denoted ρ_{ZX}.

If a test is lengthened by combining K unit-length parallel tests, the relationship between the reliability and validity of the unit-length test and the lengthened test are known (Lord and Novick, 1968):

$$\rho_K = \frac{K\rho_{XX'}}{1 + (K-1)\rho_{XX'}} \tag{3}$$

and

$$\rho_{ZX_K} = \sqrt{\frac{K}{1 + (K-1)\rho_{XX'}}}\, \rho_{ZX} \tag{4}$$

where the subscript K denotes the test lengthened by a factor of K.

EFFECT OF RELIABILITY

Consider a simple fixed-effects, one-way analysis of variance. If the analysis is performed on the true scores, the model is

$$T_{ig} = M + A_g + B_{ig} \quad \begin{array}{l} g = 1, \ldots, G \\ i = 1, \ldots, N \end{array} \tag{5}$$

where T_{ig} = the true score for individual i in group g

M = a constant

A_g = the component of the true score which is due to the effect of treatment g

B_{ig} = the deviation of an individual's score from the group mean (the error of the analysis-of-variance model)

The B_{ig} are assumed to be independently and normally distributed with expected value of zero and common variance, σ_B^2. The A_g are unknown fixed constants.

If the null hypothesis of no difference among groups $\left(\sum_g A_g^2 = 0 \right)$ is true, the test statistic for the group effect (the ratio of the between-groups mean-square to the within-groups mean-square) is distributed as central F with $(G - 1)$ and $G(N - 1)$ degrees of freedom. If the null hypothesis is not true, the test statistic is distributed as noncentral F with the same degrees of freedom and noncentrality parameter,

$$\delta_T^2 = \frac{N \sum_g A_g^2}{\sigma_B^2} \qquad (6)$$

If, rather than true scores, observed scores are used in the analysis, the model is

$$X_{ig} = M + A_g + B_{ig} + E_{ig} \qquad (7)$$

where X_{ig} = the observed score of individual i in group g

E_{ig} = the measurement error for individual i in group g

and M, A_g, and B_{ig} are the same as in the true-score model.

The measurement errors, E_{ig}, are assumed, as before, to be independently and normally distributed with expected value of zero and variance, σ_E^2. Since test theory assumes that true and error scores are independent, the E_{ig} and B_{ig} are independent.

If the null hypothesis is true, the test statistic has the same distribution as in the error-free case, central F with $(G - 1)$ and $N(G - 1)$ degrees of freedom. However, if the null hypothesis is false, the test statistic is distributed as noncentral F with the same degrees of freedom, but with noncentrality parameter,

$$\delta_X^2 = \frac{N \sum_g A_g^2}{\sigma_B^2 + \sigma_E^2} \qquad (8)$$

The numerator is the same as the numerator of the true-score non-centrality parameter. However, the denominator (the within-group

134 T. ANNE CLEARY, ROBERT L. LINN AND G. WILLIAM WALSTER

variance) has an additional component, the variance of the error of measurement, σ_E^2.

We can write the observed score noncentrality parameter in terms of the true-score noncentrality parameter and the reliability of the observed scores. The variance of the observed scores is $\sigma_B^2 + \sigma_E^2$; the variance of the true scores, σ_B^2; and the reliability, $\sigma_B^2/(\sigma_B^2 + \sigma_E^2)$. The observed-score noncentrality parameter (8) is then

$$\delta_X^2 = \rho_{XX'}\delta_T^2 \qquad (9)$$

Since the reliability is at most one, the observed-score noncentrality parameter is always less than or equal to the true-score parameter.

Since the noncentrality parameter is merely a constant times Δ, the index of the magnitude of an effect proposed by Walster and Cleary (1970), the true and observed Δs (Δ_T^2 and Δ_X^2) will have precisely the same relationship as the true and observed noncentrality parameters:

$$\Delta_X^2 = \rho_{XX'}\Delta_T^2 \qquad (10)$$

If the reliability is known, the experimenter can specify the power he wishes against magnitudes of Δ_T^2, compute the corresponding values of Δ_X^2, and then determine the sample size and Type I error rate appropriate for an observed-score analysis.

Since the sample size required to have a specified power against a particular alternative decreases as the magnitude of the alternative increases, we can reduce the sample size required to obtain a specified power against true-score alternatives, if we can increase the reliability of the observed scores. By using equations (3) and (10) we can express Δ_X^2 in terms of the reliability of the unit-length test, the factor K by which we have lengthened the test, and Δ_T^2:

$$\Delta_{X_K}^2 = \frac{K\rho_{XX'}\Delta_T^2}{1 + (K-1)\rho_{XX}} \qquad (11)$$

In order to obtain the desired power against the Δ_T^2s of interest, it may be more efficient to add subjects, increase test length, or both, depending upon the cost of lengthening the test relative to the cost of subjects. Cleary and Linn (1969) have discussed a way to determine the allocation of resources using a simple cost model.

EFFECT OF VALIDITY

Let us consider now the effect on power of using a measure that is not perfectly valid. For example, we may be interested in true-score differences on a test that is expensive to administer. However, rather than using the expensive test, we use a less costly measure that is correlated with it. The measure for our analysis is then not perfectly valid.

We shall assume that the measure used, say Y, is linearly related to the true score of interest, T, and that this relationship is the same for all groups. In addition, we shall assume that the treatment affects Y only through its effect on T. Our model for Y is then

$$Y_{ig} = \alpha + \beta T_{ig} + \epsilon_{ig} \tag{12}$$

where Y_{ig} = the observed measure for individual i in the group g

T_{ig} = the unobserved true score of interest for individual i in group g

ϵ_{ig} = the error of estimate for individual i in group g

α and β = unknown constants

The ϵ_{ig} are assumed to be independently and normally distributed with expected value of zero and variance, σ_ϵ^2, and are assumed to be independent of the T_{ig}. The common intercept and slope parameters are α and β.

The noncentrality parameter for the analysis of Y is given by

$$\delta_Y^2 = \frac{\beta^2 N \Sigma A_g^2}{\beta^2 \sigma_B^2 + \sigma_\epsilon^2} \tag{13}$$

If we divide the numerator and denominator of equation (13) by β^2, the numerator is the same as that of the noncentrality parameter of the true scores σ_T^2—equation (6)—but the denominator has increased by $\sigma_\epsilon^2/\beta^2$. Since

$$\rho_{TY}^2 = \frac{\beta^2 \sigma_B^2}{\beta^2 \sigma_B^2 + \sigma_\epsilon^2} \tag{14}$$

we can rewrite δ_Y^2 in terms of δ_T^2 and ρ_{TY}^2

$$\delta_Y^2 = \rho_{TY}^2 \delta_T^2 \tag{15}$$

Now since the correlation between the observed scores is

$$\rho_{XY} = \rho_{TY}/\sqrt{\rho_{XX'}} \tag{16}$$

we can see the simultaneous effect of reliability and validity in the relationships between δ_Y^2 and δ_T^2

$$\delta_Y^2 = \frac{\rho_{XY}^2}{\rho_{XX'}^2} \delta_T^2 \tag{17}$$

In addition, recalling equation (9), we can see the relationship between δ_Y^2 and the observed score noncentrality parameter δ_X^2

$$\delta_Y^2 = \frac{\rho_{XY}^2}{\rho_{XX'}^2} \delta_X^2 \tag{18}$$

As in the case of reliability alone, if both the reliability of X and the validity of Y are known, the experimenter can specify the power he wishes against magnitudes of Δ_T^2, compute the corresponding values of Δ_Y^2, and then determine the sample size and Type I error rate appropriate for an analysis of the observed score, Y. The relationship between Δ_Y^2 and Δ_T^2 is

$$\Delta_Y^2 = \rho_{XY}^2 \Delta_T^2 / \rho_{XX'} \tag{19}$$

Again, by increasing test length, this time test Y, we can increase Δ_Y^2 and thus decrease the number of subjects required. Using equation (4) for the validity of measure Y increased by a factor K, Y_K, we obtain

$$\Delta_{Y_K}^2 = \frac{K}{1 + (K - 1)\rho_{YY}} \rho_{XY}^2 \Delta_T^2 / \rho_{XX'} \tag{20}$$

Depending upon the cost of subjects, the cost of the measure of interest, X, and the cost of lengthening the measure, Y, it will be possible to determine the most efficient allocation of resources to obtain the desired power against the Δ_T^2s of interest.

If the validity of Y, the correlation of Y with the measure of interest, X, is not known, there are several upper bounds that we can place on Δ_Y^2. These upper bounds will lead to lower bounds on the number of subjects. We know, for example, that the validity coefficient cannot exceed the square root of the reliability coefficient of either measure. Therefore

$$\rho_{XY} \leq \sqrt{\rho_{XX'}} \tag{21}$$

and

$$\rho_{XY} \leq \sqrt{\rho_{YY'}} \tag{22}$$

Since we have assumed that X is the expensive measure of interest, it is not unreasonable to assume that Y has a lower reliability coefficient. Therefore, let us use equation (22) to form a bound:

$$\Delta_Y^2 \leq \rho_{YY'} \Delta_T^2 / \rho_{XX'} \tag{23}$$

The bound in equation (23) can be improved by noting that the correlation between the true scores on X and the true scores on Y can be written

$$\frac{\rho_{XY}}{\sqrt{\rho_{XX'}\rho_{YY'}}} \tag{24}$$

This correlation must be less than or equal to 1.0, and therefore

$$\rho_{XY} \leq \sqrt{\rho_{XX'}\rho_{YY'}} \tag{25}$$

Substituting the relationship in equation (25) into equation (19), our bound becomes

$$\Delta_Y^2 \leq \rho_{YY'}\Delta_T^2 \qquad (26)$$

and we have reduced the bound in equation (23) by a factor of $\rho_{XX'}$. Finally, we can obtain an upper bound on Δ_{YK}^2 for the test Y increased by a factor of K if only $\rho_{XX'}$ and $\rho_{YY'}$ are known by combining equations (25) and (20):

$$\Delta_{YK}^2 \leq \frac{K}{1 + (K-1)\rho_{YY'}} \rho_{YY'}\Delta_T^2 \qquad (27)$$

Now let us consider the implications of these equations for a researcher. We shall use the example, presented by Walster and Cleary (1970), of a researcher who is interested in whether a costly training program for the unemployed improves job skills as measured by on-the-job ratings of trained observers. In order to make his decision, he designs an experiment in which subjects are randomly assigned either to the experimental training program or to a no-treatment control group. Because of the cost of implementing the program, he is interested in only large effects: he chooses to have power of 0.99 against Δ_T of 2.0 and power of 0.05 against Δ_T of 0.5. For the true-score analysis, the appropriate sample size per group is sixteen.

However, the researcher will not analyze true scores. Therefore he must choose a sample size appropriate for observed score Δs. Let us say that the reliability of the ratings of job performance is high ($\rho_{XX'} = 0.90$). From equation (10) the resulting values of Δ_X^2 are 0.225 and 3.6, and the appropriate sample size for this analysis is eighteen. If the researcher does not want to run this many subjects and is willing to double the test length (double the number of ratings), he can use equation (11) to determine values of $\Delta_{X_2}^2$ for the double-length test. The resulting values of $\Delta_{X_2}^2$ are 0.237 and 3.789, for which the appropriate sample size is seventeen. Clearly there are a number of alternatives open to the researcher. In fact, if subjects are very inexpensive, he could cut the test length and run more than eighteen subjects. If the test length is cut so that the reliability is reduced to 0.6, twenty-six subjects per cell would be required.

Now let us assume that the experimenter is considering the use of a paper-and-pencil test instead of the more expensive on-the-job ratings. The paper-and-pencil test (Y) is not perfectly valid ($\rho_{XY} = 0.50$) and, since the training is practical, the treatment can be expected to affect the paper-and-pencil scores only through its effect on the true scores of the job ratings. Thus we may use equation (19) to obtain the values of Δ_Y^2, which are 0.069 and 1.111. The resulting appropriate sample size is fifty-three. If the researcher does not want to run this many subjects, he can explore the effect on the required sample size of lengthening the paper-and-pencil test by using equation (20). Assuming that the reliability of the paper-and-pencil test is reasonably high ($\rho_{YY'} = 0.70$) and the test is doubled, the values of $\Delta^2_{Y_2}$ are 0.082 and 1.307, resulting in a required sample size of 45. If the test is tripled the values of $\Delta^2_{Y_3}$ are 0.087 and 1.389, resulting in a sample size of forty-three.

If the correlation between the paper-and-pencil test and the ratings is not known, but the reliability of both tests are known, equation (26) gives an upper bound for the values of Δ^2_Y, which are 0.175 and 2.800, resulting in a lower bound on the required sample size of twenty-two.

REFERENCES

CLEARY, T. A. AND LINN, R. L.
    1969   "Error of measurement and the power of a statistical test." *British Journal of Mathematical and Statistical Psychology* 22: 49–55.
LORD, F. M., AND NOVICK, M. R. (WITH CONTRIBUTIONS BY A. BIRNBAUM)
    1968   *Statistical Theories of Mental Test Scores.* Reading, Mass.: Addison-Wesley.
OVERALL, J. E. AND DALAL, S. N.
    1965   "Design of experiments to maximize power relative to cost." *Psychological Bulletin* 64: 339–350.
SUTCLIFFE, J. P.
    1958   "Error of measurement and the sensitivity of a test of significance." *Psychometrika* 13: 9–17.
WALSTER, G. W. AND CLEARY, T. A.
    1970   "Statistical significance as a decision rule." *Sociological Methodology* 1970: 246–254.

BIVARIATE AGREEMENT
COEFFICIENTS FOR
RELIABILITY OF DATA

Klaus Krippendorff

UNIVERSITY OF PENNSYLVANIA

The quality of data in content analysis, in surveys with open-ended questions, in the observation of unstructured social events, and so on, critically depends on the reliability with which primary observations are assigned to categories, scaled, or measured. To help assure valid interpretations, agreement between two independent observers is measured. When agreement is due merely to chance, data may have little to do with the phenomena studied. In order for such data to be empirically meaningful, a high degree of inter-observer agreement must be demonstrated.

This paper suggests that several heretofore unrelated bivariate agreement coefficients may in fact be regarded as belonging to one family. It presents a paradigm through which their formal resemblances become transparent and it proposes efficient formulas for their computation.

FAMILY OF COEFFICIENTS

Coefficients of agreement frequently assume the following form:

$$\text{agreement} = 1 - \frac{\text{observed disagreement}}{\text{expected disagreement}} \tag{1}$$

This makes the coefficient zero when agreement is merely chance, unity when agreement is perfect, and negative when agreement is below chance. In contradistinction to this form, it should be noted, several known coefficients take some measure of the maximum disagreement (that is, of the total observed covariance) as denominator, which makes them vary between zero and one only. Two familiar examples of the latter are Kendall's (1948) coefficient of concordance and Robinson's (1957) statistical measure of agreement. Because such coefficients assume no definite value for chance agreement, they do not seem suited for evaluating reliability. Therefore concern is limited to coefficients based on equation (1) above.

To be more specific, data gathered to assess the agreement between two independent observers can always be represented in a square matrix:

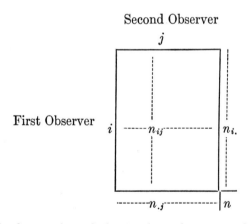

where n_{ij} is the number of observations that are assigned to category (or scale value) i by the first observer and to category (or scale value) j by the second, $n_{i.}$ is the frequency with which the category (or scale value) i is used by the first observer, and n is the total number of units recorded by both.

The diagonal of this square matrix, with entries n_{ii}, contains the incidents of agreement. When scales are categorial or nominal, that is, in the unordered case, any deviation from the diagonal constitutes disagreement. Thus when computing the observed disagreement the entries n_{ij} have to be weighted by a function d_{ij}:

$$d_{ij} = \begin{cases} 0 \text{ if } i = j \\ 1 \text{ if } i \neq j \end{cases} \tag{2}$$

When categories imply a metric, constitute interval scales, or are ranked, such a function would be quite inappropriate because disagreement then becomes a function of the difference between scale values. A suitable function[1] for assessing the degree of disagreement analogously to the above is:

$$d_{ij} = (i - j)^2 \tag{3}$$

The evaluation of the frequencies that are expected when the two observers are not influenced by their observations and agreement is due to chance always relies on the marginal distributions. However, differences emerge depending on whether disagreements between observers regarding their use of categories or scale values are considered or ignored. If the expected frequencies, e_{ij}, are computed on a joint marginal distribution, that is, on the average frequencies in categories i and j, then:

$$e_{ij} = \frac{1}{n}\left(\frac{n_{i.} + n_{.i}}{2}\right)\left(\frac{n_{.j} + n_{j.}}{2}\right) \tag{4}$$

If the expected frequencies are based on the observer's respective marginal distribution then:

$$e_{ij} = \frac{1}{n} n_{i.} n_{.j} \tag{5}$$

With

$$\Sigma\Sigma n_{ij} d_{ij}$$

as a measure of the observed disagreement and

$$\Sigma\Sigma e_{ij} d_{ij}$$

as a measure of the disagreement obtained by chance, equation (1) can be given the following form:

---

[1] As far as this family of agreement coefficients is concerned, there is no inherent reason for squaring the differences between scale values. In fact, any monotonically increasing function of these differences would be appropriate. The most simple form of such a function would be $d_{ij} = |i - j|$. The use of some weight of these differences has been recommended by Goodman and Kruskal (1954). However, the use of squares leads to several desired properties and to two familiar interpretations of the resulting agreement coefficients as will be shown below.

$$a = 1 - \frac{\Sigma\Sigma n_{ij}d_{ij}}{\Sigma\Sigma e_{ij}d_{ij}} \tag{6}$$

Equation (6) defines the common features of a family of agreement coefficients, the members of which are obtained through the variation of d_{ij} and e_{ij} respectively.

KNOWN INTERPRETATIONS

Let the observed proportion of agreement be defined by

$$P_0 = \frac{1}{n} \sum n_{ii}$$

and the expected proportion of agreement be

$$P_e = \frac{1}{n^2} \sum \left(\frac{n_{i.} + n_{.i}}{2} \right)^2$$

Now, if equations (2) and (4) are inserted into equation (6), the agreement coefficient can be rewritten as follows:[2]

$$a_\pi = 1 - \frac{\displaystyle\sum_{i \neq j} n_{ij}}{\displaystyle\frac{1}{n} \sum_{i \neq j} \left(\frac{n_{i.} + n_{.i}}{2} \right) \left(\frac{n_{.j} + n_{j.}}{2} \right)} = \frac{P_0 - P_e}{1 - P_e} \tag{7}$$

Its numerator is a measure of the above-chance agreement observed and its denominator is a measure of the above-chance agreement maximally possible. The term a_π is exactly Scott's (1955) widely used coefficient of inter-coder agreement, π.

Let the observed proportion of agreement be

$$P_0 = \frac{1}{n} \sum n_{ii}$$

as above but let the proportion of agreement obtained by chance now be defined by

$$P_e = \frac{1}{n^2} \sum n_{i.}n_{.i}$$

When equations (2) and (5) are inserted into equation (6), then

---

[2] Since the proofs regarding the relation between known coefficients and the measures defined in equations (2) through (6) are lengthy, they can be obtained from the author. The following section discusses only the results.

$$a_\kappa = 1 - \frac{\displaystyle\sum_{i \neq j} n_{ij}}{\displaystyle\frac{1}{n} \sum_{i \neq j} n_{i.} n_{.j}} = \frac{P_0 - P_c}{1 - P_c} \tag{8}$$

which is another though less familiar agreement coefficient proposed by Cohen (1960), called κ. Thus a_π and a_κ merely vary with the way the expected frequencies e_{ij} are computed.

A quite unexpected result is obtained when equations (3) and (4) are inserted into equation (6). If $\langle X, Y \rangle$ denotes a pair of observations with values $\langle i, j \rangle$ and if sums are taken over n such pairs rather than with reference to the values i and j, then

$$\Sigma n_{i.} i = \Sigma X, \ \Sigma n_{i.} i^2 = \Sigma X^2, \text{ and so on.}$$

With $\bar{M} = (\Sigma X + \Sigma Y)/2n$ the coefficient can now be rewritten as follows:

$$a_R = 1 - \frac{\Sigma\Sigma n_{ij}(i - j)^2}{\displaystyle\frac{1}{n} \sum \sum \left(\frac{n_{i.} + n_{.i}}{2}\right)\left(\frac{n_{.j} + n_{j.}}{2}\right)(i - j)^2}$$
$$= \frac{2\Sigma(X - \bar{M})(Y - \bar{M})}{\Sigma(X - \bar{M})^2 + \Sigma(Y - \bar{M})^2} \tag{9}$$

This is the intra-class correlation coefficient as proposed by Pearson (1901). The coefficient is computed exactly like the product moment coefficient except that all pairs of observations are entered twice, once as $\langle X, Y \rangle$ and once as $\langle Y, X \rangle$ so that $\bar{M}$ is the common mean and the resulting distribution is symmetrical with regard to the diagonal of the matrix.

Finally, if equations (3) and (5) are inserted into equation (6), and sums are taken as above, but where

$$\bar{X} = \frac{1}{n} \sum X \quad \text{and} \quad \bar{Y} = \frac{1}{n} \sum Y$$

are the individual means, the coefficient now assumes the following form:

$$a_{\bar{r}} = 1 - \frac{\Sigma\Sigma n_{ij}(i - j)^2}{\displaystyle\frac{1}{n} \sum \sum n_{i.} n_{.j}(i - j)^2}$$
$$= \frac{2\Sigma(X - \bar{X})(Y - \bar{Y})}{\Sigma(X - \bar{X})^2 + \Sigma(Y - \bar{Y})^2 + \Sigma(\bar{X} - \bar{Y})^2} \tag{10}$$

This coefficient apparently has not been used before. Its numerator is a measure of covariation, just as in the product moment coefficient. However, instead of taking the geometric mean over the individual variances as an estimate for the expected covariation, the denominator of $a_{\bar{r}}$ consists of the sum of the individual variances plus the variation of the two means.

If each of the available categories or scale values is used only once by the observers, then equations (4) and (5) are identical: $e_{ij} = 1/n$. If under this restriction equation (3) is inserted into equation (6) and if $\Sigma\Sigma n_{ij}(i - j)^2$ is expressed as the sum over the n-squared differences, Σd^2, then:

$$a_R = a_{\bar{r}} - 1 - \frac{\Sigma\Sigma n_{ij}(i - j)^2}{\dfrac{1}{n^2} \sum\sum (i - j)^2} = 1 - \frac{6\Sigma d^2}{n(n^2 - 1)} \qquad (11)$$

which is the well-known Spearman rank order correlation coefficient, sometimes called *rho*. It is not surprising that this particular association measure is a member of the family of agreement coefficients while many others are not. Here, any deviation from perfect agreement also counts as a deviation from perfect association. However, in assessing association by the product moment formula, for example, only deviation from a perfect linear dependency, $X = a + bY$ and $Y = a' + b'X$, are considered. It would thus be improper to regard all association measures as measures of agreement.

DIFFERENTIATING PROPERTIES AND RELATIONS

The alternatives for d_{ij} and e_{ij} now lend themselves to the following typology shown in Table 1.

TABLE 1
Typology of Agreement Coefficients

$a = 1 - \dfrac{\Sigma\Sigma n_{ij}d_{ij}}{\Sigma\Sigma e_{ij}d_{ij}}$	$d_{ij} = \begin{cases} 0 \text{ if } i = j \\ 1 \text{ if } i \neq j \end{cases}$	$d_{ij} = (i - j)^2$	
$e_{ij} = \dfrac{1}{n}\left(\dfrac{n_{i.} + n_{.i}}{2}\right)\left(\dfrac{n_{.j} + n_{j.}}{2}\right)$	a_π	a_R	True agreement
$e_{ij} = \dfrac{1}{n} n_{i.}n_{j.}$	a_κ	$a_{\bar{r}}$	Partial agreement
	Unordered (Nominal Scales)	Ordered (Ordinal and Interval Scales)	

It is possible to compare the properties of the four coefficients. These properties are normally hidden behind divergent notational styles and different computational formulas. As discussed above, equation (6) implies that all coefficients assume unity as their maximum value when the numerator $\Sigma\Sigma n_{ij}d_{ij} = 0$, that is, agreement is perfect. When for all cells in the matrix $n_{ij} = e_{ij}$, the coefficients are zero, indicating that the observed agreement is due merely to chance. For example,

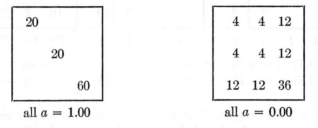

20		
	20	
		60

all $a = 1.00$

4	4	12
4	4	12
12	12	36

all $a = 0.00$

Negative values appear when agreement is below chance, a case which should rarely occur in estimates of reliability. Coefficients are also negative or zero when either one or both of the observers fail to exhibit variations in their use of categories or scale values. More generally, situations that are characterized by high chance agreements require relatively more observed agreements than situations in which agreements are less likely achieved by accident. For example,

100	

all $a = 0.00$

7	3
3	87

all $a = 0.67$

23	3	4
3	23	4
4	4	32

all $a = 0.67$

In comparing the differential effects of e_{ij} on the agreement coefficients, it can be shown that $a_\kappa \geq a_\pi$ and $a_\mp \geq a_R$. If the two distributions over the marginals are the same for the two observers, that is, $n_{i\cdot} = n_{\cdot i}$ for all i (as in the third of the following three examples), then equations (4) and (5) produce the same expected frequencies and $a_\kappa = a_\pi$ and $a_\mp = a_R$. However, if the two distributions differ (as in the first and second of the following examples), discrepancies between a_κ and a_π and between $a_\mp$ and a_R reflect the individual proclivity of observers to disagree regarding their use of categories or regarding preferences for particular scale values. Since a_π and a_R are sensitive to this disagreement whereas a_κ and $a_\mp$ are not, the former can therefore be called coefficients of true agreement while the latter might be called partial agreement coefficients. Consider the following:

4		2	6
	1	1	2
		2	2
4	1	5	10

20		10	30
	5	5	10
		10	10
20	5	25	50

40		10	50
	10	5	15
10	5	20	35
50	15	35	100

$a_\pi = 0.50$ $a_R = 0.31$ $a_\pi = 0.50$ $a_R = 0.31$ $a_\pi = a_R = 0.50$
$a_\kappa = 0.53$ $a_{\bar r} = 0.49$ $a_\kappa = 0.53$ $a_{\bar r} = 0.49$ $a_R = a_{\bar r} = 0.31$

Moreover, the examples show that the coefficients remain unaffected by the number n of units of observation in the sample. Thus when the entries n_{ij} are multiplied by a scaler, the agreement coefficients remain invariant. The first and the second of the above examples are related in this way. When a new matrix is created by adding to a matrix its transpose, only the true agreement coefficients remain invariant. This is demonstrated by the third of the above examples, which is obtained from the second as described.

In the dichotomous case, where the matrix is just 2×2, differences between coefficients for the ordered and the unordered case do not exist, that is, $a_\pi = a_R$ and $a_\kappa = a_{\bar r}$. This not only is meaningful on intuitive grounds but can also be seen from the definitions of d_{ij}. With only one possible "degree" of disagreement, equations (2) and (3) produce identical values, that is, 0 and 1, whereby the distinction between nominal and interval scales disappears.

The condition $a_\pi = a_R$ and $a_\kappa = a_{\bar r}$ also holds where the set of scale values is used by the observers as true nominal scales, that is, disagreements are distributed evenly over the nondiagonal entries as a consequence of which numbers assigned to categories are freely interchangeable. Suppose for all cells $i \neq j : n_{ij} = be_{ij}$, where b has a value between zero and one. Then, by equation (6), for all coefficients $a = 1 - b$. Thus the difference between the ordered and unordered case is disregarded. However, if disagreements tend to cluster around the diagonal then $a_R \geq a_\pi$ and $a_{\bar r} \geq a_\kappa$; but if disagreements accumulate in the corners most distant from the diagonal, then $a_\pi \geq a_R$ and $a_\kappa \geq a_{\bar r}$. Thus the difference between the two coefficients reflects the information implicit in the ordering of categories or scale values. For example,

9	2	2
2	9	2
2	2	9

all $a = 0.54$

9	3	
3	9	3
	3	9

$a_\pi = a_\kappa = 0.54$
$a_{\bar{R}} = a_{\bar{r}} = 0.75$

9	1	4
1	9	1
4	1	9

$a_\pi = a_\kappa = 0.54$
$a_R = a_{\bar{r}} = 0.36$

It is clear then that an appropriate application of these coefficients in a given situation requires two independent decisions. First, is a possible metric among categories or intervals between values to be ignored (the unordered case) or considered significant (the ordered case)? Second, is the observers' tendency to disagree over the marginal distribution to be considered in (true agreement) or not in (partial agreement) the measure? Each of the four coefficients of this family have meaningful reliability interpretations which have become transparent in discussing their formal relations above.

COMPUTATIONAL FORMULAS

For efficient computation of the agreement coefficients the following formulas are offered.[3]

$$a_\pi = \frac{4n\Sigma n_{ii} - \Sigma(n_{i.} + n_{.i})^2}{4n^2 - \Sigma(n_{i.} + n_{.i})^2} \qquad (12)$$

Here, Σn_{ii} is the sum over the diagonal and represents the actual number of agreements among the two observers. The term $\Sigma(n_{i.} + n_{.i})^2$ is the sum of squares of the joint marginal entries by two observers. When marginal frequencies are equal, that is, $n_{i.} = n_{.i}$ for all i, which can be achieved either by averaging or by adding to each square matrix its transpose, then

$$a_\pi = a_\kappa = \frac{n\Sigma n_{ii} - \Sigma n_{i.}^2}{n^2 - \Sigma n_{i.}^2} \qquad (13)$$

When marginal frequencies are not equal the equality $a_\pi = a_\kappa$ does not hold and a_κ must be computed by:

$$a_\kappa = \frac{n\Sigma n_{ii} - \Sigma n_{i.} n_{.i}}{n^2 - \Sigma n_{i.} n_{.i}} \qquad (14)$$

[3] Proofs may be requested from the author.

where $\Sigma n_{i.}n_{.i}$ is the sum of the products of the individual marginal entries by the two observers. However, the computation of a_R and $a_{\bar{r}}$ is not so simple:

$$a_R = 1 - \frac{\Sigma\Sigma n_{ij}(i - j)^2}{\sum n_{i.}i^2 + \sum n_{.j}j^2 - \frac{1}{2n}\left(\sum n_{i.}i + \sum n_{.j}j\right)^2} \tag{15}$$

$$a_{\bar{r}} = 1 - \frac{\Sigma\Sigma n_{ij}(i - j)^2}{\sum n_{i.}i^2 + \sum n_{.j}j^2 - \frac{2}{n}\left(\sum n_{i.}i\right)\left(\sum n_{.j}j\right)} \tag{16}$$

When marginals are equal, that is, $n_{i.} = n_{.i}$ for all i:

$$a_R = a_{\bar{r}} = 1 - \frac{\frac{1}{2}\sum\sum n_{ij}(i - j)^2}{\sum n_{i.}i^2 = \frac{1}{n}\left(\sum n_{i.}i\right)^2} \tag{17}$$

The denominator can be computed as follows: if the square matrix has $k \times k$ cells then the k diagonal entries can be ignored. The sum of the entries in the $2(k - 1)$ cells next to the diagonal has to be multiplied by 1^2, the content of the $2(k - 2)$ cells next to the above is multiplied by 2^2, and so on, until the content of the two most distant cells is multiplied by $(k - 1)^2$. Usually, there should be few deviations from the diagonal, which makes the computation of the numerator easy. The expressions in the denominator are computed from the marginal entries. Thus $\Sigma n_{i.}i^2$ involves multiplying the frequencies with which a scale value is used by its square, and so on.

Although usually more tedious, a_R and $a_{\bar{r}}$ can also be computed from a list of couples $\langle X, Y \rangle$. With the notational conventions of correlational analysis:

$$a_R = \frac{4n\Sigma XY - (\Sigma X + \Sigma Y)^2}{2n(\Sigma X^2 + \Sigma Y^2) - (\Sigma X + \Sigma Y)^2} \tag{18}$$

$$a_{\bar{r}} = \frac{2n\Sigma XY - 2(\Sigma X)(\Sigma Y)}{n(\Sigma X^2 + \Sigma Y^2) - 2(\Sigma X)(\Sigma Y)} \tag{19}$$

To exemplify the computation, let the results of a duplicate recording of $n = 16$ observations be given in the following square matrix. Although a small sample size may not lead to significant conclusions, it will serve the purpose of illustration:

Second Observer

		0	1	2	3	
First Observer	0	4	1		2	7
	1		3		1	4
	2			2	2	4
	3				1	1
		4	4	2	6	16

According to equation (12):

$$a_\pi = \frac{4 \cdot 16(4 + 3 + 2 + 1) - [(4 + 7)^2 + (4 + 4)^2 + (2 + 4)^2 + (6 + 1)^2]}{4 \cdot 16^2 - [(4 + 7)^2 + (4 + 4)^2 + (2 + 4)^2 + (6 + 1)^2]} = 0.49$$

According to equation (14):

$$a_\kappa = \frac{16(4 + 3 + 2 + 1) - [4 \cdot 7 + 4 \cdot 4 + 2 \cdot 4 + 6 \cdot 1]}{16^2 - [4 \cdot 7 + 4 \cdot 4 + 2 \cdot 4 + 6 \cdot 1]} = 0.52$$

According to equation (15) (products with zero omitted):

$$a_R = 1 - \frac{(1 + 2)1^2 + 1 \cdot 2^2 + 2 \cdot 3^2}{4 \cdot 1^2 + 2 \cdot 2^2 + 6 \cdot 3^2 + 4 \cdot 1^2 + 4 \cdot 2^2 + 1 \cdot 3^2} = 0.41$$
$$- \frac{1}{2 \cdot 16}(4 \cdot 1 + 2 \cdot 2 + 6 \cdot 3 + 4 \cdot 1 + 4 \cdot 2 + 1 \cdot 3)^2$$

According to equation (16) (products with zero omitted):

$$a_{\bar{r}} = 1 - \frac{(1 + 2)1^2 + 1 \cdot 2^2 + 2 \cdot 3^2}{4 \cdot 1^2 + 2 \cdot 2^2 + 6 \cdot 3^2 + 4 \cdot 1^2 + 4 \cdot 2^2 + 1 \cdot 3^2} = 0.46$$
$$- \frac{2}{16}(4 \cdot 1 + 2 \cdot 2 + 6 \cdot 3)(4 \cdot 1 + 4 \cdot 2 + 1 \cdot 3)$$

Such a result would normally preclude the use of these data. A comparison of the coefficients reveals first, that observers disagree regarding their marginal distributions. This is indicated by noting that $a_\pi < a_\kappa$ and $a_R < a_{\bar{r}}$. That is, the true agreement measures are smaller than those for partial agreement. Second, the fact that $a_\pi > a_R$ and $a_\kappa > a_{\bar{r}}$, that is, coefficients for nominal scales are larger than those for interval scales, suggests that no advantage is gained in treating the data as exhibiting an order or an interval scale.

    The fact that the agreement coefficients are insensitive to the number of categories involved is illustrated by attempts to merge the categories of this example. In eight out of thirteen possible mergers, a_π further declines. The most immediate gain is obtained by lumping 2 and 3, the categories in which confusion is heaviest, and then a_π becomes 0.62. A further improvement is made by merging 0, 2, and 3, resulting in $a_\pi = 0.67$. But such gains are evidently paid for with the loss of information (discriminability, sensitivity) which a research project might not be able to afford. However, if categories are redundant then the family of agreement coefficients offers opportunities for optimizing reliability.

REFERENCES

COHEN, J.
    1960   "A coefficient of agreement for nominal scales." *Educational and Psychological Measurement* 20 (1): 37–46.
GOODMAN, L. A. AND KRUSKAL, W. H.
    1954   "Measures of association for cross-classification." *Journal of the American Statistical Association* 49: 732–764.
KENDALL, M. G.
    1948   *Rank Correlation Methods.* London: Griffin.
PEARSON, K.
    1901   "Mathematical contributions to the theory of evolution. IX: On the principle of homotyposis and its relation to heredity, to variability of the individual, and to that of race. Part I: Homotyposis in the vegetable kingdom." *Philosophical Transactions of the Royal Society* (London) Series A, 197: 385–479.
ROBINSON, W. S.
    1957   "The statistical measure of agreement." *American Sociological Review* 22: 17–25.
SCOTT, W. A.
    1955   "Reliability of content analysis: The case of nominal scale coding." *Public Opinion Quarterly* 19: 321–325.

VALIDITY AND THE
MULTITRAIT-MULTIMETHOD
MATRIX

Robert P. Althauser

PRINCETON UNIVERSITY

Thomas A. Heberlein

UNIVERSITY OF WISCONSIN

This chapter is the revision of the first part of a paper read at the September 1969 meeting of the American Sociological Association, entitled "Reliability and Validity, Methods of Data Collection, and the Multitrait-Multimethod Matrix." For helpful comments on previous versions, we wish to thank Robert Scott, Charles Werts, Robert Linn, Roger V. Burton, and David Heise.

Recent applications of path analysis and causal inference to the study of measurement error (Siegel and Hodge, 1968; Heise, 1969b) have focused more on the reliability of measures than on their validity (with exceptions—Costner, 1969; Blalock, 1969). Where to draw the distinction between these two concepts (and whether to draw one at all) is still an unsettled question in methodology. An assessment of either must begin with multiple indicators or measures of underlying concepts. Reliability for some (Siegel and Hodge, 1968; Campbell and Fiske, 1959) is a function of the consistency of measures (of the same underlying concept) using "identical, repeated" items or "maximally similar methods" of measurement. On the same view, the consistency of "alternative measures" or measures by "maximally different" methods reflects valid measurement.

Unfortunately, this line between identical and nonidentical measures and between nonindependent and independent methods of measurement is a thin one, logically and empirically (Campbell and Fiske, 1959, p. 83). We concur with Werts and Linn (1969b) that what better distinguishes questions of reliability from validity is the assumption that only underlying concepts and random error affect measures. In contrast, matters of validity arise when other factors—more than one underlying construct or methods' factors or other unmeasured variables—are seen to affect the measures in addition to one underlying concept and random error.[1]

Ideally, we should "develop models for simultaneously assessing both questions of reliability . . . and validity" (Siegel and Hodge, 1968, p. 56). That is, models containing underlying constructs, multiple indicators of constructs, random and systematic sources of error in the indicators should be specified and tested. Unhappily, we will be unable to identify the unknown relationships in many such models. In other words, there will be too few observable correlations from which to estimate the unknown relationships among constructs, indicators, and sources of error (Heise, 1969a). We see an example of this situation in a later discussion of the model in Figure 1.

Recent work sensitive to this problem has converged on the conclusion that to solve the identification problem, one must have at least three measures (Costner, 1969; Werts and Linn, 1969a)[2] or three or more measures of each concept over time (Heise, 1969b). However, one may well question whether research practices and methodology texts will adjust themselves to this conclusion. Including multiple indicators

---

[1] Accordingly, there is no viable distinction between "reliability" and Campbell and Fiske's notion of "convergent validity," as defined below (Werts and Linn, 1969b).

[2] Identification of a model containing two measures (of two traits) and five methods was also found possible, so the convergence of conclusion must be slightly qualified.

of important concepts at the cost of measuring additional variables may be impractical to many researchers. Are there any procedures, then, for assessing the validity of measures in models which cannot be identified?

One impressive attempt at such a procedure is Campbell and Fiske's "multitrait-multimethod matrix." This is a matrix of intercorrelations among measures of more than one concept using more than one method of measurement. They proposed several criteria by which to gauge the validity of measures. These criteria are functions of the size and differences between certain of these correlations.

In this paper we begin our study of validity by critically reviewing the inferences about validity proposed by Campbell and Fiske. Using a causal model to interpret the correlations in the matrix, we decompose the correlations and find that only one of the four ways of assessing validity proves sound. We then propose an alternative approach using Costner's "consistency criterion" (1969). Since the causal model underlying the matrix cannot be identified, a simpler overidentified model with measures unaffected by the different methods of collecting data is tested against the alternative of the causal model for the matrix. Small observed correlations between measures are an obstacle to the use of Costner's procedure, however, and two amendments to this approach are proposed. Both have the effect of increasing the size of the observed correlations without altering the test of the overidentified model. The first is that validity be tested by examining correlations among theoretically related measures. The second is a (provisional) correction for attenuation.

THE MULTITRAIT-MULTIMETHOD MATRIX

Campbell and Fiske (1959) have recommended two major criteria for establishing the validity of a measure. A test should demonstrate (1) convergent validity; that is, show a high correlation with another measure of the same trait; and (2) discriminant validity; that is, show low correlations with other tests from which they were intended to differ. Furthermore, a test may be thought of as a "trait method unit, a union of a particular trait content with a measurement procedure not specific to content" (p. 81). To demonstrate convergent and discriminant validity and to obtain some idea of the impact of method variance, Campbell and Fiske proposed the multitrait-multimethod matrix in which the same set of traits is measured by several different methods.

A generic form of the matrix is presented in Table 1. There are three sets of correlations in the matrix: (1) correlations between measures of the same concept by different methods, denoted by vs; (2) correlations between measures of different concepts using different methods, denoted by hs; and (3) correlations between measures of different concepts using the same methods, denoted by ms. This corresponds to some terminology used by Campbell and Fiske in designating parts of the matrix: vs are the measures of "convergent validity"; the hs are off-diagonal correlations in the "heteromethod" blocks of the matrix; and the ms are off-diagonal correlations in the "monomethod" blocks.[3]

TABLE 1

A Multitrait-Multimethod Matrix with Measures of Three Traits Obtained by Two Methods

Method	Measures of	Interview			Questionnaire		
		X	Y	Z	X'	Y'	Z'
	X	r_x					
Interview	Y	m_{yx}	r_y				
	Z	m_{zx}	m_{zy}	r_z			
	X'	$v_{x'x}$	$h_{x'y}$	$h_{x'z}$	$r_{x'}$		
Questionnaire	Y'	$h_{y'x}$	$v_{y'y}$	$h_{y'z}$	$m_{y'x'}$	$r_{y'}$	
	Z'	$h_{z'x}$	$h_{z'y}$	$v_{z'z}$	$m_{z'x'}$	$m_{z'y'}$	$r_{z'}$

Convergent validity is established when traits measured by one method are correlated significantly greater than zero with the criterion. In this case the criterion is the same trait measured by another method. That is, the higher the vs in Table 1, the greater the convergent validity.

To establish "discriminant validity," three comparisons of correlations are proposed. First, one desires a higher correlation between measures of the same concept using different methods than the correlation between measures of different concepts using different methods. This involves a comparison of the measures of validity (vs) as found in the diagonals of the heteromethod block with the off-diagonal correlations within that block (the hs). If each v in a given row and column of the matrix is clearly greater than the hs in the same row *or* column, this desideratum is met. Thus, $v_{y'y}$ should be greater than the hs with y' or y in their subscripts: $v_{y'y} > h_{y'z}, h_{x'y}, h_{y'x}, h_{z'y}$.

Second, different concepts measured by the same method should not correlate more highly than do measures of the same concept using different methods. Otherwise, we could be tempted to attribute such a higher correlation to the sameness of method rather than sameness of the concepts being measured. Correlations between different concepts measured by the same methods are symbolized by the ms, the off-diagonal correlations in the two monomethod blocks. If an m in a given row or column is high and approaches or surpasses the vs in the same row

[3] More precisely, the "heterotrait-heteromethod" and "heterotrait-monomethod" triangles of each block.

or column, it could indeed be due to the communality of methods (or "common methods' variance") absent in the heteromethod blocks. Thus $v_{y'y}$ should be greater than m_{zy}, m_{yx}, $m_{y'x'}$, and $m_{z'y'}$.

Third, regardless of the methods used, the same pattern of off-diagonal correlations (hs, ms) should hold. This would reflect an underlying matrix of substantive or "true" correlations between concepts that is maintained in spite of possible methods' effects. If the same pattern of relative sizes among corresponding hs and ms is observed, this desideratum is met. (More precisely, we could define this requirement as follows: $m_{y'x'} - m_{z'x'} = m_{yx} - m_{zx} = h_{y'x} - h_{z'x}$; and $m_{zx} - m_{zy} = h_{z'x} - h_{z'y} = m_{z'x} - m_{z'y'}$ and . . . , for all possible paired comparisons between corresponding correlations.)

Campbell and Fiske (1959) describe two ways in which methods affect the correlations among variables. The first involves the component of spuriousness in the correlations among measures in monomethod blocks. This can be referred to as *common methods' variance*. In factor analytic terms, we posit the operation of individual methods' factors specific to each method used to gather data, for example, a questionnaire or interview factor.

The second way noted by Campbell and Fiske is present to the degree that the different methods involved lack complete independence. Lack of independence is reflected in modest off-diagonal correlations (positive or negative hs) in heteromethod blocks. This lack of independence can also be conceptualized as a *general methods' factor* by viewing different methods as categories of such a factor.

The structure of inference behind these procedures depends upon whether the desiderata are met. If they are, we are to infer that methods' effects are unimportant, and that substantive relationships among variables are small. The latter assures us that two items are not measuring the same thing. If they are not met, however, the inferences above do not hold.

We can more clearly examine the viability of this line of reasoning by examining the causal model which underlies a somewhat reduced multitrait-multimethod matrix, shown in Table 2. The path diagram

TABLE 2

Observed Correlations Among Measures of X and Y

Methods	Measures:	Interview		Questionnaire	
		X'_I	Y'_I	X'_Q	Y'_Q
Interview	X'_I				
	Y'_I	$r_{Y'_IX'_I}$			
Questionnaire	X'_Q	$r_{X'_QX'_I}$	$r_{X'_QY'_I}$		
	Y'_Q	$r_{Y'_QX'_I}$	$r_{Y'_QY'_I}$	$r_{Y'_QX'_Q}$	

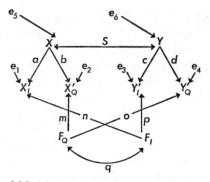

Figure 1. Causal Model of Measures (X', Y'), Underlying Concepts (X, Y), and Methods' Factors (F_Q, F_I).

presented in Figure 1 portrays the relationships among two underlying concepts X and Y, two measures of each concept (X_I', X_Q', Y_I', Y_Q'), and two methods' factors F_Q and F_I, where X_I' denotes a measure of X using interview data, Y_Q' represents a measure of Y using questionnaire data, F_Q represents a questionnaire factor, and so on. The "true" or substantive relationship between the two underlying concepts (or traits) is labeled S. The epistemic paths between each concept and its two measures are denoted by a, b, c, and d.

The specific methods' paths for questionnaire and interview factors are denoted by m, o and n, p, respectively. The correlation q denotes the extent to which the independence of these two methods is absent. Error terms $e_1 \ldots e_4$ are shown affecting each measure, and terms e_5 and e_6 are shown affecting the underlying concepts X and Y. The model assumes that these terms are correlated neither with each other nor with measures or concepts other than the one to which they are assigned.

Note that X, Y, F_I, and F_Q are all unmeasured variables. F_I and F_Q are best conceived of as symbols for extraneous variables which are peculiar to each method of collecting data. For example, the respondent's need for acceptance or approval, his willingness to confide confidential information, his need for achievement as expressed in his "performance" as a respondent, or his sensitivity to the researcher's expectations are all extraneous variables which may be differentially represented in the methods' factors.

There are six observed correlations in this model, but nine paths (or ten, counting the unknown correlation q) to be estimated. For it to be possible to estimate these paths, we must have at least an equal number of knowns—correlations here—and unknowns (paths) (Heise, 1969a). Hence we cannot estimate or identify these paths. However, this model mains useful   as a basis for studying the suggested inferences about validity. To proceed, we use path analysis to derive expressions for the correlations being compared in Campbell and Fiske's assessment of validity.

PATH EQUATIONS FOR CAUSAL MODEL

The path equations for the six correlations between X' and Y' in the multitrait-multimethod matrix (see Tables 1 and 2, and Figure 1) are shown below:

Hetermethod block, diagonal correlations (the vs)

$$v_{x'x} = r_{X'_Q X'_I} = ab + nqm \tag{1}$$
$$v_{y'y} = r_{Y'_Q Y'_I} = cd + oqp \tag{2}$$

Hetermethod block, off-diagonal correlations (the hs)

$$h_{y'x} = r_{Y'_Q X'_I} = aSd + nqo \tag{3}$$
$$h_{x'y} = r_{X'_Q Y'_I} = bSc + mqp \tag{4}$$

Monomethod block, off-diagonal correlations (the ms)

$$m_{yx} = r_{Y'_I X'_I} = aSc + np \tag{5}$$
$$m_{y'x'} = r_{Y'_Q X'_Q} = bSd + mo \tag{6}$$

Turning to the comparisons of correlations proposed by Campbell and Fiske, it will suffice for us to examine one example of each comparison.

Convergent Validity

To establish convergent validity, the vs must be large. As can be seen from either equation (1) or equation (2), inferring convergent validity from the observation of large v requires the assumption that the epistemic paths involved are large and equal and that the methods are largely independent ($q = 0$). When this cannot be assumed, the inference is not safe. Although the first of these assumptions may not be unreasonable, the assumption of independence of methods is more difficult to meet. How different in format are questionnaire and interview? When two paper-and-pencil tests, administered at the same session, are viewed as separate methods, the problem increases. In short, even this most appealing criterion for validity may lead to incorrect inference about the validity of measures.

Discriminant Validity

First Comparison. The first of three measures of discriminant validity requires a comparison of diagonal and off-diagonal correlations in the heteromethod block (vs and hs). For example,

$$v_{x'x} - h_{y'x} = r_{X'_QX'_I} - r_{Y'_QX'_I} = (ab - aSd) + nq(m - o) \qquad (7)$$

As we will see in the later comparisons as well, the correlation difference above has two components, one a function of the substantive relation S and of epistemic paths, the second of methods' paths. Recalling the inference structure described above, we can see that the first component and not the second should contribute to the difference *if* the desideratum is to hold. That is, the difference should primarily be a function of a small S or large $(1 - S)$. In other words, the inferences above assume a correspondence between the observation of a large positive difference of correlations (or of constant differences in the third comparison below) and the twin conditions of insubstantial methods' effects and small substantive relations between underlying concepts. (Likewise, it assumes a correspondence between the observation of a small, zero, or negative difference and the existence of serious methods' effects or a high substantive relationship.)

We can see, however, that the structure supporting these inferences has some weaknesses, particularly in this first comparison of correlations. If the desiderata hold, then the first component should dominate the differences observed. But for this component to be a function primarily of S, certain epistemic paths must be approximately equal ($b = d$ in equation (7)).

The second component may make no contribution to these differences or the equality because methods' paths are properly small. But this component is always a function of a product of one method's path, a difference of two other methods and the dependence of methods (q). It may be making no contribution because there is a small difference of methods (for example, $[m - o]$ in equation (7)) or independence of methods ($q = 0$). An interpretation that a large correlation difference primarily reflects the first component may therefore be assuming an equality of methods' paths.

Unfortunately, the desideratum could also be met (and the differences be quite positive) if the methods' coefficients were all equal *and large*. Indeed, their very equality would obscure the effects of methods on measures, while we infer that there are no methods' effects.

So, the first assessment of validity appears virtually untenable without assuming what we are assessing—the absence of a strong method's effect. It will be helpful and reasonable in the other comparisons to make additional assumptions to support the proposed interpretation, for example, that certain epistemic paths are approximately equal (and of like sign) and that the two paths from each respective method are of like sign. But in this first comparison, these are of no help.

Second Comparison. The second of three measures of discriminant validity requires a comparison of the diagonal in the heteromethod block with the off-diagonal in the monomethod blocks (vs and ms). For example,

$$v_{x'x} - m_{yx} = r_{X'_I X'_Q} - r_{X'_I Y'_I} = (ab - aSc) + n(qm - p) \qquad (8)$$

As before, the difference in correlation has two components. The first reflects a term approximately equal to $(1 - S)$ if we assume two epistemic paths (b, c) equal. Assuming positive epistemic paths, this first component will be positive, and unless the paths from one of the methods (p and n from F_I) are of unlike sign, the second component will usually be a negative function of methods' paths and intercorrelation (negative because the product of two paths, q and m, is usually less than a single path coefficient, p).[4] Note that this second component will tend to be larger than in the other comparisons. It is essentially a product of two paths, whereas in the other comparisons, the second component is a product of three paths.

The size of the difference thus hinges on the size of this usually negative second component. In many of the illustrations provided by Campbell and Fiske, there are comparatively large ms which are taken to reflect the method's factor common to that monomethod block. This factor is assumed to enlarge to a spurious extent these observed correlations, thus reducing the difference between observed correlations. The effect of the second component is quite consistent with this assumption. If the path n were large, for example, then the product of it and the usually negative difference ($qm - p$) would tend to reduce the contribution of the positive difference ($1 - S$) to the overall positive difference. The result would be a combination of components producing a very small positive, zero, or negative difference (that is, m greater than v).

Yet, the hazards of underidentification to such an inference are not entirely circumvented without additional assumptions: (1) that the epistemic paths are equal and of like sign (so that the hopefully dominant first component will be a true function of $[1 - S]$; and (2) that the methods' paths from each method's factor are of like sign. The former

---

[4] Even if the term *is* positive in the unusual circumstance that, for example, $p = 0.6$ and $qm = 0.81$, other comparisons will correct any faulty inferences thereby. Thus, the expression for $v_{y'y} - m_{y'x'} = (cd - bSd) + o(qp - m)$ would entail a negative second component, even though $n(qm - p)$ in equation (8) was positive. To be safe, all comparisons involving the concepts X and Y should satisfy the desideratum. Of course, if m (or q) is negative, the second term becomes even more negative than otherwise. To qualify the inference that the desideratum is especially well satisfied, all other comparisons must be made again.

assumption is a little easier to make than the latter, because common sense or theory can be used to define measures so as to meet the assumption.[5] The latter requires more theoretical bravado, but it is actually necessary only when there is grave doubt as to the absence of independence between methods' factors, that is, if $(q \neq 0)$.

If the desideratum of a positive difference is not met, however, the suggested inference of serious methods' effects or methods' dependence appears sound. That is, there is no way we could falsely conclude that our measures fail to discriminate when, in fact, they do or when methods' effects are insubstantial.

Third Comparison. The third of three measures of discriminant validity entails comparisons of off-diagonal correlations in corresponding positions in a heteromethod and monomethod block. The desideratum suggested is a common pattern of "trait interrelationships" among off-diagonal correlations in monomethod and heteromethod blocks. This amounts to constant differences between pairs of correlations in corresponding positions of either block. For example, the following equation should hold:

$$m_{yx} - m_{zx} = h_{y'x} - h_{z'x} \qquad (9)$$

To define m_{zx} and $h_{z'x}$, equations (3) and (5) are utilized, substituting Z for Y in the model in Table 1 and denoting the paths to Z as primes of the paths to Y:

$$m_{zx} = aS'c' + np' \qquad (10)$$

$$h_{z'x} = aS'd' + nqo' \qquad (11)$$

Substituting equations (3), (5), (10), and (11) into equation (9), we have

$$(aSc + np) - (aS'c' + np') = (aSd + nqo) - (aS'd' + nqo') \qquad (12)$$

After grouping like terms, we have

$$a(Sc - S'c') + n(p - p') = a(Sd - S'd') + nq(o - o') \qquad (13)$$

Each side of the equation has two components, one a function of epistemic paths, one of the methods' paths. The situation which undermined the first comparison returns again. Two pairs of methods' paths, here p, p' and o, o', could be quite large but equal, causing the second components on each side to vanish and contributing to the equality of

---

[5] To illustrate, suppose x = religious liberalism and y = devotionalism; x' = "Do you believe in hell? (yes, no)"; y' = "How often do you pray a week? (every day or oftener, twice a week, once a week or less)." The epistemic path $x - x'$ is negative, while $y - y'$ is positive. One could simply "run" liberalism's measure in the opposite direction (no, yes) to make $x - x'$ positive.

sides (again assuming some epistemic paths—$c = c'$; $d = d'$). The sug-·
gested inference that methods' paths are insubstantial would be incorrect
in that event.

In sum, we find that the criteria for convergent validity can be
met, when in fact the measures do not converge since the vs can be
inflated by correlated methods. Discriminant validity does not fare much
better since we find that only one of three criteria can be interpreted
as Campbell and Fiske suggest. An alternative approach is obviously
needed to detect the presence of methods effects.

CAUSAL APPROACH

One such approach drawing upon the work of Costner (1969),
Blalock (1964), and others is to test the model previously discussed
(Figure 1). A direct test of this model is hindered, of course, by the
underidentification of its path components. Using Costner's "consistency
criterion," however, it is possible to start with an overidentified model
such as in Figure 2 and test it against various alternative models including the one previously discussed (Figure 1). The overidentified model

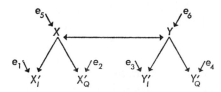

Figure 2. Overidentified Model of Measures (X', Y') and Underlying Concepts
(X, Y).

posits no influence of methods' factors on measures of X and Y, while, of
course, the alternative model does. It also assumes that errors are uncorrelated. Starting with this overidentified model, we can deduce the
following equality, the "consistency criterion":

$$(r_{X'_I Y'_Q})(r_{X'_Q Y'_I}) = (r_{X'_I Y'_I})(r_{X'_Q Y'_Q}) \qquad (14)$$

There are many conceivable alternative models against which the
simpler overidentified model *may* be testable. One could imagine models
which reflect the influence of diverse extraneous variables: social desir-
ability, reactive effects, relationships between concept X and measure
Y' (Costner, 1969). We will confine ourselves here to the alternative
model showing the influence of methods' factors.

While this alternative cannot be identified, we have already
written path expressions for the four correlations in equation (14) (see
equations (3), (4), (5), and (6)). To simplify this calculation, let us

assume that the methods' effects are independent and, hence, $q = 0$. Equation (14) can now be written:

$$(aSc + np)(bSd + mo) = (aSd)(bSc) \tag{15}$$

or

$$abS^2cd + npbSd + moaSc + npmo = abS^2cd \tag{16}$$

We can see from equation (16) that the consistency criterion would not hold if the alternative model were correct. In Costner's terms, this (and any other) alternative model suggests a form of "differential bias" (or "specification error"—Heise, 1969a) in the basic, overidentified model. If this bias is present, then equation (14) should not hold.

If the observed correlations are now substituted into equation (14) and the criterion holds, we can reject this alternative model and any other for which the criterion would not hold. If, on the other hand, the criterion does not hold, we could reject the basic overidentified model, but without any indication of which among many plausible alternative models (or forms of differential bias) is more appropriate.

Unfortunately, for models with less than three measures per concept, there are also alternative models for which the criterion is satisfied, as Costner shows. Against such alternatives, the test of the basic model is not viable. We cannot in this instance determine which of the many models for which the criterion holds might be the most appropriate.

Returning to the alternative model above, the criterion will not be met in the slightly more complicated case where $q \neq 0$ unless two unlikely conditions are both satisfied:[6] (1) $q = \pm 1$ and (2) $c/d = \pm p/o$ or $a/b = \pm n/m$ or both. The latter could obtain, for example, if $c = d$ and $p = o$, or $a = b$ and $n = m$. Certainly this cannot be ruled out entirely, but if the methods are at all dissimilar, it is unlikely that they will be perfectly dependent.

EXAMPLE

Let us apply the approach suggested above to an illustration comprised of hypothetical correlations between measures of three concepts (X, Y, Z) using two methods of data collection—interviews and

---

[6] In the case where $q \neq 0$, we have $(aSc + np) (bSd + mo) = (aSd + nqo) \times (bSc + mqp)$. Multiplying through each side and grouping like terms, one may write either $mnop(1 - q^2) + nSb(pd - ocq) + aSm(co - pdq) = 0$ or $mnop(1 - q^2) + oSc(am - bnq) + dSp(bn - amq) = 0$. For these two respective expressions to equal zero (and for the consistency criterion to be met, therefore), $q = \pm 1$, and assuming that, it must also be true that $c/d = \pm p/o$ or $a/b = \pm n/m$.

questionnaires. The correlations are arrayed in the multitrait-multi-method matrix in Table 3.

TABLE 3

Simulated Multitrait-Multimethod Matrix

Method of Data Collection	Concepts	Interview			Questionnaire		
		X'_I	Y'_I	Z'_I	X'_Q	Y'_Q	Z'_Q
Interview	X_I						
	Y_I	0.10					
	Z_I	0.30	0.30				
Questionnaire	X_Q	0.50	0.10	0.25			
	Y_Q	0.05	0.50	0.30	0.05		
	Z_Q	0.20	0.30	0.30	0.30	0.30	

We will test three basic, overidentified models against the alternative model discussed above: the model shown in Figure 2, where X causes Y, a model identical in structure with Y replaced by Z (hence X causing Z), and one with Y causing Z.

The appropriate expressions for the consistency criterion in each case are equation (14) for the first test and equation (17) for the second:

$$(r_{Z'_Q X'_I})(r_{X'_Q Z'_I}) = (r_{Z'_I X'_I})(r_{Z'_Q X'_Q}) \tag{17}$$

Substituting (from Table 3), we have for the first test

$$(0.05)(0.10) = (0.10)(0.05) \quad (\text{criterion } holds), \tag{18}$$

and for the second,

$$(0.20)(0.25) = (0.30)(0.30) \tag{19}$$

Forming a difference, we have

$$0.04 = (0.09) - (0.05) \tag{20}$$

To determine whether the criterion holds in this and similar instances, we must see whether the difference above, called the "tetrad difference," is significantly different from zero. According to Spearman and Holzinger (1924), the standard error of this difference is approximately:[7]

$$\sigma_{dif} = 2r(1 - r)/\sqrt{N} \tag{21}$$

where r is the average of the four correlations in the difference and N is the sample size. This gives a standard error of 0.035 for this difference, which means that the above difference is *not* significantly different from

[7] This holds unless both N and r are small. The difference between this expression and a slightly more rigorous one in the case of $N = 70$ and $r = 0.30$ was about 0.002.

zero. Hence, we may be inclined to conclude that the criterion holds. Inasmuch as the criterion also holds for a third test of a basic model in which Y causes Z, we might conclude that differential bias of the sort proposed by the alternative model in Figure 1 was absent. The threat to the validity of our measures posed by the different methods of data collection would appear to be negligible.

This would not, of course, preclude such a high substantive path coefficient (S) as to undermine the other threat to discriminant validity: the possibility that X and Y measure the same thing. However, with the assurance that differential bias (at least of the form just anticipated) is not present, we can proceed to estimate the paths in the basic over-identified model and, in particular, the one for the underlying "true" relationship between concepts. Using the formula derived by Costner, we find that $p_{YX} = 0.14$, $p_{zy} = 0.77$, and $p_{zx} = 0.66$ (an average, as explained later). Depending on his theory and the substantive meanings of X, Y, and Z, a researcher can decide if these paths (actually, correlations here) suggest the measurement of the "same thing."

However, there is a problem with Costner's procedure that arises in its application to the study of these matrices and that will arise whenever the average of the four correlations in the consistency criterion is small (roughly, less than 0.30). The problem is deliberately illustrated in the test of the model where X causes Z. It will become apparent after a little reflection that "tetrad differences" comprised of such small correlations will rarely be significantly different from zero. The differences between the products of correlations this size are simply too small for the tests of the basic models to have any power against the alternative models. Only if the average size of the correlations being multiplied is roughly greater than 0.30 can a test of a model acquire reasonable power.

CORRECTION FOR ATTENUATION

There are two ways around this problem. The first, previously suggested by Heberlein (1969), is that the traits or concepts chosen for a validity study be theoretically related. What is important to show in a validity study is that, through using various methods of measurement, traits which might be expected to be related on theoretical grounds are empirically distinct. Suggestions about the validity of a mathematics ability test are strengthened if it is compared with verbal ability and IQ within a multitrait-multimethod matrix rather than with attitudes toward authority and self-acceptance. In short, if we concern ourselves with the discriminant validity of measures that quite possibly measure the "same thing" or whose underlying concepts at least predict one another for substantive reasons, our assessment of validity will be more meaningful.

The important result of following this suggestion is that the correlations in the matrix will be considerably higher, particularly in the off-diagonal cells of the heteromethod block. The net effect on the use of the consistency criterion will be that the test of the basic, over-identified models will acquire considerably more power against alternative models. This result will be illustrated below.

The other way of handling the problem is to correct these correlations for attenuation (also suggested by Heberlein, 1969). The correction is provisional because it and the overidentified model both assume that methods' factors are not present (or, more generally, that the error terms in the model are uncorrelated). It is this assumption that we are about to test. If we subsequently reject the overidentified model and infer that methods may systematically affect our measures, then the correction for attenuation cannot be safely interpreted[8] (Heberlein, 1969, p. 18; Bohrnstedt, 1969).

This correction for attenuation is illustrated in Table 4. There is some controversy over which procedure for estimating reliability is most adequate: split-half correlation (Guttman, 1945; Johnson, 1950), Cronbach's α (Lord and Novick, 1968) or test-retest correlations (Heise, 1969b).

TABLE 4

Simulated Multitrait-Multimethod Matrix Corrected for Attenuation

Method of Data Collection		Interview			Questionnaire		
	Concepts	X'_I	Y'_I	Z'_I	X'_Q	Y'_Q	Z'_Q
	X'_I						
Interview	Y'_I	0.20					
	Z'_I	0.76					
	X'_Q	1.00	0.20	0.63			
Questionnaire	Y'_Q	0.10	1.00	0.77	0.10		
	Z'_Q	0.51	0.77	1.00	0.76	0.77	

However, we can estimate the paths in the basic, overidentified model (in Figure 2) and thereby obtain estimates of reliability, avoiding the controversy. The formula for the five path coefficients in the basic model (X causes Y) are reproduced below from Costner (1969),[9] with

[8] In general, the estimates of disattenuated correlations may be either falsely inflated or reduced by correlated errors. Hence disattenuation reflects, and would not alter, the effects of methods or any other source of correlated error.

[9] The reader should note Costner's footnote 4 (1969) before using these formulas.

the subscripts changed from numbers to letters designating interviews (I) or questionnaires (Q):

$$S^2 = \frac{(r_{X'_I Y'_Q})(r_{X'_Q Y'_I})}{(r_{X'_I X'_Q})(r_{Y'_I Y'_Q})} = \frac{(r_{X'_I Y'_I})(r_{X'_Q Y'_Q})}{(r_{X'_I X'_Q})(r_{Y'_I Y'_Q})} \tag{22}$$

$$a^2 = (r_{X'_I X'_Q})\frac{(r_{X'_I Y'_Q})}{(r_{X'_Q Y'_Q})} = (r_{X'_I X'_Q})\frac{(r_{X'_I Y'_I})}{(r_{X'_Q Y'_I})} \tag{23}$$

$$b^2 = (r_{X'_I X'_Q})\frac{(r_{X'_Q Y'_Q})}{(r_{X'_I Y'_Q})} = (r_{X'_I X'_Q})\frac{(r_{X'_Q Y'_I})}{(r_{X'_I X'_I})} \tag{24}$$

$$c^2 = (r_{Y'_I Y'_Q})\frac{(r_{X'_Q Y'_I})}{(r_{X'_Q Y'_Q})} = (r_{Y'_I Y'_Q})\frac{(r_{X'_I Y'_I})}{(r_{X'_I Y'_Q})} \tag{25}$$

$$d^2 = (r_{Y'_I Y'_Q})\frac{(r_{X'_Q Y'_Q})}{(r_{X'_Q Y'_I})} = (r_{Y'_I Y'_Q})\frac{(r_{X'_I Y'_Q})}{(r_{X'_I Y'_I})} \tag{26}$$

Using these equations, S, a, b, c, and d were estimated for models similar to the one in Figure 2, showing X causing Y, X causing Z, and Y causing Z. For example, the estimates for the first model (X causes Y) were: $S = 0.14$; $a = b = 0.707$; $c = 1.00$; $d = 0.50$.[10] These are next substituted into a typical expression for the correction for attenuation:

$$r^{*}_{X'_I Y'_I} = r_{X'_I Y'_I}/\sqrt{R_{XX'}R_{YY'}} \tag{27}$$

where $r^{*}_{X'_I Y'_I}$ is the corrected correlation, and $R_{XX'}$ and $R_{YY'}$ the reliability estimates. These latter, in turn, are equal to

$$R_{XX'} = ab \tag{28}$$

and

$$R_{YY'} = cd \tag{29}$$

Carrying out the correction expressed in equation (27) using our illustrative data, we have

$$r^{*}_{X'_I Y'_I} = 0.10/\sqrt{(0.707)(0.707)(1.0)(0.50)} = 0.20 \tag{30}$$

---

[10] The estimates for the model X causes Z were $S = 0.67$, $a = 0.67$, $b = 0.76$, $c = 0.58$, and $d = 0.52$. For model Y causes Z, $S = 0.77$, $a = b = 0.707$, $c = d = 0.55$. With overidentified models, estimates need not be consistent. That is, the two expressions for each path coefficient, equations (22) to (26), need not empirically agree. This poses a general problem: which inconsistent estimate or what function (for example, an average) of these estimates should we use? In this example, estimates were consistent for the coefficients in models X causes Y and Y causes Z. This was not true for the coefficients in the model X causes Z. The inconsistent estimates here were averaged. For a discussion bearing on this problem, see Goldberger (1969, 1970).

Similarly, the remaining correlations[11] were provisionally corrected for attenuation and are displayed in Table 4. Notice that the average size of these correlations has increased over the uncorrected correlations.

If we now return to our test of the models previously considered, we still find that the criterion holds for the models, X causes Y and Y causes Z. But the "tetrad" difference of correlations in the test of the model, X causes Z, is now:

$$(0.76)(0.76) - (0.51)(0.63) = 0.2563 \qquad (31)$$

Since the standard error of this difference is 0.045, we can see that this is significantly different from zero and that the consistency criterion does not hold, after all. Making the correction for attenuation raised the average level of the four correlations from 0.225 to 0.665, providing the difference in the power of our test needed to give us a higher probability of detecting differential bias in the basic model. We conclude in this instance that there is such bias. What, then, can we conclude about the discriminant validity of our individual measures?

There are two general ways of proceeding to this conclusion. The first is to reason from the total configuration of our tests of basic models. We infer from above that there is some kind of methods' effects on the model, X causes Z, and presumably on X or Z or both. It can be shown that for the criterion not to hold, at least one method must be influencing the measures of both X and Z, though perhaps much more Z than X (Althauser, 1969, Appendix 4-3). Measures of Y, by contrast, are free of any methods' effects because Y is not included in any model having differential bias.

We can fall back on Campbell and Fiske's second comparison of correlations, however, for a further clue. It is obvious from Table 3[12] that the diagonal correlation $r_{Z'_Q Z'_I}$ is not appreciably greater than the

[11] The disattenuation of the vs, for example, $r_{X'_Q X'_I}$, $r_{Y'_Q Y'_I}$, and $r_{Z'_Q Z'_I}$ may depend, using this procedure, on the positions of X, Y, and Z in a particular model. For example, the denominator of equation (27) for $r^*_{X'_Q X'_I}$ would be $\sqrt{(1.00)^2(0.50)^2}$. When the model was X causes Y, but $\sqrt{(0.707)^2(0.707)^2}$ when the model was Y causes Z. Should the disattenuated correlations be different for different models (they were not for any of the above), an average of the disattenuated correlations might be required. However, this dependence on the model bears only on the calculation and interpretation of the disattenuated correlations themselves, since these vs do not appear in equation (17), used to test the models.

[12] It would be inappropriate to refer to Table 4. The overidentified model X causes Z has just been rejected, hence the disattenuated correlations involving measures of X and Z cannot be safely interpreted.

off-diagonal correlations involving measures of Z in the monomethod blocks. In fact, for all four possible comparisons, there is a difference of exactly zero. Hence it would appear that measures of Z have been most influenced by the methods of collecting data.[13]

[13] In some conceivable instances, a three-variable recursive model of $X \longrightarrow Y$

$$\searrow \swarrow$$
$$Z$$

would better describe the relations among three different measures of the same concept or of different concepts. In such instances, the results of a test of the random error assumption (that is, the use of Costner's consistency criterion) is the same as above (see Blalock, 1969). The difference which adopting the recursive model makes is in the estimates of the "true" relations among underlying concepts. It is relatively simple to solve for the true paths in such a recursive, using the previously estimated paths (which are correlations). In the above example, we would get $p_{yx} = 0.14$ as before, $p_{zx} = 0.57$ (versus 0.67 before), and $p_{zy} = 0.67$ (versus 0.77 before).

REFERENCES

ALTHAUSER, R. P.
    1969   "Reliability and validity, Methods of data collection and the multitrait-multimethod matrix." Princeton University (mimeo).
BLALOCK, H. M., JR.
    1964   *Causal Inference in Nonexperimental Research.* Chapel Hill: University of North Carolina Press.
    1969   "Multiple indicators and the causal approach to measurement error." *American Journal of Sociology* 75: 264–272.
BOHRNSTEDT, G. W.
    1969   "Observations on the measurement of change." In E. F. Borgatta (Ed.), *Sociological Methodology 1969.* San Francisco: Jossey-Bass.
CAMPBELL, D. T. AND FISKE, D. W.
    1959   "Covergent and discriminant validation by the multitrait-multimethod matrix." *Psychological Bulletin* 56: 81–105.
COSTNER, H. L.
    1969   "Theory, deduction and rules of correspondence." *American Journal of Sociology* 75: 245–263.
GOLDBERGER, A. S.
    1969   "On Boudon's method of linear causal analysis." SSRI Workshop Series, EME-6914, University of Wisconsin.
    1970   "On Boudon's method of linear causal analysis." *American Sociological Review* 35: 97–101.
GUTTMAN, L. A.
    1945   "A basis for analyzing test-retest reliability." *Psychometrika* 10: 255–282.
HEBERLEIN, T. A.
    1969   "The correction for attenuation and the multitrait-multimethod matrix: Some prospects and pitfalls." M. A. thesis, University of Wisconsin.
HEISE, D. R.
    1969a   "Problems in path analysis and causal inferences." In E. F. Borgatta (Ed.), *Sociological Methodology 1969.* San Francisco: Jossey-Bass.

1969b "Separating reliability and stability in test-retest correlation." *American Sociological Review* 34: 93–101.

JOHNSON, H. C.
1950 "Test reliability and correction for attenuation." *Psychometrika* 15: 115–119.

LORD, F. M. AND NOVICK, M. R.
1968 *Statistical Theories of Mental Test Scores*. Reading, Mass.: Addison-Wesley.

RICHARDSON, S. A., DOHRENWEND, B. S. AND KLEIN, D.
1965 *Interviewing: Its Forms and Functions*. New York: Basic Books.

SIEGEL, P. M. AND HODGE, R. W.
1968 "A causal approach to the study of measurement error." In H. M. Blalock, Jr. and A. B. Blalock (Eds.), *Methodology in Social Research*. New York: McGraw-Hill.

SPEARMAN, C. AND HOLZINGER, K.
1924 "The sampling error in the theory of two factors." *British Journal of Psychology* 15: 17–19.

WERTS, C. E. AND LINN, R. L.
1969a "Path analysis: Psychological examples." *Psychological Bulletin* (forthcoming).
1969b "Cautions in applying various procedures for determining the reliability and validity of multiple-item scales." Educational Testing Service (mimeo).

$\mathcal{X}10\mathcal{X}$

VALIDATION OF REPUTATIONAL LEADERSHIP BY THE MULTITRAIT-MULTIMETHOD MATRIX

Gene F. Summers
UNIVERSITY OF WISCONSIN

Lauren H. Seiler
UNIVERSITY OF ILLINOIS

Glenn Wiley
WATSEKA COMMUNITY HIGH SCHOOL

The preparation of this paper was supported by PHS Research Grant 1R11 MH-02592-01 from the National Institute of Mental Health and Illinois Agricultural Experiment Station (AES) Project 05-396, contributing to NC-80. Lauren Seiler's participation was supported (in part) by National Institutes of Health Fellowship 1-F1-MH-41983-01 BEH from the National Institute of Mental Health. We wish to express appreciation to the editors for making available to us the manuscript of the Althauser and Heberlein chapter. The difficulties in assessing validation by the multitrait-multimethod matrix which they note are important. However, in the analysis which follows we have avoided them in a manner which is consistent with the logic of the Althauser and Heberlein argument.

Reputational methods for identifying community leaders are well established judging from their continued use. Their apparent popularity notwithstanding, reputational methods received considerable criticism from Wolfinger (1960), Polsby (1959), Dahl (1958), and others. These criticisms focused largely on the validity of the methods and to a lesser degree on their reliability. The objections raised include the following: (1) the final list of nominees may include too many people, thereby including nonleaders; (2) too few persons may be nominated, thereby excluding some leaders; (3) respondents may be inaccurate sources of data; (4) the investigator and the respondent may not share meanings attached to such terms as *power, influence, leadership,* or whatever term is used in the interview; and (5) the leadership structure is an artifact of the reputational method. Furthermore, Wolfinger (1960, p. 636) doubts the credibility of the assumption "that reputations for influence are an index of the distribution of influence." All of these reservations question the validity of reputational methods.

What is needed is empirical investigation to determine the degree of validity one may attribute to reputational methods. While there are several approaches available for such an assessment,[1] this analysis examines the convergent and discriminant validity (Campbell and Fiske, 1959) of four reputational techniques for identifying general community leaders and educational leaders. A second purpose of the analysis is to illustrate the utility of the multitrait-multimethod matrix for the solution of measurement problems in sociology.

What is required to demonstrate convergent and discriminant validity is evidence of convergence among independent efforts to measure a single leadership structure, while simultaneously demonstrating discrimination among several types of leadership. Assuming the methods to be reliable, failure to obtain convergence would indicate the methods

---

[1] The reader who wishes to become acquainted with previous empirical assessments of reputational methods will find the following of interest: Schulze and Blumberg (1957), D'Antonio *et al.* (1961), D'Antonio and Erickson (1962), D'Antonio and Form (1965), Ehrlich (1967), Scoble (1961), Freeman *et al.* (1963), Freeman (1968), Agger *et al.* (1964), Blankenship (1964), Jennings (1964), Presthus (1964), Wildavsky (1964), Abu-Luban (1965), Laskin and Phillet (1965), Gamson (1966a and 1966b), and Walton (1966).

are not measuring the same underlying leadership structure. This would support some critics of reputational methods. Failure to find discrimination among types of leadership would argue for a monolithic rather than a pluralistic power structure. That is, if efforts to identify various types of leaders, such as business, government, educational, political, or religious, all produce the same list of persons with consistent internal rankings, the evidence would be consistent with critics who maintain that reputational methods reveal monolithic power structures as artifacts of the method.

Since method dissimilarity increases the rigor of the test of convergent validation in a multitrait-multimethod design, one would like to compare reputational methods with decisional methods, participant observation, and other techniques. Unfortunately, our data do not permit us to examine such widely diverse methods, but do allow us to examine four reputational methods in conjunction with two leadership types.

SETTING AND PROCEDURES

Because of serendipitous circumstances, data from two studies of leadership structures in the same community became available to us. During summer, 1966, Summers and associates conducted a survey[2] in a midwestern county which was restudied by Wiley in spring, 1967. Neither was aware of the other's research until some months later at which time the data were pooled to permit the analysis presented here. Before we examine the multitrait-multimethod matrix, a brief description of the communities, the two studies, and the reputational methods used will be instructive.

Community

The community consists of three townships in a small midwestern county. According to the 1960 U.S. Census the county was 100 per cent

[2] The Rural Industrial Development Project is an interdisciplinary analysis of the impact of rapid industrialization of a rural-agricultural area. The research design includes an unmatched but highly similar rural region which is not experiencing rapid industrialization. Thus, the design is quasi-experimental. Data collection will be on a longitudinal basis over a five-year period, and is intended to provide information necessary to assess the impact of industrialization. Aspects of community change which are of special interest include migration patterns, ecology of land use patterns, demographic composition, farming practices, labor use patterns, family composition, bureaucratization of social control agencies, articulation of values of religious agencies, work orientations and educational and occupational aspirations of youth, mental health indices, leadership structure, and attitudes toward a number of change-related objects.

rural and predominantly rural-farm with a population of approximately 4,500. There were six incorporated places, the largest having approximately 1,000 inhabitants. The area is in the heart of the nation's corn belt, urban oriented, and near the national average in per capita income.

In April, 1965, a major steel producer announced plans for the development of a production complex within the county. The first phase of construction was completed in late 1968 at a cost exceeding 150 million dollars. By 1969 the plant employed approximately 800 with an estimated annual payroll of five million dollars.

The collection of data concerning reputational leaders took place during the period of plant construction and at a time when expectations of massive industrial expansion were running high.

Rural Industrial Development Project

The Rural Industrial Development Project (July to November, 1966) is a longitudinal study of the area undergoing industrial development. One of the objectives of the research is to examine the changes which occur in a community as industrial development progresses. The data for this report were taken from the benchmark survey. The sample consists of 196 heads of households selected by an area probability sampling procedure with a 1:7 sampling ratio.[3]

Each head of household was asked to nominate three leaders in each of three areas of activity. The question asked was, "Would you please suggest three persons in this community you think are most important in influencing the decisions that are made concerning: (1) business and economic development, (2) educational matters, and (3) matters of local government?" There was freedom to nominate the same person in all three areas. These nominations produced two leadership scores. The educational leadership score was the total nominations received for educational matters. A general community leadership score was created by summing nominations for matters of local government and business and economic development.[4]

Wiley Study

The Wiley study (March to May, 1967) centered around a 1965 school district reorganization that merged three townships into a single school district. One purpose was to identify the most influential individuals in the three townships (Wiley, 1967, p. 249).

---

[3] A similar procedure was used by Singh (1964).

[4] Pooling of nominations in these two areas was done to maximize comparability with Wiley's measure of general community leadership.

Initially, Wiley selected two nominating panels and a third panel was derived from their nominations. The first panel consisted of twenty-one school leaders, that is, "those individuals serving as top school administrators or school board members in school districts at the time just prior to school district reorganization" (Wiley, 1967, pp. 54–55). This panel is referred to as school officials hereafter. The second panel was composed of twenty-two heads of chartered voluntary organizations in the area, a procedure similar to that used by Schulze and Blumberg (1957). Organization heads who were school board members, former school board members, and others closely associated with schools, such as teachers and administrators, were excluded from this panel (Wiley, 1967, p. 79). This panel will be referred to as organization heads.

The school officials and organization heads were asked five questions which served as a basis for determining the leadership structure in the area.[5] The first four questions dealt with general community leadership while the fifth question dealt specifically with the school district reorganization. Each panel member could nominate as many leaders as he wished.

The fifteen most often nominated individuals from each panel were used to create the third panel of nominators, designated as popular judges. Since eleven of the fifteen persons nominated most often by school officials were also among those most frequently chosen by organization heads, there were only nineteen popular judges. They were interviewed in the same way as were the first two panels.

While Wiley's procedure of panel formation prohibited overlap between school officials and organization heads, it permitted overlapping membership between either of these panels and the popular judges panel. Indeed, four school officials and two organization heads were also popular judges. In order to maximize method independence in the multitrait-multimethod matrix, overlapping panelists were as-

---

[5] The five questions were: (1) "Suppose a major project was before your community, one that required decision by a group of leaders whom nearly everyone would accept. Which people would you choose to make up this group—regardless of whether or not you know them personally?" (2) "In most communities certain persons are said to have a lot to say about programs that are planned, projects, and issues that come up around the community. What persons in the community are influential in this way?" (3) "If a decision were to be made in the state capital that affected your community, who, besides local area members of the legislature, would be the best individuals to contact state officials?" (4) "Who in your community would be the best people to get in touch with federal officials in the state capital or Washington, D.C.?" and (5) "One of the issues that was recently brought before the community concerned school district reorganization. What persons in the community were influential in bringing about this reorganization?"

signed to the popular judges panel only. Thus the analysis which follows is based upon the nominations of three completely nonoverlapping panels adapted from the Wiley study—seventeen school officials, twenty organization heads, and nineteen popular judges.

Some heads of households included in the area probability sample were also members of Wiley's panels. Of the 196 heads of households interviewed one was a school official, two were organization heads, and five were popular judges. Whereas overlapping membership among Wiley's panels was avoided, overlap between them and the area probability sample was retained. Removal of overlapping panelists would have destroyed the integrity of the area probability sample. Any representative probability sample of a community will include reputational leaders. If such persons were removed from the sample, one no longer would have an unbiased probability sample.

From each of Wiley's three nominating panels, two sets of community leadership scores were calculated—general community leadership and educational leadership. General community leaders were those persons receiving at least one nomination as decision maker on a major community project, as being influential in community programs, projects, or issues, or as a good contact with state or federal officials (questions 1–4). A nominee's score was the total number of nominations received. The educational leadership score was the total nominations for being influential in bringing about the school district reorganization (question 5).

RESULTS

Multitrait-multimethod matrix. A brief description of the matrix is in order for those persons unfamiliar with its structure. Reference to Table 1 will reveal two traits (community and educational leadership), each measured by four methods (school officials, organization heads, popular judges and heads of households), producing eight variables. The main diagonal of the matrix represents the reliability coefficients for each trait-method unit. These are in parentheses when they are known, and when unknown, the parentheses are empty. The reliability diagonal can be broken into four reliability diagonals, one for each method. Adjacent to each reliability diagonal (the monotrait-monomethod values) is a heterotrait-monomethod triangle. In Table 1 this triangle is formed by the reliability figure and the parentheses near it. Each reliability diagonal and its heterotrait-monomethod triangle make up a monomethod block. A heteromethod block consists of a validity diagonal (monotrait-heteromethod values) and the two heterotrait-heteromethod triangles on either side of it. In Table 1 the validity diagonal values are in italics and the heterotrait-heteromethod triangles are represented by the regular-type figures above and below.

Convergent Validity

The evidence for convergent validation—confirmation of reputed leadership by independent procedures—is found in the validity diagonals. These values should be significantly greater than zero and large enough to encourage further investigation. The values obtained (Pearson product moment correlations) range from 0.66 to 0.87 with a median of 0.795. Both desiderata for convergent validation are clearly met. In this regard it is instructive to consider the two leadership types separately. For general community leadership the convergent validity values ranged from 0.66 to 0.87 with a median of 0.725 whereas the comparable values for educational leadership were 0.74 to 0.87 and 0.855. Thus, it is apparent that all four methods identified substantially the same persons as general community leaders and were even more convergent in identifying educational leaders. Furthermore, the internal ranking of leaders was quite consistent among methods. Assuming the methods are independent there is evidence of substantial convergence.

Discrimination Validity

In addition to the requirement that methods converge in their measurement of a given trait one must have evidence of their ability to discriminate among traits. The evidence of discriminant validity can be observed in at least three ways. First, a validity diagonal value must be larger than the values in its row and column of the heterotrait-heteromethod triangle. That is, the correlation of two measures of the same underlying trait of leadership (for example, A_1 and A_2) should be larger than correlations of that variable with any other variable having neither trait nor method in common. An example from Table 1 may be helpful.

There should be more agreement between school officials and heads of organizations in their nominations of community leaders than between officials' nominations of community leaders and heads' nominations of educational leaders ($r_{A_1A_2} > r_{A_1B_2}$). Similarly their agreement on community leaders should be greater than the officials' list of educational leaders and the heads' community leader nomination ($r_{A_1A_2} > r_{A_2B_1}$). A comparable pattern of discrimination should be observed for every validity diagonal value in each heteromethod block.

It is clear that this criterion is met for all cases in our matrix. In all heteromethod blocks the validity diagonal values are greater than

TABLE 1

Multitrait-Multimethod Matrix of Reputational Leadership ($N = 290$)[a]

		School Officials		Organization Heads		Popular Judges		Heads of Household	
		A_1	B_1	A_2	B_2	A_3	B_3	A_4	B_4
School Officials									
Community	A_1	( )							
Educational	B_1	63	( )						
Organization Heads									
Community	A_2	78	50	( )					
Educational	B_2	69	86	56	( )				
Popular Judges									
Community	A_3	87	58	81	62	( )			
Educational	B_3	69	87	53	85	66	( )		
Heads of Household									
Community	A_4	67	42	66	39	66	42	( )	
Educational	B_4	59	77	41	87	55	74	23	( )

[a] All persons receiving one or more nominations are included. Cell entries are Pearson product moment correlation coefficients with decimal points omitted.

the heterotrait-heteromethod entries. This is an extraordinary finding in that this criterion is seldom completely met.

A second criterion of discriminant validation is that each entry in the validity diagonal must have a value greater than the correlation of the trait with any other trait sharing the method. For a given variable (A_1), this involves comparing its correlations with other measures of the same trait ($r_{A_1A_2}$, $r_{A_1A_3}$, and $r_{A_1A_4}$) and its correlation with other traits measured by the same method ($r_{A_1B_1}$). According to Campbell and Fiske (1959, p. 83), a variable must "correlate higher with an independent effort to measure the same trait than with measures designed to get at different traits which happen to employ the same method." An examination of Table 1 indicates that every variable meets this criterion except one, $r_{A_3B_3} = r_{A_3A_4}$. It should be noted, however, that the validity coefficients involving heads of households as nominators of general community leaders (A_4) does not manifest the degree of convergence apparent among the other three methods of measuring general community leaders. Nevertheless, the validity diagonal values of A_4 compare quite favorably with the correlation among heads of households' nominations of educational leaders (0.67, 0.66, 0.66 versus 0.23). Thus, again the data indicate a satisfactory discriminant validation.

The third criterion of discriminant validation suggested by Campbell and Fiske (1959, p. 83) can be applied to the data of Table 1 in only an approximate manner. The criterion "is that the same pattern of trait interrelationship be shown in all of the heterotrait triangles of both the monomethod and heteromethod blocks." Since all of these triangles contain only one value a pattern cannot be observed in the sense intended. However, one can note that all such values are positive and of moderate magnitude.

CONCLUSIONS

These findings present substantial evidence that several reputational methods are capable of identifying the same persons as leaders in a rural county and of rank ordering the persons consistently. Even though the three techniques used by Wiley are similar they diverge from the heads of household probability sampling technique. This is of interest theoretically as well as methodologically. It indicates that whatever meanings are attributed by researchers and community residents to such concepts as leadership, power, and influence, the shades of difference do not preclude a common interpretation, as is evident in the convergent validity values. The results argue strongly that reputational leaders can be identified by a probability sample of heads of households in rural communities. However, care must be exercised in generalizing this finding to metropolitan areas or to other types of leadership.

Equally important, it is apparent that for our data, reputational methods do not artifactually produce evidence of monolithic power structures. There is evidence in the discriminant validity coefficients that general community and educational leadership structures were moderately independent. Even though the coefficients are higher than would be preferred (0.39 to 0.69), the amount of independence is noteworthy with these rural data. It is in rural communities that monolithic leadership structures are most likely to occur.

Aside from indicating a somewhat pluralistic leadership structure in the county being studied, the evidence from the multitrait-multimethod matrix makes it clear that these reputational methods are capable of detecting pluralistic structures. However, this became apparent only when more than one trait *and* method were incorporated in the research design. This means that whenever possible studies of community leadership structure should attempt to identify more than one structure with several methods. Doing so allows the leadership structure to be described with greater confidence.

The generally high values in the heteromethod blocks require some comment. We noted above that methods should be maximally dissimilar or independent. When there is overlap in method variance all values in the heteromethod block will be elevated; elevation increases as the common variance of methods increases. Since all four methods are reputational some method overlap is expected. Empirical evidence of this can be seen by comparing the values of the heteromethod block involving heads of household with those in which it is not involved. Throughout they are smaller, which is consistent with our knowledge of procedural similarities among the four methods. Since the elevation of the validity diagonal values above the heterotrait-heteromethod values remains comparable throughout, the relative validity can still be evaluated. However, interpretation of the validity diagonal values in an absolute sense would be inappropriate because that would require complete independence of traits and methods, represented by zeros in the heterotrait-heteromethod triangles. This is seldom achieved in practice. Clearly there is still a need to include decisional methods and participant observer methods in a multitrait-multimethod matrix analysis, to examine the predictive validity of reputational methods, to pursue cross-validation studies, and to examine the convergent-discriminant validation of other types of leadership.

REFERENCES

ABU-LUBAN, B.
1965 "The reputational approach to the study of community power: A critical evaluation." *Pacific Sociological Review* 8 (Spring): 35–42.
AGGER, R. E., GOLDRICH, D. AND SWANSON, B. E.
1964 *The Rulers and the Ruled: Political Power and Impotence in American Cities.* New York: Wiley.
BLANKENSHIP, L. V.
1964 "Community power and decision-making: A comparative evaluation of measurement techniques." *Social Forces* 43 (December): 207–216.
BONJEAN, C. M.
1963 "Community leadership: A case study and conceptual refinement." *American Journal of Sociology* 68 (May): 672–681.
BORGATTA, E. F.
1968 "My student, the purist: A lament." *Sociological Quarterly* 9 (Winter): 29–34.
CAMPBELL, D. T. AND FISKE, D. W.
1959 "Convergent and discriminant validation by the multitrait-multimethod matrix." *Psychological Bulletin 56* (March): 81–105.
DAHL, R. A.
1958 "A critique of the ruling elite model." *American Political Science Review* 52 (June): 463–469.
D'ANTONIO, W. V. AND ERICKSON, E. C.
1962 "The reputational technique as a measure of community power: An evaluation based on comparative and longitudinal studies." *American Sociological Review* 27 (June): 362–376.
D'ANTONIO, W. V. AND FORM, W. H.
1965 *Influentials in Two Border Cities: A Study in Community Decision-Making.* Notre Dame, Ind.: University of Notre Dame Press.

D'ANTONIO, W. V., FORM, W. H., LOOMIS, C. P. AND ERICKSON, E. C.
   1961   "Institutional and occupational representatives in eleven community systems." *American Sociological Review* 26 (June): 440–450.

EHRLICH, H. J.
   1967   "The social psychology of reputations for community leadership." *Sociological Quarterly* 8 (Autumn): 514–530.

FREEMAN, L. C., FARARO, T. J., BLOOMBERG, W., JR. AND SUNSHINE, M. H.
   1963   "Locating leaders in local communities." *American Sociological Review* 28 (October): 791–798.

FREEMAN, L. C.
   1968   *Patterns of Local Community Leadership.* Indianapolis: Bobbs-Merrill.

FRENCH, R. M. AND AIKEN, M.
   1968   "Community power in Cornucopia: A replication in a small community of the Bonjean technique of identifying community leaders." *Sociological Quarterly* 9 (Spring): 261–270.

GAMSON, W. A.
   1966a "Rancorous conflict in community politics." *American Sociological Review* 31 (February): 71–81.
   1966b "Reputation and resources in community politics." *American Journal of Sociology* 72 (September): 121–131.

JENNINGS, M. K.
   1964   *Community Influentials: The Elites of Atlanta.* New York: Free Press.

LASKIN, R. AND PHILLET, S.
   1965   "An integrative analysis of voluntary associational leadership and reputational influence." *Sociological Inquiry* 35 (Spring): 176–185.

MILLER, D. C. AND DIRKSEN, J. L.
   1964   "The identification of visible, concealed, and symbolic leaders in a small Indiana city: A replication of the Bonjean-Noland study of Burlington, North Carolina." *Social Forces* 43 (May): 548–555.

POLSBY, N. W.
   1959   "The sociology of community power: A reassessment." *Social Forces* 37 (March): 232–236.

PRESTHUS, R.
   1964   *Men at the Top: A Study in Community Power.* New York: Oxford University Press.

SCHULZE, R. O. AND BLUMBERG, L. U.
   1957   "The determination of local power elites." *American Journal of Sociology* 63 (November): 290–296.

SCOBLE, H.
   1961   "Leadership hierarchies and political issues in a New England town." In M. Janowitz (Ed.), *Community Political Systems.* New York: Free Press.

SINGH, A.
   1964   "Reputational measure of leadership: A study of two Indian villages." Unpublished paper, Mississippi State University.

WALTON, J.
   1966   "Substance and artifact: The current status of research on community power structure." *American Journal of Sociology* 71 (January): 430–438.

WILDAVSKY, A.
   1964   *Leadership in a Small Town.* Totawa, N.J.: Bedminster Press.

WILEY, G. E.
    1967   "Issues and influentials: The decisional process in school district re-
          organization." Unpublished Ph.D. dissertation, Illinois State University.
WOLFINGER, R.
    1960   "Reputation and reality in the study of community power." *American
          Sociological Review* 25 (October): 636–644.

PART THREE

STATISTICAL
TECHNIQUES

❧11❧

STATISTICS ACCORDING TO BAYES

Gudmund R. Iversen

UNIVERSITY OF MICHIGAN

Valuable comments on an earlier draft were provided by Helmut Norpoth.

Thomas Bayes may not have foreseen that a paper he wrote and friends of his published in 1763, after his death, would serve to tie his name to a branch of statistics that has come into prominence today. Bayesian statistics gets its name from the use and special interpretation of what is known as Bayes' theorem, a simple identity in conditional and unconditional probabilities, contained in the paper by Bayes (1763).

The rise of Bayesian statistics in the last couple of decades has been prompted mainly by dissatisfaction with what sometimes is called classical statistics. This is the statistics of hypothesis testing with errors of two kinds and the statistics of confidence intervals, as developed by Neyman and Pearson in this century. Their formalizations were a major achievement, but in practice difficulties are found with classical statistics.

One such difficulty rests with the specification of the value of the parameter that is tested in the null hypothesis. In the case of a correlation coefficient, for example, one usually sets the population parameter equal to zero in the null hypothesis and investigates whether the sample result is in line with this value. What can be said if the null hypothesis is rejected? By rejecting the null hypothesis we have essentially eliminated zero as a possible value of the parameter. But that still leaves an infinite number of other possible values of the parameter, and even though the value representing no relationship has been eliminated, the population parameter could equal 0.01, say, and that value does not represent a very strong relationship between the two variables. The complete power curve for the test could help us decide about parameter values other than zero, but this curve is difficult to obtain for many tests and is seldom made available by the investigator.

If the null hypothesis is not rejected we are not very far along either. The evidence in the sample used for the test does not permit acceptance of the value of the parameter specified in the null hypothesis when the null hypothesis is not rejected. Nonrejection means that the null value is only one of many possible values of the population parameter.

The major difficulty with classical statistics is perhaps best seen in the concept of a confidence interval. In almost anyone's learning of confidence intervals appears a statement which seems to say that the probability equals $1 - \alpha$ that the population parameter has a value that lies between the two numbers A and B. At the moment one is about to accept this statement, which seems intuitively so correct, the instructor drones on with the clarification that it really is the interval from A to B that contains the parameter with probability $1 - \alpha$.

Thus, in classical statistics the unknown parameter values are fixed, and given these values of the parameters, probability statements are made about the known sample result. Bayesian statistics reverses this procedure. The reversal consists of considering the sample result after it has been observed as fixed; and, conditional on this fixed sample information, making probability statements about the unknown parameter values.

BAYES' THEOREM

The joint probability of D and H_k, discussed further below, can be written as the product of the conditional probability of D given H_k and the unconditional probability of H_k, as expressed in the equation

$$P(DH_k) = P(D|H_k)P(H_k) \qquad (1)$$

Similarly, by interchanging D and H_k the joint probability of D and H_k can be written

$$P(DH_k) = P(H_k|D)P(D) \qquad (2)$$

Since the left sides of the two equations above are identical, the two right sides can be set equal to each other.

$$P(D|H_k)P(H_k) = P(H_k|D)P(D) \qquad (3)$$

Solving for the conditional probability $P(H_k|D)$, equation (3) becomes

$$P(H_k|D) = \frac{P(D|H_k)P(H_k)}{P(D)} \qquad (4)$$

If H can take on the mutually exclusive and exhaustive alternatives $H_1, H_2, \ldots, H_k$ there is an identity from the theory of probability which states that the probability $P(D)$ can be written

$$P(D) = P(D|H_1)P(H_1) + \cdots + P(D|H_k)P(H_k) \qquad (5)$$

Substituting for $P(D)$ from equation (5) into equation (4), we get the equation

$$P(H_k|D) = \frac{P(D|H_k)P(H_k)}{\sum_k P(D|H_k)P(H_k)} \qquad (6)$$

This equation is Bayes' theorem.

Classical and Bayesian statistics take very different approaches to statistical inference. Statisticians in both groups, however, do not disagree about Bayes' theorem as such. Even a believer in classical statistics may have reason to use Bayes' theorem from time to time if the $P(H_k)$s are known.

What separates the two lines of thought is the special interpretation given to equation (6) by Bayesian statisticians. Let H stand for hypothesis and H_k for the kth hypothesis which states that the parameter in question, θ, takes on the specific value θ_k, that is, $H_k: \theta = \theta_k$. The presentation here is restricted to the analysis of one parameter at a time even though it is possible to consider the joint investigation of several parameters. Let D stand for the sample data. The so-called posterior probability $P(H_k|D)$ on the left side of equation (6) gives the probability of the hypothesis H_k being true conditional on the given data in the sample. According to Bayes' theorem this probability equals a fraction where the numerator is the product of two probabilities. The first of these, $P(D|H_k)$, is the probability of the data D conditional on the kth hypothesis, that is, the probability of the sample data D if the parameter in question has the value specified in the hypothesis H_k. This probability is called a *data probability*.

The second factor in the numerator of Bayes' theorem is the probability $P(H_k)$. This is the unconditional probability of the hypothesis

H_k, often called the *prior probability* of that hypothesis. This probability is assessed before the sample is taken. Bayes' theorem calls for the probabilities $P(H_1)$, $P(H_2)$, . . . , $P(H_k)$. These probabilities specify a probability distribution over the values of the parameter given by the K hypotheses. This distribution, called the *prior distribution*, is determined by the investigator before the data are collected. The prior distribution is intended to represent the existing knowledge of how probable the various values of the parameters are before additional sample information is obtained.

The denominator $P(D)$ in Bayes' theorem is the *unconditional probability* of the observed data. This probability is obtained as the sum in equation (5) where each data probability is weighted by the corresponding prior probability. $P(D)$ acts as a normalizing constant for the probabilities in the numerator, and one is seldom interested in $P(D)$ by itself.

Using Bayes' theorem the information contained in the observed data is merged with the prior information about the parameter being studied. The outcome of this merger is the posterior probabilities $P(H_k|D)$. The posterior probability distribution represents the knowledge accumulated after the prior knowledge and the current data are examined and the posterior probability distribution is arrived at using the sample data to update the prior probability distribution.

NUMERICAL EXAMPLE

A group of five people consists either of two revolutionaries and three moderates or four revolutionaries and one moderate. The actual group composition is unknown to us and we attempt to determine the group composition using Bayes' theorem by observing the distribution in a sample of one person. Let π be the proportion of revolutionaries in this population of five. The population parameter π can therefore take on the value 0.4 or 0.8. The corresponding two hypotheses become

$$H_1: \pi = 0.4 \qquad H_2: \pi = 0.8$$

Let us assume that according to current knowledge we believe the two group compositions to be equally likely. Thus, the prior probability distribution can be written

$$P(H_1) = 0.5 \qquad P(H_2) = 0.5$$

The random sample of size one turns out to consist of a moderate. Let the data D therefore be denoted M. If the hypothesis H_1 represents the true state of affairs, there are three moderates in the population of five, and for that reason the probability of a random person being moderate is taken to be 0.6. This data probability can be written

$$P(M|H_1) = 0.6$$

Similarly, if H_2 represents the true group composition we have the data probability

$$P(M|H_2) = 0.2$$

According to Bayes' theorem we have

$$P(H_1|M) = \frac{P(M|H_1)P(H_1)}{P(M)} = \frac{P(M|H_1)P(H_1)}{P(M|H_1)P(H_1) + P(M|H_2)P(H_2)}$$

$$= \frac{(0.6)(0.5)}{(0.6)(0.5) + (0.2)(0.5)} = \frac{0.3}{0.4} = 0.75$$

For the second hypothesis the similar computation gives $P(H_2|M) = 0.25$. The computations necessary to find the posterior probability distribution on the basis of the prior probability distribution and the data probabilities are conveniently summarized in Table 1.

TABLE 1
Example of Computations Using Bayes' Theorem

Hypothesis	Population Proportion	Prior Distribution	Data Probability	Product	Posterior Distribution
H	π	$P(H)$	$P(M|H)$	$P(M|H)P(H)$	$P(H|M)$
H_1	0.4	0.5	0.6	0.3	0.75
H_2	0.8	0.5	0.2	0.1	0.25
Total		1.0		$P(F) = 0.4$	1.00

Observing one moderate has changed our opinion about the unknown composition of the group. Rather than believing that the two compositions are equally likely we believe, after sampling one person, that the 2-3 composition is three times as likely as the 4-1 composition. The hypothesis H_1 has become more likely by observing one moderate since under that hypothesis there are more moderates in the group than under the competing hypothesis.

Rather than talking about prior and posterior probability distributions over the set of hypotheses it is possible to denote these distributions as distributions over the parameter. In this example one could write $P(\pi)$ and $P(\pi|M)$ for prior and posterior distributions, respectively.

SUBJECTIVE PART OF BAYESIAN STATISTICS

The prior distribution needed for Bayesian analysis is provided by the investigator before the new data are collected. That gives him a unique opportunity to make his study fit into a cumulative framework. His past knowledge of the subject matter at hand is explicitly built into the current study by means of the prior distribution. This distribution is then modified by the information contained in the sample data. Anyone wanting to study the topic further can use this past posterior distribution as the new prior distribution and proceed with data collection at that point.

The prior probability distribution reflects the investigator's opinion of what the true value of the parameter is. In Bayesian as well as in classical statistics it is thought that the sample data have been generated on the basis of some fixed parameter value. Because there is uncertainty about what that one value really is, one assigns a probability distribution to the parameter as a measure of this uncertainty.

In the end, however, the prior distribution is specific to the investigator, and two investigators are usually not expected to provide identical prior probability distributions. This means that the posterior distribution, representing the outcome of the study, might differ for two investigators analyzing the same data. For that reason Bayesian statistics has been classified as a statistical theory dealing with personal probabilities. The phrase *subjective probabilities* is also used, partly to imply that the classical theory of statistics somehow deals with more objective probabilities.

The fact that the posterior distribution may not be unique has been taken to introduce some doubt about the inherent scientific objectivity of Bayesian statistics. Personal considerations that affect the final conclusions are, however, always introduced in any scientific endeavor. For example, using classical statistics the level of significance for a test is chosen by the investigator. For mildly unlikely data this leaves the investigator with the possibility of calling his results significant or not by suitably choosing the significance level. Using Bayesian statistics one is forced to be specific about the subjectivity that enters the analysis, since the subjectivity has to be expressed in the prior distribution. By having to be specific about these matters it becomes easier to determine the effects of the subjective choices on the final conclusions.

In the face of conclusive results in the data the effect of the prior distribution is negligible, given that the prior distribution is not too extreme. One extreme situation consists of giving some parameter value a prior probability of zero. With such a value no data evidence can prevent the posterior probability for that parameter value from also becoming zero. But even wildly different prior distributions converge rapidly to about the same posterior distribution when the sample size increases and the sample contains conclusive evidence about the parameters being studied.

Classical and Bayesian statistics view the concept of probability very differently. Classical statistics takes the probability of an event to be the relative frequency of the occurrence of the event as the number of trials becomes large. With this definition of probability it makes no sense to talk about the probability that a parameter has a specific value. The value of the parameter is usually unknown, but this value is some fixed number. At most the classical statistician will say that the probability is either one or zero that the parameter equals any specific value depending upon whether the value is the true value. Bayesian statistics interprets probability to be a measure of the uncertainty a person has about whether an event will occur. This measure of uncertainty is specific to the person. It can be based on an observed relative frequency but is not restricted to such a definition.

Since Bayesian statistics permits probability statements to be made expressing one's uncertainty of what the world is like one may make probability statements about what the unknown value of a statistical parameter is. Thus, a typical Bayesian use of probability is to say that the probability is 0.95 that the value of the parameter lies between the two numbers A and B. Short of being told the actual value of the parameter, statements of this type represent the kind of information most investigators want about what is being studied.

With this concept of probability Bayesian statistics permits probability statements about events that cannot be repeated. Considering the abundant use of probability statements in daily life most people make use of Bayesian probabilities to guide their actions. "It will probably not rain today and I therefore leave the umbrella at home" refers to the specific day which is never to return again and the statement is therefore a Bayesian probability statement. Just as we are uncertain about the weather we are uncertain about the true values of statistical parameters, and Bayesian statistics permits the assignment of probabilities to these unknown parameter values.

An actual prior probability distribution is usually determined more by hunches and vague opinions than by some well-defined earlier posterior distribution. Most sociological research is undertaken just because not much past knowledge is available. The researcher is therefore faced with a translation of more or less well-defined impressions into a probability distribution over a statistical parameter. This process is not always simple, but it usually results in the investigator's having to think harder about the early aspects of his study than otherwise might have been the case. Depending upon the parameter in question there may be certain mathematical considerations entering into the specification of the prior distribution. Beyond that the form of the prior distribution rests with the investigator. For an instructive illustration of how a prior distribution can be set up on the basis of some vague impressions see the dialogue by Raiffa (1968, pp. 161–168).

INFERENCE ABOUT A POPULATION PROPORTION

The numerical example above represents a simple case of determining a population proportion. In the example the proportion can take on only two possible values, and the sample consists of one person. Here the general case is considered where the population proportion π of people with some specific characteristic can taken on any value between zero and one, and the simple random sample consists of n persons.

The binomial probability distribution gives the probability of obtaining x people with the given characteristic in a simple random sample of size n when the probability of a person's in the population having this characteristic is π. This probability π is unknown, but with an observed sample with known n and x the data probability can be expressed, using the binomial distribution, as a function of the unknown parameter. The data distribution becomes

$$p(x|\pi) = \binom{n}{x} \pi^x (1 - \pi)^{n-x} \qquad (7)$$

Since we are here dealing with continuous functions of the unknown parameter π we change the notation from P, standing for probability, to p, standing for probability density.

First the prior probability distribution $p(\pi)$ must be assessed. It is sometimes tempting to believe that one does not know anything about the parameter in question. But there is no way of expressing total ignorance by means of a prior distribution. The closest one can come to not having much previous knowledge is usually to state that prior to observing any data one believes that each value of the parameter is equally likely in the case of a discrete parameter, and all intervals of the same length are equally likely to contain the parameter in the case of a continuous parameter. If, upon further reflection, one finds that certain values of the parameter are thought to be more, or less, probable than other values, these opinions should be contained in the prior distribution.

Because of the form of the data probability in the case of binomial sampling it is mathematically convenient to have the prior distribution expressed in the form

$$p(\pi) = \frac{1}{B(a, b)}\, \pi^{a-1}(1 - \pi)^{b-1} \qquad a > 0, b > 0 \qquad (8)$$

Equation (8) is known as the beta distribution. The term $B(a, b)$ is a constant that makes the area under the curve equal to one. The terms a and b are constants, and for various numerical combinations of these parameters the beta distribution takes on a wide range of shapes. For a discussion of the versatility of the beta distribution see Mosteller and Tukey (1968, pp. 175–177). The mean and variance of π from the distribution in equation (8) are $a/(a + b)$ and

$$\left[\frac{a}{a + b}\left(1 - \frac{a}{a + b}\right)\right] \Big/ (a + b + 1)$$

With the prior distribution and the data distribution specified above, Bayes' theorem provides the posterior distribution of π as given in the expression

$$p(\pi|x) = \frac{1}{B(a - x, b + n - x)}\, \pi^{a+x-1}(1 - \pi)^{b+n-x-1} \qquad (9)$$

This distribution is also a beta distribution, but with parameters $a + x$ and $b + n - x$. The constant which makes the area under the curve equal to one is $B(a + x, b + n - x)$. When a and b are integers we have

$$\frac{1}{B(a + x, b + n - x)} = \frac{(a + b + n - 1)!}{(a + x - 1)!(b + n - x - 1)!} \qquad (10)$$

From equation (9) the posterior mean and variance are obtained to be $(a + x)/(a + b + n)$ and

$$\left[\frac{a + x}{a + b + n}\left(1 - \frac{a + x}{a + b + n}\right)\right] \Big/ (a + b + n + 1)$$

Assume that we were to take another simple random sample of size n_2 from this population and use the posterior distribution in equation (9) as the new prior distribution. If the second sample consists of x_2 people with the characteristic being studied and $n_2 - x_2$ people without, the theory outlined above can be used to find the new posterior probability distribution of π. This distribution becomes

$$\frac{1}{B[a + x + x_2, b + (n - x) + (n_2 - x_2)]}\, \pi^{a+x+x_2-1}(1 - \pi)^{b+(n-x)+(n_2-x_2)-1}$$

The number of people in the second sample with the characteristic is added on to the exponent for π and the number of people without the characteristic is added on to the exponent for $1 - \pi$. From this addition in the exponents it can be said that the information in the initial prior distribution in equation (8) is equivalent to having an initial sample of size $a + b$ where a people have the characteristic and b people do not.

Increasing the exponents in the posterior distribution has the effect of reducing the variance of π since the denominator in the expression for the variance is one larger than the sum of the two exponents in the beta distribution. As an example of the magnitude of the uncertainty attached to the population proportion using the posterior distribution, we find that with a sample size n around 100 and the posterior mean anywhere from 0.40 to 0.60, the posterior standard deviation is around 0.05 when a and b are small.

Thus, by selecting a beta prior and having data that fit the binomial distribution the posterior distribution of π is a beta distribution as shown in equation (9). This posterior distribution is used in order to draw inferences about the parameter π.

USE OF POSTERIOR DISTRIBUTION

The posterior probability distribution over the possible values of the parameter results from the merger of the prior information about the parameter and the information contained in the sample data. This distribution typically represents one of the final steps of a Bayesian statistical analysis. The distribution may be in the elegant mathematical form exemplified by equation (9) or the distribution may be computed using more approximate and numerical methods. In either case the posterior distribution represents current knowledge about the parameter.

The posterior distribution can be used to calculate summary measures of the posterior knowledge we have about the parameter. The mode of the distribution tells which value, or small interval, of the parameter is the most likely. The mode is the measure simplest to obtain when the posterior distribution is computed using numerical methods. When the mathematical form of the posterior distribution is known, as in equation (9), formulas for the mode, median, and mean are usually available. The posterior distribution provides, in addition to measures of central tendency, information about how precisely the value of the parameter can be assessed after the sample data have been analyzed. The posterior standard deviation can be used to measure how probable it is that the true value of the parameter lies as much as some number c standard deviation away from the posterior mean, or any other value of the parameter.

From the posterior distribution it is also possible to conclude that the probability equals some fraction, say 0.95, that the unknown parameter lies between two numbers A and B, using tables or numerical methods. For any fixed probability $1 - \alpha$ we find an interval from A to B so that

$$P(A < \theta < B) = 1 - \alpha \qquad (11)$$

A and B are usually chosen to make the interval between the two numbers as short as possible. The probability statement above is to be read as it stands, "the probability equals $1 - \alpha$ that the value of the parameter θ lies between the numbers A and B." This is the way the classical confidence interval so intuitively is interpreted, but it is not until one makes use of Bayesian statistics that one can correctly make such a statement. This in spite of the fact that the formal expressions in both cases look like equation (11).

Various summary uses can be made of the posterior distribution. A good strategy, however, may be to make the whole distribution available. That way the reader can reach his own conclusions about the unknown parameter value. Making the whole posterior distribution public also makes it possible for other investigators to use this posterior distribution in future studies of the same kind.

How are the results from a Bayesian and a classical statistical analysis different? The main difference lies in the philosophical foundations of the two schools of thought. However— setting these differences aside for a moment—the practical consequences for the investigator may not always be great. The width and location of the confidence interval are not very different from the width and location of the Bayesian probability interval, if the prior probability distribution is gentle in the area of interest. Similarly, if a null hypothesis is rejected the value of the parameter specified in this hypothesis is usually found in one of the tails of the posterior distribution, again if the prior distribution does not have too much effect on the determination of the posterior distribution. Noticeably different conclusions from use of the two methods usually result from well-specified prior probabilities.

But the philosophical differences will forever separate the two ways of thinking. If probability measures uncertainty and one is uncertain about the true parameter value, the Bayesian way is the way to proceed. If probability is measured by relative frequencies and the unknown parameter value is fixed, meaning that probability statements are made about the sample results, the classical way is the way to proceed. These are two fundamentally different approaches to data analysis. Most of us were brought up according to the classical way of thinking, but it may well be that the Bayesian way will serve us better.

STOPPING RULES

The fact that a posterior probability is a conditional probability can be used to show another feature of Bayesian statistics. An investigator using classical statistics must bring to his analysis not only the observed data but also parts of the design of the data collection process. Parts of the design are necessary in order not to violate the frequency definition of probability under which he operates. The intentions of the investigator do not have the same importance when Bayesian statistics are applied.

More specifically, it can be shown that the probability of getting x observations with a certain characteristic in a sample of n observations is different from the probability of getting observation number x with the characteristic as exactly the nth observation. Assuming that this is independent sampling and the probability is π that an observation has the characteristic, then the first probability is obtained from the binomial distribution and becomes

$$P_1(x|\pi) = \binom{n}{x} \pi^x (1 - \pi)^{n-x} \qquad (12)$$

The second probability is obtained from the negative binomial distribution as

$$P_2(x|\pi) = \binom{n-1}{x-1} \pi^x (1 - \pi)^{n-x} \qquad (13)$$

This means that

$$P_1(x) = (n/x)P_2(x) \qquad (14)$$

and the two probabilities can differ considerably, depending upon the values of n and x. The fact that different probability distributions are used means that when inferences are desired about the probability π one first has to establish from which distribution the available data have come.

But how is the choice to be made between these two probabilities? When the investigator is asked about what his intentions were on how to collect the data he says he just sort of stopped; the budget was getting low, he had been interrupted by a meeting and having observed that the last observation had the characteristic being studied he was beginning to think that he had enough observations.

Here the Bayesian statistician steps in and says nothing matters but the data themselves, not whether they were collected under one scheme or another, as long as there was simple random sampling of the observations. The information in the data is contained in the likelihood

$$L(\pi; x, n) = \pi^x(1 - \pi)^{n-x} \tag{15}$$

which is a function of the unknown π for given x and n. It is through the likelihood function that data influence the posterior distribution. Going back to Bayes' theorem the constant $\binom{n}{x}$ in the case of binomial sampling or the constant $\binom{n-1}{x-1}$ in the case of negative binomial sampling appears in both the numerator and the denominator and therefore cancels out. Thus, the distinction between the two intentions above is not relevant for Bayesian statistics. The analyst is free to stop collecting his data when the money runs out, when the phone rings, or for any other reason he might have.

LITERATURE ON BAYESIAN STATISTICS

The writings on Bayesian statistics are voluminous and quite scattered. Specialized topics have been pursued in statistical journals while broader expositions have been appearing in journals oriented toward substantive areas. Psychologists have been exposed to Bayesian statistics through a paper by Edwards, Lindman, and Savage (1963). *The Review of Educational Research* presented a paper by Meyer (1966). Bayesian statistics has been discussed for social psychologists by Mosteller and Tukey (1968).

In spite of these papers it has been difficult for the uninitiated to gain a working knowledge of Bayesian statistics. This difficulty has been eased by the appearance of the first elementary introduction to Bayesian statistics, written by Schmitt (1969). Much of the recent interest in Bayesian statistics can be traced to the writings of Savage (1962, 1964). He presents compelling arguments in favor of the Bayesian approach. These are arguments that have forced many people to reevaluate their preconceptions of what are the very foundations of statistics.

BAYESIAN STATISTICS IN SOCIOLOGY

For anyone attracted to data analysis from the Bayesian point of view the task is clear. After determining what parameter is to be examined a prior probability distribution is specified over the possible values of the parameter. This distribution summarizes the existing knowledge about the missing parameter value up to the point when new data are sought. The information available in the data is expressed in the various data probabilities. Through Bayes' theorem we arrive at a posterior distribution of the parameter, incorporating the two sources of information.

How to obtain the posterior distribution of a population proportion has been discussed in some detail above. Another well-developed area of Bayesian statistics, inferences about parameters of the normal distribution, can be found described in Schmitt (1969). Simple Bayesian regression analysis is also presented in the same book. In short, Bayesian counterparts exist for many simpler statistical techniques.

For a sociologist wanting to do a more complex analysis the situation becomes more complicated. A multiple regression analysis with K variables, for instance, requires a $K + 2$ dimensional joint prior distribution over the parameters. It is difficult to think in many dimensions, let alone incorporate scattered and imprecise previous knowledge in a prior distribution. Another difficulty, sometimes overlooked, has to do with the data probabilities. Bayes' theorem assumes we know the probability distributions for the variables being studied, but that is not always the case.

Particularly in multivariate analysis the mathematics of finding the univariate posterior distribution for each of the parameters easily becomes complicated. This, however, is a problem that numerical methods and computers can help solve.

Bayesian statistical methods have not been common in sociological research. Part of this is ignorance about the Bayesian way of looking at data analysis; part of this is a lack of development of appropriate Bayesian techniques. For Bayesian statistics to take hold in the near future a certain amount of retooling among current sociologists is necessary. But even if this retooling was not to take place the teaching of Bayesian methods that is beginning to take hold is almost certain to have its effect on the profession. The appeal of Bayesian statistics is not lost on students in methodology and statistics courses, and the first traces of Bayesian analysis may come from these students.

REFERENCES

BAYES, T.
    1763   "An essay towards solving a problem in the doctrine of changes." *Philosophical Transactions* (Royal Society, London) 53:370–418. Reprinted in *Biometrika* 45 (1958): 293–315.

EDWARDS, W., LINDMAN, H. AND SAVAGE, L. J.
1963   "Bayesian statistical inference for psychological research." *Psychological Review* 70 (May): 193–242.

MEYER, D.
1966   "Bayesian statistics." *Review of Educational Research* 36: 503–516.

MOSTELLER, F. AND TUKEY, J.
1968   "Data analysis including statistics." Pp. 160–183 in G. Lindzey and E. Aronson (Eds.), *Revised Handbook of Social Psychology*. Reading, Mass.: Addison-Wesley.

RAIFFA, H.
1968   *Decision Analysis*. Reading, Mass.: Addison-Wesley.

SAVAGE, L. J.
1962   "Subjective probability and statistical practice." Pp. 9–35 in L. J. Savage *et al.*, *Foundations of Statistical Practice*. New York: Wiley; London: Methuen.

SAVAGE, L. J.
1964   "The foundations of statistics reconsidered." Pp. 173–188 in H. E. Kyburg, Jr., and H. E. Smokler (Eds.), *Studies in Subjective Probability*. New York: Wiley.

SCHMITT, S.
1969   *Measuring Uncertainty*. Reading, Mass.: Addison-Wesley.

✖12✖

UNCERTAINTY ANALYSIS APPLIED TO SOCIOLOGICAL DATA

Doris R. Entwisle

THE JOHNS HOPKINS UNIVERSITY

Dennis Knepp

UNIVERSITY OF PENNSYLVANIA

This research was supported by National Science Foundation Grant GE 9846.

In sociological research, *multivariate analysis* usually means analysis of survey data or counts that have been cross-tabulated on several independent categoric variables. Voters, for example, may be classified by sex and party (two independent categoric variables) and then the number of votes in favor of an issue can be tallied by each sex-party category. The strategy of examining data by repetitive cross-tabulations as variables are added or held constant is perhaps the most common kind of analysis employed by sociologists. (See, for example,

200

Lazarsfeld, 1955.) This variety of multivariate analysis is *not* the "multivariate analysis" of mathematical statistics which analyzes multiple measurements (continuous variables) made upon a number of persons or objects. Techniques such as the analysis of variance and covariance, factor analysis, and multiple regression all fall under the latter rubric, and because the form of the underlying distribution of at least the error component of these models is assumed to be normal, they are conveniently, and less confusingly, classified as parametric methods.

There is no body of techniques to use with count data that can be compared directly to the parametric techniques available for interval data. In a parametric analysis, a large body of data can be subjected to an analysis of variance, for example, before examining differences between specific cells, and only if the overall analysis points to significant differences are smaller analyses undertaken. This provides a safeguard against paying undue attention to vagaries in data that stem from sampling fluctuations, and it also provides an overall evaluation for all effects in one summary table. Uncertainty analysis, the topic of this paper, provides a systematic way for scrutinizing a large body of data and leads to a summary for all effects in one compact array. This paper gives some notions of: (1) how uncertainty analysis has been developed in other fields, (2) the mathematical basis for the analysis, (3) application of the method to sociological data, (4) the usefulness of the method both in providing an overall summary of data and in respect to other problems of data analysis, and (5) the relation of uncertainty analysis to other techniques especially those developed by Goodman and Coleman. Computer programs (in Basic and in Fortran) for performing uncertainty analysis have been prepared.[1]

DEVELOPMENT OF UNCERTAINTY ANALYSIS

Uncertainty analysis has been developed and used extensively in other fields, especially in psychology and communications engineering. To our knowledge this technique has so far not been applied to sociological data. (The only exception appears to be that Coleman (1964) used Shannon's information measure to analyze hierarchization of choices in a sociometric matrix.) In sociology applications of uncertainty analysis are somewhat different from applications in other fields because the sociologist's major source of data is the survey and he is rarely able

---

[1] Listings of a FORTRAN IV program and a BASIC program, with instructions, are available from the National Auxiliary Publication Service, % CCM Information Corp., 909 Third Ave., New York, N.Y., 10022. Tables of $-p \log_2 p$ (with argument and function to four decimal places) are available from the authors.

to manipulate predictor variables. By contrast, the psychologist manipulates the stimuli (predictors) and observes differences in response. Uncertainty analysis is derived from the theory of information and gives a measure of how much can be told about a dependent variable from knowledge of independent variables. It is especially useful for studying multivariate attribute data in a preliminary way. For instance, if we know a respondent's social class, his religion, and his age, we may be able to guess better how he will vote on fluoridation than we could guess without knowledge of his background characteristics.

In uncertainty analysis it is assumed that the information associated with each variable is measured and is additive: the information associated with each predictor adds to give the total amount of information available to predict the dependent variable. For instance, knowledge of husbands' voting intentions can help predict wives' intentions but also a woman's previous voting record might help predict her voting behavior. The matrix of women's intentions could be classified according to husbands' intentions (Republican/Democrat) and according to previous voting record (Republican/Democrat). An uncertainty measure would tell how predictable women's intentions were from both independent variables and also how the two independent variables interact.

The number of possible outcomes for an event is a measure of uncertainty. If the outcome of a coin toss is already known, there is no uncertainty and so no information is to be gained by tossing the coin. Before the coin is tossed, however, if a head or a tail is equally probable, uncertainty is at a maximum because there is no advantageous choice between the two outcomes. One guess is as good as another. On the other hand, if the coin is slightly biased in the direction of falling heads and we know this, we could predict heads on every throw and be right more often than we were wrong. This is the intuitive notion behind uncertainty analysis. In a state of complete ignorance, we may have no choice but the equivalent of a 50–50 coin toss. Our predictions may improve after study of a situation, however, once we establish associations between different factors. Since there may be many factors, and since they may exert their influence singly, two at a time, three at a time, and so on, a procedure is required to assess simultaneously the impact of all the factors in all possible combinations. Uncertainty in a given matrix may be partitioned into portions associated with each of the predictor variables, much the way sums of squares are partitioned in a variance analysis.

Intuitively the "amount of information" contained in an event is related to the number of possible outcomes—when a die is tossed the outcome is more uncertain than when a coin is tossed because the first results in establishing one outcome out of six possible outcomes and the second decides between only two outcomes. Therefore throwing a die gives more information than tossing a coin but the number of possible outcomes cannot itself serve as a measure of uncertainty reduction, as the reader will quickly see. If one coin toss gives us two units of information (because of two possible outcomes) then each successive coin toss should give that much more information. But three tosses have eight outcomes, not six, and this is four times as much "information" as two outcomes. We need a measure that is monotonically related to the number of outcomes but that gives the same amount of information with each successive event. A measure satisfying these conditions is a logarithmic one:

$$U = c \log k$$

where U is the required measure of uncertainty, k is the number of possible outcomes, and c is a proportionality constant. It is conventional to use logarithms to the base 2 for this measure (entirely an arbitrary choice, and any other base would be workable), and to let c equal unity. This choice then gives as a unit of measurement (bit), the uncertainty involved in an event with two possible and equally likely outcomes. The reader should consult Garner (1962) for a more extensive description and history of the measure.

Perhaps the most valuable feature of uncertainty analysis is the evaluation of interaction effects. Absence of father, for instance, may not affect school performance except when it occurs for families toward the low end of the social class continuum. If father absence and social class interact, it could be misleading to conclude that father absence has a small overall effect rather than that there is no effect for some class levels and a marked effect for others. Interaction uncertainties could account for uncertainty in addition to that accounted for by either father absence or social class considered separately (a positive interaction), or the interaction could show how much prediction from one variable was duplicated by the other (a negative interaction). Perhaps knowing whether father is present or absent does not improve prediction beyond knowing social class alone, a negative interaction uncertainty, as would be the case if almost all of the absent fathers occurred at one class level.

After showing in some detail how to analyze uncertainty, its specific application to sociological data and its advantages for sociological analysis will be discussed. In particular the analysis of interaction uncertainties will be stressed.

MATHEMATICAL BASIS FOR ANALYSIS

Uncertainty,[2] U, is defined as:

$$U = \log_2 R$$

where R is the number of equally likely possible outcomes. Since the probability associated with an event is the reciprocal of the number of things that can occur, the uncertainty equation can be rewritten in terms of probabilities. For equally likely events:

$$U = \log_2 (1/p)$$
or
$$U = -\log_2 (p)$$

When events are not equally likely the uncertainty of a particular outcome is weighted by the likelihood of occurrence of that outcome:

$$U(x) = - \sum_i p(x_i) \log p(x_i)$$

A biased coin, 75–25, has less total uncertainty associated with it than a fair coin. For the biased coin the uncertainty is

$$0.3113 + 0.5000 = 0.8113$$

whereas for a fair coin it is

$$0.5000 + 0.5000 = 1.0000$$

Knowledge of the biasing reduces the uncertainty by 0.1887. In the same manner if one wished to predict religious affiliation and knew only that there were three possibilities, Catholic, Protestant, and Jewish, he would guess that they occurred equally often. After a survey, however, one would know that the three possibilities are not equally likely, and this knowledge improves prediction and reduces uncertainty.

With two variables, the uncertainty partitioning occurs in terms of the *joint* uncertainty:

$$U(x, y) = - \sum_{i,j} p(x_i, y_j) \log p(x_i, y_j)$$

where $p(x_i, y_j)$ is the joint probability of occurrence of the two variables. The maximum joint uncertainty is the sum of the uncertainties of each variable taken alone:

---

[2] Methods for uncertainty analysis are discussed extensively in Garner (1962) and this presentation is a summary of his work.

$$U(x) = - \sum_i p(x_i) \log p(x_i)$$

$$U(y) = - \sum_j p(y_j) \log p(y_j)$$

$$U_{max} = U(x) + U(y)$$

The *contingent* uncertainty, $U(x:y)$, is the difference between the maximum joint uncertainty, $U_{max}(x, y)$, and the actual joint uncertainty, $U(x, y)$.

$$U(x:y) = U_{max}(x, y) - U(x, y)$$

In the 2×2 case this procedure is equivalent to applying the χ^2 test of independence assuming all margins fixed. (For a discussion of contingent uncertainty, especially its relation to variance and correlation analyses, see Garner (1962), pp. 59–62.)

The *conditional* uncertainty is the average amount of uncertainty associated with one variable while the other variable is held fixed.

$$U_x(y) = U(x, y) - U(y)$$

It is symmetrical, that is,

$$U_y(x) = U(x, y) - U(x)$$

because $\qquad U(x:y) = U(y) - U_x(y)$

and also $\qquad U(x:y) = U(x) - U_y(x)$

The term $U\overline{(xyz)}$ is the *interaction* uncertainty between x, y, and z, and is the unique uncertainty associated with the joint impact on x of y and z, beyond that associated with each variable considered alone:

$$U\overline{(xyz)} = U_y(x:z) - U(x:z)$$

This is symmetric in x, y, and z. The interaction uncertainty is equal to the contingent uncertainty between x and z within the categories of y, less the contingent uncertainty neglecting the y division.

The approach generalizes readily to three or more variables. As new predictor variables are added, the further reductions in uncertainty can be measured.

APPLICATIONS TO SOCIOLOGICAL DATA

Numerical Example. Most sociological studies are concerned with complex situations reflecting the influence of many variables. For instance, Breton and McDonald (1967) studied high school students'

TABLE 1
Cross-Tabulation of Educational Aspirations of Ontario High School
Students (adapted from Breton and McDonald, 1967)
Variables
Dependent: Educational aspirations (EDA)
Independent: (1) Sex (*S*)
(2) Grade (*GR*)
(3) Parental desires (*PAR*)
(4) Peer plans (*PP*)

Independent Variable Number 1234	High Educational Aspirations	Low Educational Aspirations	
1111	74	15	
1112	21	8	
1121	24	21	
1122	9	28	
1211	61	16	
1212	37	13	
1221	15	25	
1222	35	61	
2111	81	8	
2112	15	2	
2121	16	23	
2122	5	22	
2211	51	15	
2212	28	5	
2221	9	26	
2222	16	46	
Total	497	334	831

educational aspirations in relation to sex, grade, parents' desires, and peer-group plans. The total uncertainty in a matrix produced by cross-tabulating one small part of their survey data (Table 1) can be partitioned into many components. The impact of the predictor variables can be considered one at a time, and in all possible combinations. The most useful partitioning is in terms of contingent uncertainties for pairs of variables and all interactive terms. This division of uncertainty resembles the division in variance analysis for a complete factorial design when variance is partitioned for variables taken singly, and then in all possible interactive combinations.

The computation for the data of Table 1 is illustrated classifying educational aspirations (high-low) of Ontario high school students in terms of four predictor variables. First, from a four-fold table showing the breakdown of students in terms of educational aspirations versus peer plans, the marginal proportions and interior proportions are computed and shown in Table 2.

TABLE 2

	Number of Students Educational Aspirations			Proportions of Students Educational Aspirations		
	High	Low	Total	High	Low	Total
Consistent Peer Plans	331	149	480	0.3983	0.1793	0.5776
Inconsistent	166	185	351	0.1998	0.2226	0.4224
	497	334	831	0.5981	0.4019	1.0000

The next step is to find the uncertainty associated with each p-value, $-p \log_2 p$, by consulting a table (Knepp, 1967; see footnote 1). The uncertainty is shown in matrix in Table 3.

TABLE 3
Uncertainty Matrix

0.5290	0.4446	0.4574
0.4641	0.4825	0.5251
0.4435	0.5286	

The contingent uncertainty between educational aspirations (EDA) and the other predictor variables, sex (SEX), grade (GR), and parents' desires (PAR) (Table 4), is also computed by the same method.

TABLE 4
Uncertainty Partitioning for Data of Table 1

Term No.	Term	U	χ^2 1.3863 n U	Significance Level
1	$U(EDA:SEX)$	0.0000	0.00	N.S.
2	$U(EDA:GR)$	0.0090	10.39	0.01
3	$U(EDA:PAR)$	0.1778	204.83	0.001
4	$U(EDA:PP)$	0.0344	39.63	0.001
5	$U(EDA\ SEX\ GR)$	0.0010		
6	$U(EDA\ SEX\ PAR)$	0.0064		
7	$U(EDA\ GR\ PAR)$	−0.0051		
8	$U(EDA\ SEX\ PP)$	0.0001		
9	$U(EDA\ GR\ PP)$	−0.0018		
10	$U(EDA\ PAR\ PP)$	−0.0288		
11	$U(EDA\ SEX\ GR\ PAR)$	0.0006		
12	$U(EDA\ SEX\ GR\ PP)$	−0.0001		
13	$U(EDA\ SEX\ PAR\ PP)$	0.0009		
14	$U(EDA\ GR\ PAR\ PP)$	0.0074		
15	$U(EDA\ SEX\ GR\ PAR\ PP)$	0.0002		
	Algebraic Sum	0.2018		

The contingent uncertainty is found by subtracting the actual joint uncertainty from the maximum joint uncertainty:

$$
\begin{aligned}
U(EDA:PP) &= U_{max}(EDA, PP) - U(EDA, PP) \\
&= (0.4435 + 0.5286 + 0.4574 + 0.5251) \\
&\quad - (0.5990 + 0.4641 + 0.4446 + 0.4825) \\
&= 0.0344
\end{aligned}
$$

The next step is to compute the triple interactions. These all follow a similar pattern, so only one is illustrated, in Table 5. For $U(EDA\ PAR\ PP)$ we need the number of students with high and low educational aspirations for each PAR-PP combination.

TABLE 5
Parents' Desires

	High Educational Aspirations		Low Educational Aspirations	
	High	Low	High	Low
Consistent	267	54	64	95
Peer Plans				
Inconsistent	101	28	65	157

The interaction is

$$
U(\overline{EDA\ PAR\ PP}) = U_{PAR}(EDA:PP) - U(EDA:PP)
$$

The second term on the right has already been computed and is 0.0344. $U_{PAR}(EDA:PP)$ is the contingent uncertainty within each PAR group between PP and EDA, appropriately weighted. The group having high parents' desires (54.2 per cent) is shown in Table 6.

TABLE 6

	Educational Aspirations		
	High	Low	
Consistent	267	54	321
Peer Plans			
Inconsistent	101	28	129
	368	82	450

$$
U(EDA:PP) = 0.0023
$$

The group with low parent desires (45.8 per cent) is shown in Table 7. The contingent uncertainties for high and low parents' desires groups are then weighted by the proportions with high and low parents' desires:

$$
U_{PAR}(EDA:PP) = 0.542(0.0023) = 0.458(0.0094) = 0.0056
$$

Finally, to get the interaction uncertainty we take the difference:

TABLE 7

	Educational Aspirations		
	High	Low	
Consistent	64	95	159
Peer			
Plans			
Inconsistent	65	157	222
	129	252	381

$$U(EDA:PP) = 0.0094$$

$$U(\overline{EDA\ PAR\ PP}) = U_{PAR}(EDA:PP) - U(EDA:PP)$$
$$= 0.0056 - 0.0344 = -0.0288$$

By the same method the other triple interactions are calculated (Table 4). To compute higher order interactions essentially the same procedure is followed.[3] In the present example there are four quadruple interactions and a quintuple interaction. This completes the partitioning of the uncertainty.

To interpret the results for the numerical example shown in Table 4, we suggest steps as follows. First, SEX (Term 1) by itself does not reduce uncertainty and it is not a component of any sizeable interaction except $\overline{EDA\ SEX\ PAR}$ (Term 6). This interaction is small in magnitude compared with PAR alone (0.0064 vs. 0.1778).

Next, GR (Term 2) is small, though significant, by itself, and is not included in any large interactions except for $\overline{EDA\ GR\ PAR}$ (Term 7) and $\overline{EDA\ GR\ PAR\ PP}$ (Term 14).

The triple interaction involving GR is negative (-0.0051) and the quadruple interaction involving GR is positive ($=0.0074$). The difference between these interactions is small ($0.0074 - 0.0051 = 0.0023$), suggesting no overall gain in predictive power from including both these interactions. One would therefore probably be willing to

---

[3] For example, the contingent terms needed to compute the quintuple interaction $U(\overline{D1234})$, where 1 to 4 are the independent variables and s_i represents the number of categories on the ith variable, are

$$U(\overline{D1234}) = (-1)^2 U_{C_1}(D:4) + (-1)^3 U_{C_2}(D:4)$$
$$+ (-1)^4 U_{C_3}(D:4) + (-1)^5 U_{C_4}(D:4)$$

where C_1 is all combinations of three of the variables taken three at a time (not including variable 4), C_2 is all combinations of the 123 variables taken two at a time, and C_3 is just each variable separately. C_4 is C_0^3, which is none of the variables.

Thus:
$$U(\overline{D1234}) = U_{123}(D:4) - U_{12}(D:4)$$
$$- U_{13}(D:4) - U_{23}(D:4) + U_1(D:4)$$
$$+ U_2(D:4) + U_3(D:4) - U(D:4)$$

neglect both *GR* and *SEX* as independent variables, and confine attention to the remaining variables.

To recapitulate, by evaluating the uncertainty associated with each variable, alone or in combination with others, we have a measure of the importance of each in predicting the dependent variable. All interactions are isolated and their sign tells whether they add or subtract from predictive power. In the numerical example presented, it appears that almost all the useful information in the 2^4 table can be summarized in a 2×2 table where educational aspirations are cross-tabulated against parents desires and peer plans, and where grade and sex are neglected. After making this decision one could of course use any of the conventional methods for judging the significance of the 2×2 table.

USEFULNESS OF UNCERTAINTY ANALYSIS

Uncertainty analysis provides an objective procedure for structuring research problems, especially surveys. Some perplexing questions for which uncertainty analysis offers help follow. What particular variables should be included in a study (or excluded)? For example, if data can be secured on sex, age, income, and so on, how many independent variables, or which of these variables, will be most fruitful to consider?

In the example above it turned out that two independent variables contributed almost nothing to an understanding of the data, but one would hesitate to discard them in the absence of knowledge concerning their interactions. Uncertainty analysis provides a rapid assessment of all interactions *in relation to* other interactions. With one higher order interaction positive and a second negative, as in the example, it is clear that the overall gain is slight. Even with large numbers of cases, there are limits on the number of independent variables that one can reasonably consider; those that contribute little information can be discarded in favor of others containing more.

Does one phrasing of a question elicit more information, or different information, than alternate phrasing does? For example, students can be asked whether they plan to continue school or to drop out. Although both questions are similar and presumably should elicit the same information, a survey researcher would not be surprised if one phrasing produced rather different patterns from another.

Again an overall summary of the total uncertainty associated with each, which can be obtained quickly and mechanically and will evaluate higher order interactions, will greatly aid in choosing between questions. This also suggests a way to improve reliability of scales. Uncertainty analysis, besides indicating that an item is not producing variance among respondents, can indicate much faster than an item analysis what ills the item suffers from—whether it is discriminating between certain groups and not others, whether an adjustment of a cutting point would help, and so on. The uncertainty associated with any attribute, or any set of data, has a maximum which can be calculated. Various ways of specifying a problem can be evaluated with respect to this maximum, and with the aid of a computer it is feasible to select the division closest to the maximum.

Uncertainty analysis also can measure the increase in predictive power as variables are added to a study, both as the added variables act independently, and as they act in concert with one or more of the other predictor variables. This kind of approach, which is reminiscent of multiple regression, may avoid errors often made in interpreting regression or factor analyses. Also, one can compare degrees of association for variables with different metrics; for example, in a study directed at understanding school achievement, one might ask whether association is greater between high verbal ability and number of siblings or between high verbal ability and dollar income. The fact that number of siblings and dollar income have different metrics poses no difficulty. For the same reason it is possible to consider and evaluate the information produced by different questions in an interview schedule. Uncertainty analysis thus seems to offer help for a number of important methodological problems of concern to sociologists.

RELATION TO OTHER TECHNIQUES

Several good basic texts explain the mathematical basis of uncertainty analysis, but are oriented toward psychological or communications engineering applications (see Garner, 1962; Attneave, 1959; Abramson, 1963). This paper presents a brief overview of the mathematical basis for the technique, but its main purpose is to call attention to sociological applications.

Uncertainty analysis has the same kind of generality and presents the same kind of overall summary of a set of data as variance analysis. Because of lack of independence in the data matrix, however, significance tests like those associated with variance analysis are contraindicated. Absolute amounts of uncertainty can be compared, but except for contingent uncertainties between pairs of variables, significance tests analogous to F-tests in variance analysis are lacking. A codistribution of education and income, for instance, does not assume that the probability of observing a high education is independent of the probability of observing a high income. (A variance model guarantees orthogonality of effects by its assumption of additive constants that sum to zero across any row or down any column. Interactions in a variance analysis are likewise modeled by additive constants.) Interest in uncertainty analysis is not in testing an observed relationship against the null hypothesis of independence but rather in estimating the strength of the relationship between variables and how the strength of relationship varies with other covariates. Fortunately, as remarked earlier, the significance testing problem is frequently irrelevant anyway in sociological problems.

For pairs of variables it turns out that $1.3863nU(X:Y)$ is distributed approximately as χ^2, where n is the number of observations in the entire table. There is no way to evaluate the magnitude of the interaction terms, however. They are distributed as the difference of two χ^2 distributions, a difference function studied in some detail by Pearson, Stouffer, and David (1932) and more recently by Knepp and Entwisle (1969). But since the χ^2s in uncertainty analyses are not independent, it is not clear how to develop significance tests. The magnitude of the simple contingent uncertainty terms can be evaluated directly using a standard χ^2 table (see first four lines of Table 4), but other comparisons cannot be evaluated in similar terms.

The determination of the relative magnitudes of interaction uncertainties can be especially illuminating in sociological data analysis. It is important to emphasize that the meaning of interaction is not identical with the meaning of interaction in other contexts: interaction in uncertainty analysis is a contingent uncertainty that is not zero. In analysis of variance, interaction is the failure of differences across rows or between columns to be the same. Interaction in uncertainty analysis is a failure of additivity *as long as the proportions have been converted to uncertainties* (basically logarithms). The additivity property of the information measure is a basic reason for its selection in preference to other possible measures. A dependent variable is accounted for in terms of two predictors, A and B, by the sum of the separate relations with A and B plus the joint relation with all possible A-B combinations.

One important property of uncertainty analysis is that negative interactions occur frequently. Negative interactions in variance analysis can occur only when variables are not orthogonal, an impossibility with most designs. If—in uncertainty analysis—two predictor variables are correlated, then the reduction in uncertainty accomplished by the first variable will partly overlap the uncertainty reduction achieved by the second. This overlap produces a negative interaction between the two predictor variables. There is thus provided a measure of the redundancy between predictor variables, a matter of universal concern in sociological research.

The ability to evaluate interactions for many attributes in all possible combinations systematically can be of great help in clarifying sociological data, especially as a form of preliminary analysis. With computer programs we have developed, it is possible to go directly from a cross-tabulation program to an uncertainty analysis program. Uncertainty analysis does not yield *different* information from what one gets if he uses another measure, but it is often easier to compute and sometimes has more intuitive meaning than do other measures. For instance, high occupational status is often associated with high income and very little additional information may be provided by using both indices rather than one. Uncertainty reductions could be computed for status and income taken as individual predictors of some dependent variable, and then the interaction uncertainty could be computed for the two predictors. These uncertainties measure the relative utility of the two classification variables taken by themselves and the extent to which they are redundant. For some surveys one predictor could be more useful, cheaper, or more reliable than another even though the two predictors overlapped generally. The data of Table 1, for instance, show a negative interaction, -0.0288, among educational aspirations, parents' desires, and peer plans. This suggests that parents' desires and peer plans overlap one another. The contingent uncertainty for each of the predictors is 0.1778 and 0.0344 respectively. The interaction uncertainty is almost as large as the uncertainty associated with peer plans, so knowing peer plans does not contribute much predictive power in addition to what is obtained from knowing only parents' desires. One could do something exactly analogous to stepwise regression here, looking at additional uncertainty due to each added variable. Uncertainty analysis gives a rapid preview and suggests how a parametric analysis might be structured. In some cases multiple contingencies can be large even with small lower order contingencies. A study of pretesting effects, for instance, has shown bright boys to be adversely affected and bright girls to be aided with *no* overall difference for pretesting or lack of pretesting (Entwisle, 1961).

One property of uncertainty analysis is that the elimination of some variables does not affect the analysis for the remaining variables. For example, if GR and SEX of Table 4 are eliminated, PAR and PP are unaffected. The total uncertainty accounted for by PAR and PP is 0.1834, which underscores again the negligible influence of GR and SEX. GR and SEX plus all their interactions (twelve terms) yield a small net gain of $0.2018 - 0.1834 = 0.0184$. We can compare the net gain from including PP over PAR alone by looking at the magnitudes of PP and the $\overline{PP\,PAR}$ interaction $(0.0344 - 0.0288 = 0.0045)$ and this turns out to be small in magnitude compared with *PAR* alone. As mentioned earlier, peer plans contribute very little net gain in predictive power because of the negative interaction (Term 10). Parents' desires are apparently a strong force in educational aspiration of Ontario youth, and peer plans are consistent with parents' desires.

Further decisions about variables to include and exclude would depend on specific circumstances. Rather than eliminating peer plans as a variable, one might wish to observe the interaction of parents' desires and peer plans over youth groups of different social statuses. It could turn out, for example, that the interaction varies in a meaningful way over social status, with peer plans and parents' desires being less consistent for groups of low social status. The uncertainty measure allows comparison of amounts of association across status levels.

Two points deserve emphasis: (1) comparisons between terms of different orders are reasonable *only* when all variables are dichotomous; and (2) once categories are defined, each variable's contribution to uncertainty reduction remains constant.

Multivariate analysis of attribute data has received much attention also from both Goodman and Coleman over the past few years in an effort to quantify and make rigorous the intuitive procedures outlined by Lazarsfeld and others. Goodman (1965) points out that the difference between the degree of association (Yule's Q coefficient) in two 2×2 tables can be tested by a W^2 statistic which is asymptotically distributed as χ^2. Alternatively an analogous statistic Z^2, based on odds ratios, may be used if principal interest attaches to relative magnitude of the size of odds in one set of cells compared with another. The W^2 and Z^2 statistics contain the same information. Both are based on the assumption that the dependent variable can be expressed in terms of multiplicative combinations of predictor variables taken singly and in interaction. Extension of the tests to polytomous variables is by way of the Goodman-Kruskal λ, which permits comparison of two or more contingency tables. Goodman's tests have the advantage of supplying legitimate significance tests. Both Goodman's statistic and uncertainty partitioning are independent of the order in which variables are taken. Goodman's technique provides a method for significance testing of all components with any number of categories per variable, but is limited to three-variable analyses.

In Coleman's general method for multivariate analysis (1964), probabilities are assumed to be additive. His method resembles uncertainty analysis in that the magnitudes of separate predictors may be compared. Coleman's method is reminiscent of a fixed-effects analysis of variance with ps describing main effects behaving like the additive constants of the variance model. However, there is no normally distributed error term with mean zero in Coleman's model such as the random normal deviates with zero mean that appear in a variance model. Instead, variability associated with main effects is assumed to be binomial (or multinomial) and significance tests based on this assumption are constructed. Coleman's analysis generalizes to any number of predictor variables but computer routines presently available consider only main effects (no interactions). However, the method can easily be extended to include interactions for dichotomous data.

Aside from practical considerations, the choice between Coleman's analysis and uncertainty analysis would seem to depend on which model, the additive or the multiplicative, is more reasonable. In fairly extensive computations on further data from Breton's Ontario study, results from uncertainty analysis and Coleman's analysis were almost always consistent for effects of a single predictor.

REFERENCES

ABRAMSON, N.
    1963   *Information Theory and Coding.* New York: McGraw-Hill.
ATTNEAVE, F.
    1959   *Applications of Information Theory to Psychology.* New York: Holt, Rinehart, and Winston.
BRETON, R. AND MCDONALD, J. C.
    1967   *Career Decisions of Canadian Youth: A Compilation of Basic Data.* Ottawa: Department of Manpower and Immigration.
COLEMAN, J. S.
    1964   *Introduction to Mathematical Sociology.* New York: Free Press.
DUNCAN, O. D.
    1966   "Path analysis: Sociological examples." *American Journal of Sociology* 72 (July): 1–16.
ENTWISLE, D.
    1961   "Interactive effects of pretesting." *Educational and Psychological Measurement* 21 (Autumn): 607–620.
GARNER, W. R.
    1962   *Uncertainty and Structure as Psychological Concepts.* New York: Wiley.
GOODMAN, L. A.
    1965   "On the multivariate analysis of three dichotomous variables." *American Journal of Sociology* 71 (November): 290–301.
GOODMAN, L. A. AND KRUSKAL, W. H.
    1954   "Measures of association for cross classifications." *Journal of the American Statistical Association* 49 (December): 732–764.
GOODMAN, L. A. AND KRUSKAL, W. H.
    1959   "Measures of association for cross classifications. Further discussion and references." *Journal of the American Statistical Association* 54 (March): 123–163.

KNEPP, D. L.
    1967   "Table of $-p \log_2 p$ with function and argument to four decimal places."
          Department of Social Relations, The Johns Hopkins University (mimeo.).
KNEPP, D. L. AND ENTWISLE, D. R.
    1969   "Testing significance of differences between two chi-squares." *Psy-*
          chometrika 34 (September): 331–333.
LAZARSFELD, P. F.
    1955   "Interpretation of statistical relations as a research operation." Pp.
          115–125 in P. F. Lazarsfeld and M. Rosenberg (Eds.), *The Language of*
          Social Research. New York: Free Press.
PEARSON, K., STOUFFER, S. A., AND DAVID, F. N.
    1932   "Further applications in statistics of the $T_m(x)$ Bessel function." *Bio-*
          metrika 24 (November): 293–350.

𝒴13𝒳

MULTIVARIATE ANALYSIS
FOR ATTRIBUTE DATA

James S. Coleman
JOHNS HOPKINS UNIVERSITY

There has developed in the past several years far wider use of measures expressing the relation between qualitative attributes than had developed in previous periods. These measures can be separated into two classes: measures which are symmetric vis-à-vis the two attributes, and measures which are asymmetric. The former class, including measures like γ, Q, and Goodman-Kruskal λ, is appropriate in those applications where no causal asymmetry is being examined with the measure, comparable to the case of correlation coefficients for continuous variables. The latter class is, on the other hand, composed of measures designed to express the effect of one attribute on the other, comparable to the case of regression coefficients for continuous variables.

This paper gives an exposition and further development of one approach to measures of the latter kind, an approach first introduced in 1964. The approach has been used by a number of investigators since then, but there has been no comprehensive and straightforward exposition, although there have been various developments including Boyle (1966), Boudon (1967), and Coleman (1964, 1968). In addition, a measure for interaction effects using this approach is developed and new estimation procedures for panel data are introduced. This exposition covers the model through which effects are postulated, a measure of effect for cross-sectional data with dichotomies, multivariate measures, a measure of interaction effects, weighting, and a measure of effect for panel data with two waves.

One aspect of the approach, the generalization to ordered and unordered categorical data beyond two states, will not be discussed. Exposition of this may be found in Coleman (1964, Chapter six).

MODEL

Although understanding and use of the measures introduced here does not depend on a full comprehension of the mathematical model underlying them, it is useful to gain a sense of the assumptions of the model. It is especially important that measures used to describe causal relations be based on an explicit dynamic mathematical model, and it is valuable in the use of such a measure to be aware of the model underlying it.

The model of causation used here is a continuous-time Markov process with two states, representing the two possible responses on the dichotomous dependent attribute, as in Figure 1. Each individual is assumed to have the potential for moving from the state he is currently in to the other state, a potential which is measured by the quantity q_{ij} shown in the figure. This quantity, which we will call a transition rate, may be thought of as a probability per unit time of movement, or as a constant potential for movement from state i to j at every point in time. Since the process is continuous in time, there is a continuous potential acting at all times, rather than a transition probability which operates at discrete points in time, as in a discrete-time Markov chain. The explicit and exact meaning of q_{ij} can be given by stating that in an

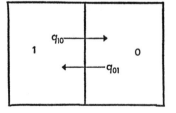

Figure 1

infinitesimally small period of time, dt, there is a probability $q_{ij}dt$ of moving from state i to j. Thus if there is only this one state j to which an individual may move, the rate of reduction in an individual's probability of being in state i is this infinitesimal transition probability times the probability that the individual is in state i: $dp_i = -q_{ij}dtp_i$.

If, as in the case considered here, there is a rate of movement in both directions, then the equation for the rate of change in p_1 is based on two rates of movement, and becomes, after dividing through by dt,

$$\frac{dp_1}{dt} = -q_{10}p_1 + q_{01}p_0 \tag{1}$$

This is the equation on which the measures of effect of independent attributes are based. The way in which these effects are assumed to occur is through differences in the values of q_{ij}. Heuristically, suppose a second attribute has an effect such that if the individual is in state 1 on the second attribute, he will be in state 1 on this attribute as well more frequently than if he is in state 0 on the second attribute. If the individual's behavior is described by this model, then the only way this effect can occur is for the size of q_{01} relative to q_{10} to be larger for the individual who is in state 1 on the second attribute than for the individual who is in state 0. There are a number of ways this can occur, but we will assume here that this occurs through a component added to the basic rate from 0 to 1 when the individual is in state 1 on the second attribute, and a component added to the basic rate from 1 to 0 when the individual is in state 0 on the second attribute. The basic rate may be thought of as a "random shock" which exists in the relevant direction in the absence of an effect from the independent attribute. If the basic rate toward state 0 is c and toward state 1 is a, and the component due to the effect of the second attribute is b, then the transition rates are as follows:

When the individual is in state 1 on the second attribute:

$$q_{01} = a + b$$
$$q_{10} = c$$

When the individual is in state 0 in the second attribute:

$$q_{01} = a$$
$$q_{10} = c + b$$

If the second attribute is labeled x, with values 0 and 1, then the values of q_{10} and q_{01} may be expressed as a function of x:

$$q_{01} = a + bx \tag{2}$$
$$q_{10} = c + b(1 - x) \tag{3}$$

In uses of this model for a sample of individuals, the usual assumption made for applying stochastic processes to a set of individuals is made, with one important exception. First, it is assumed that the transition rates do not change over time, except as individuals change state on the independent attributes. Second, it is assumed that the transition rates are dependent only on the current state of the individual, and not on how long he has been there or where he came from. It is not assumed, however, that transition rates are the same for all individuals: transition rates are a function of the value of x, as indicated in equations (2) and (3). Consequently there is heterogeneity of individuals in their transition rates. For all individuals characterized by the same value of x, however, transition rates are assumed to be the same. With these assumptions, the proportion of individuals in state 1 of the dependent attribute is an estimate of the probability p_1 that any single individual is in that state. Thus data in the form of proportions may be treated as estimates of p_1 and under appropriate conditions used to estimate the fundamental parameters, a, b, and c.

This is the basic model, from which measures of effect of an independent attribute may be derived. Clearly, the parameter of effect in the basic equations is b, so that a measure of effect should be closely related to this parameter. It should also be evident that since the model is expressed as a model in which effects occur through time, it is applicable to data on the same individuals over time, such as a two-wave panel.

MEASURE OF EFFECT FOR CROSS-SECTIONAL DATA

The model expressed in equations (1), (2), and (3) gives the relation of p_1, p_0, and dp_1/dt to the transition rates q_{10} and q_{01}, which are themselves functions of x, the individual's value on the independent attribute, and a, b, and c. The probability p_0 is merely $1 - p_1$ so that the equation is in terms of p_1 and dp_1/dt. However, data from a cross-sectional survey are in terms of proportions at one point in time. Integration of the differential equation would give an equation in p_1 at *two* points in time, for which panel data could be used. But to express a, b, c, and x in terms of p_1 at one point in time requires a further assumption: that the system is at aggregate or statistical equilibrium, in effect the assumption that if a second cross-section were taken, the same relationship between attributes would be found. This is an assumption that is ordinarily made implicitly in measuring relations between attributes or variables; here it is made explicitly.

This assumption of aggregate equilibrium is an assumption that

$dp_1/dt = 0$. With this assumption, equation (1) becomes, for application to cross-sectional data:

$$0 = -q_{10}p_1 + q_{01}(1 - p_1)$$

and solving for p_1

$$p_1 = \frac{q_{01}}{q_{01} + q_{10}} \tag{4}$$

Equation (4) gives what is desired: the probability p_1, of which observed proportions constitute estimates, related to q_{01} and q_{10}, the transition rates which cannot be directly observed or estimated with observed data. Substituting from equations (2) and (3) into the right-hand side of equation (4) gives a relation between p_1 and a, b, c, and x:

$$p_1 = \frac{a + bx}{a + b + c} \tag{5}$$

The left-hand side of this equation is estimated directly by a proportion in the data, and there are two such proportions in a tabulation with one independent attribute: p_1 when $x = 0$ and p_1 when $x = 1$, as indicated in Table 1. (The letter p_i will be used henceforth to denote both the probability and the proportion that estimates it.)

TABLE 1

Format of tabulation with a dependent attribute and a single independent attribute

| | | Independent attribute x | |
		0	1
Dependent	1	$p_1(0)$	$p_1(1)$
Attribute	0	$1 - p_1(0)$	$1 - p_1(1)$
Number of Individuals		(n_0)	(n_1)

The expressions for $p_1(0)$ and $p_1(1)$ are, respectively:

$$p_1(0) = \frac{a}{a + b + c}$$

$$p_1(1) = \frac{a + b}{a + b + c}$$

and the difference in proportions is:

$$p_1(1) - p_1(0) = \frac{a + b}{a + b + c} - \frac{a}{a + b + c}$$

$$p_1(1) - p_1(0) = \frac{b}{a + b + c} \tag{6}$$

The numerator of equation (6) is the parameter of effect of the second attribute, and the denominator, $a + b + c$, is the sum of the effect parameter and both random shocks. This is as close as one can get to a direct estimate of b with cross-sectional data. The reason can be seen intuitively as follows: cross-sectional data are data at one point in time, and thus cannot give any information on absolute sizes of transition rates or their components. But a, b, and c are absolute rates. Thus cross-sectional data can give information only on the *relative* sizes of a, b, and c. An appropriate measure for the relative size of each is its size relative to the sum of the others. Thus

$$\frac{b}{a + b + c} = p_1(1) - p_1(0) \qquad (7)$$

$$\frac{a}{a + b + c} = p_1(0) \qquad (8)$$

$$\frac{c}{a + b + c} = 1 - p_1(1) \qquad (9)$$

A useful property of these measures is that they partition the interval from 0 to 1 into three parts: a part measuring the relative size of the random shock toward state 1; a part measuring the relative size of the independent attribute's effect; and a part measuring the relative size of the random shock toward state 0. It is useful to represent these by single letters, a', b', and c' respectively.

The use of a difference in proportions as a measure, b', of the effect of the independent attribute has the virtue of simplicity; and one consequence of this simplicity is the simplicity of statistical inference: since the proportions are estimates of the probabilities in equation (1) and since they are based on independent samples, the variance of b' is simply the sum of the variances of $p_1(0)$ and $p_1(1)$. If the proportions are based on independently drawn observations, as is often assumed in population samples, these variances are binomial variances, $p_1(1 - p_1)/n$.[1] In estimating these variances, the proportions $p_1(0)$ and $p_1(1)$ can be used to estimate the probabilities, so that the estimate of the variance of b' becomes:

$$\text{var}(b') = \frac{p_1(0)[1 - p_1(0)]}{n_0} + \frac{p_1(1)[1 - p_1(1)]}{n_1}$$

[1] It may sometimes be the case that multistage sampling was carried out with some clustering. When that is done, variances must be estimated by use of the results of the sample itself. See Kish (1965). Another case may arise as well: comparisons in which $p_1(1)$ and $p_1(0)$ are not based on responses from different individuals, but on responses to different questions by the same individuals. In that case, the estimate of the variance of b' is $\text{var}[p_1(1)] + \text{var}[p_1(0)] - 2\,\text{cov}[p_1(1), p_1(0)]$.

and 95 per cent confidence intervals can be obtained around b' as

$$b' \pm 1.96 \sqrt{\text{var}(b')}$$

or the test of whether b' is significantly greater than zero at the 5 per cent level for a one-tailed test is the test of whether $b' > 1.65 \sqrt{\text{var}(b')}$. The usual cautions, of course, about statistical inference from *ex post* analysis apply here.

MULTIVARIATE MEASURES

It is a simple and straightforward step to move from a single independent attribute to additional attributes. If there are $m - 1$ independent attributes, labeled 2, . . . , m, and one dependent attribute, labeled 1, then each individual is characterized by the vector $(x_1, \ldots , x_m)$, each x_i taking on values of 0 or 1. Equations (2) and (3) become:

$$q_{01} = a + \sum_{i=2}^{m} b_i x_i \tag{10}$$

$$q_{10} = c + \sum_{i=2}^{m} b_i (1 - x_i) \tag{11}$$

and after substituting in equation (4) from equations (10) and (11) for q_{01} and q_{10}, the multivariate analogue to equation (5) is:

$$p_1 = \frac{a + \sum_{i=2}^{m} b_i x_i}{a + c + \sum_{i=2}^{m} b_i} \tag{12}$$

or expressing p_1 in terms of the measures of effect a', and b_i'.

$$p_1 = a' + \sum_{i=2}^{m} b_i' x_i \tag{13}$$

For later convenience, it will be useful to use a more compact notation for p_1 and for q_{ij} than the extension of the notation used in the preceding section. The vector of values of x_i in reverse order may be treated as a binary number. Thus the state of an individual with $x_4 = 0$,

$x_3 = 0$, $x_2 = 1$, $x_1 = 1$ is represented by the binary number 0011. In decimal notation, this is 3, and the decimal representations for all states are $0, 1, \ldots , 2^m - 1$. The states will be represented by decimal representation of the binary number with 1 added so as to begin with state 1 rather than 0. Thus the state 0011 is labeled 4, and the probability of being in this state is labeled p_4. The transition rates are labeled with the same notation; for transitions on attribute 1, the dependent variable, the state of origin and destination differ by 1. Thus q_{43} and q_{34} are transitions on attribute 1 with a configuration of 0, 0, 1 for attributes 4, 3, and 2—that is, transitions between states 0011 and 0010.

It turns out that the multivariate generalization of the difference in proportions which will give a least-squares estimate of the measure of effect is simply the average of differences in proportions, where the difference is taken between proportions in which $x_i = 1$ and $x_i = 0$, with all other attributes remaining the same.[2] Consider the measure of effect b_i' for attribute i. Now consider all 2^{m-2} states in which $x_1 = 1$ and $x_i = 0$, and label this set of states S. Any state in S, say state j, is matched by another state outside it, identical except that $x_i = 1$. This is state $j + k$, where $k = 2^{i-1}$. Then the measure b_i' is given by the average of 2^{m-2} differences of proportions:

$$b_i' = \frac{1}{2^{m-2}} \sum_{j \in S} (p_{j+k} - p_j) \qquad (14)$$

This is the estimate of b_i' which minimizes the sum of squared deviations of the observed proportions from the estimated probabilities created by the sum of additive components as defined in equation (13). In this multivariate case, the estimate of a' is best obtained after calculation of all b_i', by solving equation (13) for a' and then averaging over all values of p_j:

$$a' = \frac{1}{2^{m-2}} \sum_j \left(p_j - \sum_{i=1}^{m} b_i' x_i \right) \qquad (15)$$

where the sum is taken over all states j for which $x_1 = 1$, and the values of x_i in each term of equation (15) are 0 or 1 as x_i is 0 or 1 in state j.[3] The value of c' is then a residual, obtained by the fact that

[2] By a least-squares estimate is meant that estimate which minimizes the sum of squared differences between p_i and p_i^*, where p_i is the observed proportion and p_i^* is the proportion estimated from the right side of equation (13). See Coleman (1964) for derivation of the least-squares estimates.

[3] A least-squares estimate for a' in terms solely of the proportions p_j is given in Coleman (1964, p. 196), where the letter r is used where a' is used here. However, that method is not usable for weighted measures, which are discussed below.

$$a' + c' + \sum_{i=2}^{m} b_1' = 1.$$

Example

Throughout this paper, hypothetical data are used to illustrate use of the measures. The measures have been used by a number of investigators with real data, in published work. See McDill and Coleman (1965), Pinard (1963), and McPartland (1969). Hypothetical data, generated by the stochastic model, are used here to show the correspondence between the estimates and the true values of parameters. These hypothetical data have a special virtue: they were generated by the model of equation (1), using particular known values of a, b, and c. Consequently, it will be possible to see, in each case, how closely the estimates approximate the true values. This will be especially useful in examining the movement toward equilibrium. In the computer program which generates these hypothetical data, individuals' starting positions on each variable are independently generated, so that the attributes show a zero or near-zero relation at the start.

In the computer program that generates data according to the model, the continuous-time process of equation (1) is approximated by a sequence of very small steps of size Δt, so that $\Delta p_1 = \Delta t[q_{01} - x_1(q_{10} + q_{01})]$, where $x_1 = 1$ if the individual is in state 1 on the dependent attribute, and $x_1 = 0$ if he is in state 0. The values of q_{01} and q_{10} are composed according to equations (10) and (11); and Δp_1 is the probability of moving from state 1 or into state 1 in that small increment of time Δt. This approximation can be made as close as desired to the continuous equation by making Δt very small.

The data in Table 2, using two independent variables, labeled 2 and 3, were generated by use of the following parameters: $a = 1.0$; $c = 0.1$; $b_2 = 0.4$; $b_3 = 0.8$; and $\Delta t = 0.05$. These parameters are absolute rates; the relative rates that can be estimated with cross-sectional data are:

$$b_2' = \frac{b_2}{a + c + b_1 + b_2} = \frac{0.4}{1.0 + 0.1 + 0.4 + 0.8} = 0.174$$

$$b_3' = \frac{b_3}{a + c + b_1 + b_2} = 0.348$$

$$a' = 0.435$$

$$c' = 0.043$$

The generation of data at the beginning of the process randomly allocated individuals to different states. Table 2 shows the states of indi-

viduals at the start of the process, and Table 3 shows their states after
the process has operated for twenty rounds, which brings it close to
equilibrium, but not fully there.

TABLE 2
Randomly generated data with two independent attributes and one
dependent attribute at start of process

attribute 3:		0		1	
attribute 2:		0	1	0	1
		(p_2)	(p_4)	(p_6)	(p_8)
attribute 1	p_i	0.508	0.508	0.530	0.496
	n	(250)	(244)	(262)	(244)

TABLE 3
Randomly generated data with two independent attributes and one dependent
attribute, after twenty time periods, with $\Delta t = 0.05$

attribute 3:		0		1	
attribute 2:		0	1	0	1
		(p_2)	(p_4)	(p_6)	(p_8)
attribute 1	p_i	0.444	0.598	0.786	0.889
	n	(250)	(244)	(262)	(244)

The estimates of b_2' and b_3' following equation (14) are averages of two
differences in proportions:
The general equations are:

$$b_2' = \tfrac{1}{2}(p_4 - p_2 + p_8 - p_6)$$
$$b_3' = \tfrac{1}{2}(p_6 - p_2 + p_8 - p_4)$$

For data at the start of the process:

$$b_2' = \tfrac{1}{2}(0.508 - 0.508 + 0.496 - 0.530)$$
$$= -0.017$$
$$b_3' = \tfrac{1}{2}(0.530 - 0.508 + 0.496 - 0.508)$$
$$= 0$$

For data after twenty time periods of size 0.05:

$$b_2' = \tfrac{1}{2}(0.598 - 0.444 + 0.889 - 0.786)$$
$$= 0.129$$
$$b_3' = \tfrac{1}{2}(0.786 - 0.444 + 0.889 - 0.598)$$
$$= 0.317$$

The estimates at the start of the process show b_2' and b_3' to be very close
to zero. Their deviation from zero arises only from the random process
which generated the data. As the process continues, and approaches
equilibrium asymptotically, the estimates of b_2' and b_3' approach their
true values asymptotically (subject to random fluctuations due to sample
size). After twenty time periods (so that $t = 1$, since $\Delta t = 0.05$), the

estimates of b_2' and b_3' are 0.129 and 0.317 respectively, much closer to the true values of 0.174 and 0.348. The random shock a' is obtained by subtraction of the appropriate $b_i's$ from the respective ps:

$$a' = \tfrac{1}{4}(p_2 + p_4 - b_2' + p_6 - b_3' + p_8 - b_2' - b_3')$$

For data at the start of the process:

$$a' = \tfrac{1}{4}(0.508 + 0.508 + 0.017 + 0.530 - 0 + 0.496 + 0.017 - 0)$$
$$= 0.519$$

For data after twenty time periods of size 0.05:

$$a' = \tfrac{1}{4}(0.444 + 0.598 - 0.129 + 0.786$$
$$- 0.317 + 0.889 - 0.129 - 0.317)$$
$$= \tfrac{1}{4}(0.444 + 0.469 + 0.469 + 0.443)$$
$$= 0.456$$

The estimate of a' at the start is near 0.5, as it should be, since there was random allocation of individuals among states, with equal probability. After twenty time periods, a' has been reduced to near its equilibrium value. The value of c' is obtained as a residual, since $a' + c' + \Sigma b_i' = 1$. At the start of the process, c' is estimated as 0.498, since the estimates of b_2' and b_3' are near zero. After twenty time periods, it is $1 - 0.456 - 0.129 - 0.317 = 0.092$. This estimate is still about twice the true value of 0.043, a result due to the fact that the process has still not reached equilibrium, and b_2' and b_3' are thus still below equilibrium values.

MEASURE OF INTERACTION EFFECTS

One frequent rationale for examining all cells of a cross-tabulation rather than obtaining summary measures of effects is that effects are "not linear"; certain cells are especially high or especially low. Sometimes these variations have substantive interpretations of importance: a given effect may depend jointly upon two or more variables, rather than separately upon one or the other. One way in which such nonlinear effects may be observed and interpreted is through use of a linear model, regenerating the predicted p_i^*s based on the model, and comparing them with the observed values, p_i. For the example in Table 2, the comparison between observed and predicted values is:

	p_2	p_4	p_6	p_8
observed	0.444	0.598	0.786	0.889
predicted	0.456	0.585	0.773	0.902
observed − predicted	−0.012	0.013	0.013	−0.013

In this case, the deviations are quite small, as they should be, since the model which generated the data contained no interaction effects. If the deviations were large, it would indicate that the linear model does not fit the data, and that another model is appropriate.

Such a model differing from the linear model may take on many forms, and in some substantive areas, a model embodying specific nonlinear assumptions may be useful.[4] There is, however, one extension of the linear model of rather general utility, an extension in which the linear effects are supplemented by another effect orthogonal to them. This effect is present whenever the values of attributes 2 and 3 are *alike*, and is absent when they are *different*. In the example above from Table 2, with two independent attributes, the orthogonal effect, which will be labeled b'_{23}, is present for p_2 and p_8, absent for p_4 and p_6. This may be seen by inspection of the decomposed p^*_is:

$$\begin{aligned}
p^*_2 &= a' && + b'_{23} \\
p^*_4 &= a' \times b'_2 \\
p^*_6 &= a' && + b'_3 \\
p^*_8 &= a' + b'_2 + b'_3 + b'_{23}
\end{aligned} \tag{16}$$

In the example from Table 2, the estimate of this interaction effect b'_{23} would be -0.026, as may be seen by solving the above equations for b'_{23}, and using the values of p_i from Table 2 for estimation.

To return to the basic continuous-time model of equations (1), (10), and (11), the introduction of a first-order interaction term consists of introducing a new effect parameter, b_{ij}, which is present when $x_i = x_j$, and absent when $x_i \neq x_j$, for all pairs of independent attributes i and j. The simplest way to incorporate this into the model is to define a new attribute x_{ij}, which takes on the value 1 when $x_i = x_j$, and the value 0 when $x_i \neq x_j$. With two independent attributes i and j, such an attribute is:

$$x_{ij} = x_i x_j + (1 - x_i)(1 - x_j) \tag{17}$$

With this definition of x_{ij}, the transition rates in equations (10) and (11) take on the form

$$q_{01} = a + \Sigma b_i x_i + \Sigma b_{ij} x_{ij} \tag{18}$$
$$q_{10} = c + \Sigma b_i (1 - x_i) + \Sigma b_{ij} (1 - x_{ij}) \tag{19}$$

Thus first-order interactions in the model do not affect its basic form, but merely add another term, x_{ij}, for every pair of attributes i and j. The

---

[4] Among such assumptions, one may consider a model in which all effects are multiplicative rather than linear, with $q_{ij} = \alpha \beta_2^{x_2} \beta_3^{x_3}$ where α is a random shock, and β_2, β_3 are effects of attributes 2 and 3. In this case, values of $\beta_i > 1$ produce positive effects, and values of $\beta_i < 1$ produce negative effects.

sole difference between this attribute and the original attributes is that its value is determined by combinations of their values. Equation (13), which includes only linear terms, is replaced by one which includes the new attributes:

$$p_k = a + \sum_{i=1}^{m-1} b'_i x_i + \sum_{i=1}^{m-1} \sum_{j=1}^{m-1} b'_{ij} x_{ij} \tag{20}$$

where x_{ij} is defined according to equation (16).

The least-squares estimates for the model including first-order interactions give the same form of estimate for the interaction terms as for the linear terms or main effects, b'_i: averages of proportion differences. However, because of degrees of freedom lost owing to the linear terms b'_i, there are only half as many independent estimates: whereas in estimating the b'_i, each proportion difference was an independent estimate of b'_i, four proportions are necessary to provide a single estimate of b'_{ij}, as suggested by equation (16). The least-squares estimate for b'_{ij} is formally analogous to that for b'_i in equation (14). Consider the set S of all states in which $x_1 = 1$, $x_i = 0$, and $x_j = 0$. Then for each state in that set, there are three outside, identical except that in one, $x_i = 1$, $x_j = 0$, in another $x_i = 0$, $x_j = 1$, and in the third, $x_i = 1$, $x_j = 1$. If the state in the set is labeled h_0, then these three states are $h_1 = h_0 + 2^{i-1}$, $h_2 = h_0 + 2^{j-1}$, and $h_3 = h_0 + 2^{i-1} + 2^{j-1}$. The least-squares estimate of b'_{ij} is

$$b'_{ij} = \frac{1}{2^{m-3}} \sum_{h_0 \in S} \frac{1}{2} (p_{h_0} + p_{h_3} - p_{h_1} - p_{h_2}) \tag{21}$$

It becomes immediately possible to go directly from first-order interaction terms to interaction terms involving three, four, and more attributes, always keeping the higher-order interaction terms orthogonal to the lower-order terms. In obtaining an interaction term for attributes i, j, and k, which is orthogonal to the linear effects and pairwise interactions, any one of the pairwise terms, x_{ij}, x_{jk}, or x_{ik}, may be combined with the omitted attribute, as in equation (17), to provide still a new attribute:

$$x_{ijk} = x_{ij} x_k + (1 - x_{ij})(1 - x_k) \tag{22}$$

(where the equality holds if the subscripts on the right-hand side are permuted). It is possible in this fashion to exhaust all the degrees of freedom in an analysis, obtaining a perfect fit to the data through all higher order interactions. The number of degrees of freedom is 2^{m-1}, and this is partitioned as follows:

$$2^{m-1} = \underset{\substack{\text{(random} \\ \text{shock)}}}{1} + \underset{\substack{\text{(linear} \\ \text{effects)}}}{m-1} + \underset{\substack{\text{pairwise} \\ \text{interactions}}}{\frac{(m-1)(m-2)}{2}} + \underset{\substack{\text{triplet} \\ \text{interactions}}}{\frac{(m-1)(m-2)(m-3)}{2 \cdot 3}} + \cdots + \underset{\substack{\text{N-attribute} \\ \text{interaction}}}{1}$$

It is possible to carry out such a full partitioning of the degrees of freedom in this fashion, testing every interaction to determine whether it can be assumed to have arisen by chance. However, interactions involving more than pairs of attributes are seldom useful in substantive interpretations. Consequently, a better strategy may be to examine only linear effects and pairwise interactions, without attempting to provide interpretations for joint effects involving more than two attributes.[5]

WEIGHTING

The measure of effect introduced in the section on multivariate measures is based on averages of differences between proportions. It is natural, then, to consider a weighted average of these differences, when some of the differences are based on small numbers of cases, and may give less reliable estimates than others. The most natural weighting is weighting according to the inverse of the variance of the difference $p_{j+k} - p_k$. One such method was used in the original exposition of the approach (Coleman, 1964, Chapter six) using a binomial variance for p_i, with the observed proportions as estimates of the underlying probabilities. Boyle (1966) pointed out that it was precisely in the small-sample cases that the proportions were poor estimates, and in extreme cases (when $p_i = 0$ or 1) can cause the variance estimate to become zero, and thus a given $p_{j+k} - p_j$ to have infinite weight. Boyle suggested instead weights which assume a common underlying probability, and vary only with the number of cases, n_j, on which the proportion p_j is based. Thus the effective weight proposed by Boyle for the difference $p_{j+k} - p_j$ is

$$\frac{1}{\dfrac{1}{n_{j+k}} + \dfrac{1}{n_j}} \quad \text{or} \quad \frac{n_{j+k}n_j}{n_{j+k} + n_j}$$

where n_{j+k} and n_j are the numbers of cases on which p_{j+k} and p_j are based.

Labeling this weight w_j, equation (14) becomes

[5] A program for calculating the multivariate measures a_i', b_i', and b_{ij}' described here has been placed on file in the American Documentation Institute. In addition to the measures described in the paper, the program calculates measures when some independent attributes have more than two categories. The program is written in Fortran IV, for the IBM 7094, and has the following limitations: maximum number of independent attributes, 8; maximum number of categories on any one attribute, 20; maximum number of cells, 4096. In the computer program, all interactions are obtained, together with their standard deviations, for independent attributes up to eight in number.

$$b'_i = \frac{1}{\Sigma w_j} \sum_{jS} w_j(p_{j+k} - p_j) \tag{23}$$

With this method of weighting, and assuming that $p_{j+k} - p_j$ has a variance $pq/n_{j+k} + pq/n_j$, where p is taken to give the upper bound of variance, as 0.5, then the estimate of the variance of the weighted b_i is $1/4\Sigma w_j$. This variance can then be used as in the unweighted case to test whether b'_i is significantly different from zero, to test whether two b'_i are significantly different, or to give confidence intervals for b'_i.

Since the present approach results in a linear model, it would be surprising if it were not related to other statistical procedures based on a linear model. In fact, it can be shown that its effect parameters, b'_i, are identical to regression coefficients calculated using multiple regression analysis, when the independent variables take on only the value 0 or 1 ("dummy variables"), and the dependent variable is a proportion. Two cases are of interest. First, the unweighted estimates are identical to regression coefficients based on regression analysis carried out on the p_is themselves; and second, the weighted estimates are identical to regression coefficients based on regression analysis carried out with individual observations.

Because of this identity between measures from the present approach and measures from regression analysis, the question arises when one approach should be used, and when the other. In effect, the question is, when should measures be calculated from cross-tabulations with the use of equations (14), (15), and (21), and when should they be calculated from standard regression techniques which begin with product-moment correlation matrices? In part, the answer depends on the form of the data, and the relative ease of calculation. Beyond this, no definitive answer can be given; the present approach has the virtue of deriving very simply from cross-tabulations, without the use of unnecessary calculations designed for continuous variables—and the virtue of extending very simply to panel data (see the following section). Multiple regression, however, has the virtue of allowing mixtures of attribute data and continuous variables as independent variables.

MEASURE OF EFFECT FOR PANEL DATA

There are two principal benefits of deriving measures of association from an explicit underlying stochastic model. One of these is the ability to incorporate parameters in the model which have direct causal interpretation, and to estimate their values from data. The parameters b_i introduced in equations (10) and (11) exemplify this; but one could equally well assume a causal model different from the linear, additive one, and estimate the parameters of that model.

The second benefit is of a different sort: it is the resulting ability to establish a relation between measures of effects obtained from cross-sectional data, and measures obtained from panel data. The basic equation, equation (1), is an equation expressing a process of change over time. The causal parameters b_i, which are incorporated in equation (1) through the decomposition of q_{ij} in equations (10) and (11), have their effects over time, and thus may be estimated by the changes that occur over time, as well as by the resulting associations that they create in cross-sectional data.[6] The panel data will allow estimating the absolute sizes of b_i, while the cross-sectional data, which show only the results of the process at one point in time, can only allow estimation of the relative sizes. It turns out that the estimating procedures for the panel data are very similar to those for cross-sectional data, based principally on calculation of proportion differences, as in the cross-sectional case.

To use the model for estimating causal effects with data at two points in time, two cases may be distinguished: first, when there is only one endogenous attribute, and all the other attributes are assumed independent of that attribute and of each other; in this case, the problem is simply to estimate the sizes and direction of the effects of the independent attributes. The second case is that of a system of attributes, in which any attribute may affect any other. In this case, the problem of substantive interest is often to determine whether an association between two attributes x_1 and x_2 is produced principally by effects of x_1 on x_2, by effects of x_2 on x_1, or by a third attribute affecting both. Both these problems are examined, using only two attributes for simplicity of exposition, but in a form that allows direct generalization to more than two attributes, with examples involving three attributes.

When there is a single dependent attribute, the value of the dependent attribute for an individual is labeled x_1 and the value of the independent attribute is labeled x_2, each taking on the value 0 or 1. If

---

[6] The parameters can also be estimated by continuous observations, although such data will not be considered in detail since they are so infrequently available. The quantity q_{ij} is the probability per unit time of moving from i to j, with the dimension 1/time. The *inverse* of q_{ij}, $1/q_{ij}$, is the *expected residence time* in state i beginning with any initial observation time, given that the subsequent move was to state j'. Consequently, if there is continuous observation of an individual or a sample; the inverse of the average residence time in state i before moving to j is a direct estimate of q_{ij}. With such estimates for q_{ij}s representing different configurations of values of x_ks, equations (10) and (11) can be used directly for estimating b_is, or equations (18) and (19) can be used for estimating b_is and b_{ij}s, through standard multiple regression methods.

x_2 is constant over time, the proportion of individuals at time t who began at time 0 with a given value of x_1 and x_2 is a function of these two values and of t. That proportion will be designated as $p(t)$.

If equation (1) is expanded to express q_{01} and q_{10} as functions of x_2, then it becomes:

$$\frac{dp(t)}{dt} = -[c + b_2(1 - x_2)]p(t) + (a + b_2x_2)(1 - p(t)) \qquad (24)$$

When this equation is integrated, the result is:

$$p(t) = \frac{a}{v}(1 - e^{-vt}) + p(0)e^{-vt} + \frac{b_2}{v}(1 - e^{-vt})x_2 \qquad (25)$$

where $v = a + c + b_2$. And since the values of x_1 are observed for each individual at time 0, $p(0)$ for a given individual is either 0 or 1, and is merely x_1 at time 0. Since there are four initial states $(x_1, x_2) = (0, 0)$, $(0, 1)$, $(1, 0)$, $(1, 1)$, there are four different estimates of $p(t)$ under these different conditions (which are labeled $p_1(t)$, $p_2(t)$, $p_3(t)$, $p_4(t)$, in accordance with the notation introduced above.) These are:

$$p_1(t) = \frac{a}{v}(1 - e^{-vt})$$

$$p_2(t) = \frac{a}{v}(1 - e^{-vt}) + e^{-vt}$$

$$\qquad\qquad\qquad\qquad\qquad\qquad\qquad\qquad (26)$$

$$p_3(t) = \frac{a}{v}(1 - e^{-vt}) \qquad\qquad + \frac{b_2}{v}(1 - e^{-vt})$$

$$p_4(t) = \frac{a}{v}(1 - e^{-vt}) + e^{-vt} + \frac{b_2}{v}(1 - e^{-vt})$$

These equations have the same orthogonal form as the cross-sectional equation (12), and consequently least-squares estimates of these parameters have the same form as in the cross-sectional case. First, define a^*, b_1^*, and b_2^*:

$$a^* = \frac{a}{v}(1 - e^{-vt})$$

$$b_1^* = e^{-vt}$$

$$b_2^* = \frac{b_2}{v}(1 - e^{-vt})$$

Then:

$$b_1^* = \tfrac{1}{2}[p_2(t) - p_1(t) + p_4(t) - p_3(t)]$$
$$b_2^* = \tfrac{1}{2}[p_3(t) - p_1(t) + p_4(t) - p_2(t)] \qquad (27)$$
$$a^* = \tfrac{1}{4}[\Sigma p_i(t) - 2b_1^* - 2b_2^*]$$

More generally, the estimates are based, as in the cross-sectional case, on averages of differences between proportions:

$$b_i^* = \frac{1}{2^m} \sum_{j \in S} [p_{j+k}(t) - p_j(t)] \qquad (28)$$

(where the set S includes all states in which $x_i = 0$, and the index $k = 2^{i-1}$). For weighted estimates, this is merely modified, as in the case of cross-sectional data, to become

$$b_i^* = \frac{1}{\sum_j w_j} \sum_{j \in S} w_j [p_{j+k}(t) - p_j(t)] \qquad (29)$$

where the weight $w_j = n_{j+k} n_j / (n_{j+k} + n_j)$. After estimating these parameters, the original parameters may be recovered from them as follows:

Relative sizes a/v, b_2/v, c/v, for comparison with the same estimates from cross-sectional data (since $a/v = a/(a + b_2 + c) = a'$, and so on):

$$\frac{a}{v} = \frac{a^*}{1 - b_1^*}$$

$$\frac{b_2}{v} = \frac{b_2^*}{1 - b_1^*} \qquad (30)$$

$$\frac{c}{v} = \frac{a}{v} - \frac{b_2}{v}$$

Absolute sizes a, b_2, c, as estimates of parameters of the process:

$$a = \frac{a^*}{t(b_1^* - 1)} \log b_1^*$$

$$b_2 = \frac{b_2^*}{t(b_1^* - 1)} \log b_1^* \qquad (31)$$

$$c = \frac{1}{t} \log b_1^* - a - b_2$$

Example

The example used in the section on multivariate measures had three attributes, with attribute 1 as a dependent variable, 2 and 3 as independent variables. The parameters of the process were: $a = 1.0$, $c = 0.1$, $b_2 = 0.4$, $b_3 = 0.8$. The relative sizes of these parameters, a/v, c/v, b_2/v, b_3/v, were calculated as: 0.435, 0.043, 0.174, and 0.348. After the process had operated for twenty time periods, cross-sectional data were obtained, and estimates of these parameters were: $a'(= a/v) = 0.456$, $c' = 0.092$, $b_2' = 0.129$, $b_3' = 0.317$.

For this same data generation, a panel table (Table 4) was generated, showing changes in attribute 1 between times 1 and 20, nineteen time periods of 0.05 time units each.

TABLE 4

Randomly generated data with a single dependent attribute and two independent attributes

Time $(20 \cdot 0.05) = 1$

		1	2	3	4	5	6	7	8
Time $(1 \cdot 0.05)$	1	70	56	0	0	0	0	0	0
$= 0.05$	2	69	55	0	0	0	0	0	0
	3	0	0	57	61	0	0	0	0
	4	0	0	41	85	0	0	0	0
	5	0	0	0	0	29	81	0	0
	6	0	0	0	0	27	125	0	0
	7	0	0	0	0	0	0	18	90
	8	0	0	0	0	0	0	9	127

From these data, estimates for b_1^*, b_2^*, b_3^*, may be estimated:

$$b_1^* = \frac{1}{4}\left(\frac{55}{124} - \frac{56}{126} + \frac{85}{126} - \frac{61}{118} + \frac{125}{152} - \frac{81}{110} + \frac{127}{136} - \frac{90}{108}\right)$$
$$= 0.086$$

$$b_2^* = \frac{1}{4}\left(\frac{61}{118} - \frac{56}{126} + \frac{85}{126} - \frac{55}{124} + \frac{90}{108} - \frac{81}{110} + \frac{127}{136} - \frac{125}{152}\right)$$
$$= 0.128$$

$$b_3^* = \frac{1}{4}\left(\frac{81}{110} - \frac{56}{126} + \frac{125}{152} - \frac{55}{124} + \frac{90}{108} - \frac{61}{118} + \frac{127}{136} - \frac{85}{126}\right)$$
$$= 0.312$$

$$a^* = \frac{1}{8}\left(\sum_{i=1}^{8} p_i(t) - 4(b_1^* + b_2^* + b_3^*)\right)$$
$$= 0.413$$

Relative sizes:

$$\frac{a}{v} = \frac{a^*}{1 - b_1^*} = 0.453 \qquad \text{(true value} = 0.435)$$

$$\frac{b_2}{v} = \frac{b_2^*}{1 - b_1^*} = 0.140 \qquad \text{(true value} = 0.174)$$

$$\frac{b_3}{v} = \frac{b_3^*}{1 - b_1^*} = 0.340 \qquad \text{(true value} = 0.348)$$

$$\frac{c}{v} = 1 - \frac{a}{v} - \frac{b_2}{v} - \frac{b_3}{v} = 0.067 \qquad \text{(true value} = 0.043)$$

Absolute sizes:

$$a = \frac{a^*}{t(b_1^* - 1)} \log b_1^* = 1.14 \qquad (\text{true value} = 1.00)$$

$$b_2 = \frac{b_2^*}{t(b_1^* - 1)} \log b_1^* = 0.35 \qquad (\text{true value} = 0.40)$$

$$b_3 = \frac{b_3^*}{t(b_1^* - 1)} \log b_1^* = 0.86 \qquad (\text{true value} = 0.80)$$

$$c = -\frac{c}{v}\frac{1}{t} \log b_1^* = 0.17 \qquad (\text{true value} = 0.10)$$

Weighted estimates can also be calculated in this case, by multiplying each difference in proportions by $n_{j+k}n_j/n_{j+k} + n_j$. For example, for the first term in estimating b_i^*, the weight is $124 \cdot 126/(124 + 126)$. However, because all ns are nearly the same in this case, the weighted estimates are nearly the same as the unweighted estimates (1.13, 0.33, 0.84, and 0.17).

This example shows estimation of the parameters of the process, allowing comparison both with the true parameters and with the estimates from cross-sectional data. It is useful to note that the estimates of relative sizes from the panel data are all closer to the true values than are the cross-sectional estimates. This is not merely because of the additional data provided by the panel (which give eight proportions from which to estimate parameters, rather than only four), but also because the cross-sectional data are based on the assumption of aggregate equilibrium, while the process has not yet reached such equilibrium, and the panel estimation requires no such assumption.

The second general kind of problem studied with panel data involves interdependence between two or more attributes, or more generally, the absence of constancy over time in several attributes. The estimation problems in this case are much more difficult, because the causal variables do not remain constant, nor is their change due merely to random exogenous factors. It may be due in part to the other attribute or attributes in the system. In this case, the aim is to estimate parameters of the dependence of x_1 on x_2 and the dependence of x_2 on x_1.

In such a case, there is not merely a single fundamental differential equation of the form of equation (1), but an equation for each of the attributes that changes. These equations cannot be integrated simply as in the above case, because they constitute an interdependent system. Two general strategies are possible. The first, which was used in the original investigations (Coleman, 1964, Chapter five), requires solution of the system of equations by first estimating transition proportions, using those to solve for the transition rates q_{ij}, and then estimating the parameters of effect from the transition rates, by use of equations like equations (10) and (11). This has the defect that no weighting procedure can be applied to it to compensate for the wide variability that often occurs in the number of cases on which different transition proportions are based. A second procedure, of which there is an initial exposition in Coleman (1968), is to integrate these equations separately by use of an assumption about the path of change in the independent variables. That method is further developed below.

When the assumption of constancy in the values of x_i other than the dependent variable in equation (1) is not made, then its integration is like equation (25) except that the last term is

$$b_2 \int_0^t x_2(\tau) e^{v\tau} \, d\tau$$

Since it is not known precisely how $x_2(\tau)$ changes over time, then this term cannot be integrated as it stands. However, if $x_2(\tau)$ is replaced by $p_2(\tau)$ (that is, the random variable $x_2(\tau)$ which takes on values 1 and 0 is replaced by the probability $p_2(\tau)$ that it has the value 1), and if it is assumed that $p_2(t)$ changes linearly over time, then the equation may be integrated, to give an equation of the form

$$p(t) = a^* + b_1^* x_1(0) + b_2^* x_2(0) + b_2^{**} x_2(t) \tag{32}$$

where a^* and b_1^* have the same definition as in the case where x_2 is constant, and

$$b_2^* = \frac{b_2}{v}\left(\frac{1 - e^{-vt} - vte^{-vt}}{vt}\right) \quad \text{and} \quad b_2^{**} = -\frac{b_2}{v}\left(\frac{1 - e^{-vt} - vt}{vt}\right)$$

After b_2^* and b_2^{**} are estimated, their sum takes on the same simpler form as does b_2^* in the case where independent attributes are constant:

$$b_2^* + b_2^{**} = \frac{b_2}{v}(1 - e^{-vt}) \tag{33}$$

The estimations of a^*, b_1^*, b_2^*, and b_2^{**} are just as in the preceding case, by averages of differences between proportions, where the proportions are values of $p(t)$ which differ only according to the value of the $x_i(\cdot)$ in question.

The notation introduced in the section on multivariate measures may be extended to allow labeling of cells in a cross-tabulation of the two time periods by treating the m attributes at the second time point as additional m attributes, so that indexes for cells range from 1 to 2^{2m}, in the case of two attributes, 1 to 16. Table 5 shows the labels for each cell in a sixteen-fold table.

TABLE 5
Indexing for two-wave panel data
Time t

		00	01	10	11
		1	2	3	4
Time 0	00 1	n_1	n_5	n_9	n_{13}
	01 2	n_2	n_6	n_{10}	n_{14}
	10 3	n_3	n_7	n_{11}	n_{15}
	11 4	n_4	n_8	n_{12}	n_{16}

When attribute 1 is examined as the dependent attribute, $p_i(t)$ is defined as:

$$p_i(t) = \frac{n_i}{n_j + n_i}$$

where $j = i - 2^m$. For example, $p_5(t) = n_5/(n_1 + n_5)$, representing the proportion of individuals in state 1 (on attribute 1) at time t who were in state 0 on attributes 1 and 2 at time 0 and state 0 on attribute 2 at time t. When attribute 2 is examined as the dependent attribute, the index j in the above equation is $j = i - 2^{m+1}$. The estimate for b_1^* for attribute 1 in terms of n_i is:

$$b_1^* = \frac{1}{4}\left[\frac{n_6}{n_2 + n_6} - \frac{n_5}{n_1 + n_5} + \frac{n_8}{n_4 + n_8} - \frac{n_7}{n_3 + n_7} + \frac{n_{14}}{n_{10} + n_{14}} \right.$$
$$\left. - \frac{n_{13}}{n_9 + n_{13}} + \frac{n_{16}}{n_{12} + n_{16}} - \frac{n_{15}}{n_{11} + n_{15}} \right]$$

or in terms of $p_i(t)$, where $p_i(t)$ is written simply as p_i:

$$b_1^* = \tfrac{1}{4}[p_6 - p_5 + p_8 - p_7 + p_{14} - p_{13} + p_{16} - p_{15}] \qquad (34)$$

The estimates for b_2^*, b_2^{**}, and a^* in terms of p_i are:

$$b_2^* = \tfrac{1}{4}[p_7 - p_5 + p_8 - p_6 + p_{15} - p_{13} + p_{16} - p_{14}]$$
$$b_2^{**} = \tfrac{1}{4}[p_{13} - p_5 + p_{14} - p_6 + p_{15} - p_7 + p_{16} - p_8]$$
$$a^* = \frac{1}{8}\left[\sum_{i=1}^{2^{2m}} p_i - 4b_1^* - 4b_2^* - 4b_2^{**} \right]$$

Since only the sum $b_2^* + b_2^{**}$ is used in the subsequent calculations, the procedure may be simplified by estimating only the sum, collapsing the two equations above.

$$b_2^* + b_2^{**} = \tfrac{1}{2}[p_{16} - p_6 + p_{15} - p_5] \qquad (35)$$

The estimates for attribute 2 are analogous, except that the values of $p_i(t)$ are defined differently, as the proportion positive on attribute 2 at time t and the indices in the equations differ. The estimate for b_2^* for attribute 2 in terms of n_i is:

$$b_2^* = \frac{1}{4}\left[\frac{n_{11}}{n_3 + n_{11}} - \frac{n_9}{n_1 + n_9} + \frac{n_{12}}{n_4 + n_{12}} - \frac{n_{10}}{n_2 + n_{10}} + \frac{n_{15}}{n_1 + n_{15}}\right.$$
$$\left. - \frac{n_{13}}{n_5 + n_{13}} + \frac{n_{16}}{n_8 + n_{16}} - \frac{n_{14}}{n_6 + n_{14}}\right]$$

and in terms of the proportions (which will be labeled r_i to indicate that they are not the same as p_i for attribute 1):

$$b_2^* = \tfrac{1}{4}[r_{11} - r_9 + r_{12} - r_{10} + r_{15} - r_{13} + r_{16} - r_{14}]$$
$$b_1^* + b_1^{**} = \tfrac{1}{2}[r_{16} - r_{11} + r_{14} - r_9] \tag{36}$$
$$a^* = \tfrac{1}{8}[\Sigma r_i - 4b_2^* - 4(b_1^* + b_1^{**})]$$

If weighting is used, then each difference in proportions in estimation of b_i^* is weighted by a weight for that difference, consisting of $1/(1/n_i + 1/n_j)$, where n_i and n_j are the totals on which the proportions p_i, p_j, or r_i, r_j are based. In estimation of $b_i^* + b_i^{**}$, the weights may be applied either to the separate estimates of b_i^* and b_i^{**}, in equation (33), or to the simpler estimate of $b_i^* + b_i^{**}$ in equation (34).[7] These coefficients other than b_i^*, where i is the dependent attribute in question, have the form $(b_j/v)(1 - e^{-vt})$ or $(a/v)(1 - e^{-vt})$.

Measures of relative size can be obtained by dividing through by $1 - b_i^*$; these measures constitute one basis for comparing the effects of attribute 1 on 2 and 2 on 1, since the effects on each are expressed relative to the total rates of change on that attribute. The absolute measures may be obtained by then multiplying these numbers by $-(1/t)\log b_1^*$.

Relative sizes: Attribute 1 as dependent:

$$\frac{b_2}{v} = \frac{b_2^* + b_2^{**}}{1 - b_1^*} \quad \text{(effect of 2 on 1)}$$

$$\frac{a}{v} = \frac{a^*}{1 - b_1^*} \quad \text{(random shock toward state 1)} \tag{37}$$

$$\frac{c}{v} = 1 - \frac{b_2}{v} - \frac{a}{v} \quad \text{(random shock toward state 0)}$$

---

[7] The two weighting procedures will give slightly different results, and weights applied to the estimate of $b_i^* + b_i^{**}$ will give a better estimate of that quantity. However, in the weighted results reported here, weights are applied separately to b_i^* and b_i^{**}.

Attribute 2 as dependent:

$$\frac{b_1}{v} = \frac{b_1^* + b_1^{**}}{1 - b_2^*}$$

$$\frac{a}{v} = \frac{a^*}{1 - b_2^*}$$

$$\frac{c}{v} = 1 - \frac{b_1}{v} - \frac{a}{v}$$

Absolute sizes: Attribute 1 as dependent: all relative values are multiplied by

$$-\frac{1}{t} \log b_1^*$$

Attribute 2 as dependent: all relative values are multiplied by

$$-\frac{1}{t} \log b_2^*$$

Example

Data were generated as for the preceding examples, with the following parameters:

	Changes in attribute	
	1	2
a	0.5	0.1
c	0.5	1.0
b_1	–	0.8
b_2	0.4	–

The term $\Delta t = 0.05$, time period of panel for nineteen cycles, from $t = 0.05$ (with random distribution among states at time 0) to $t = 1.0$. *Sample size:* 1000. These parameters give attribute 1 a stronger effect on 2 than is 2's effect on 1 (0.8 to 0.4), but there is also greater total change on 2 than on 1 (1.9 to 1.4). The relative sizes of effects and random shocks are:

	Changes in attribute	
	1	2
a	0.357	0.053
c	0.357	0.526
b_1	–	0.421
b_2	0.286	–
Total	1.000	1.000

The process generated the data shown in Table 6.

TABLE 6
Randomly generated data with two interdependent attributes

	Time $(20 \cdot 0.05) = 20$			
	1	2	3	4
Time $(1 \cdot 0.05) = 0.05$	194	55	5	26
	97	93	14	48
	125	38	34	38
	58	59	23	93

Using equations (34) and (35), estimates are, for attribute 1 as dependent:

$$b_1^* = \frac{1}{4}\left[\frac{93}{190} - \frac{59}{249} + \frac{59}{117} - \frac{38}{163} + \frac{48}{62} - \frac{26}{31} + \frac{93}{116} - \frac{38}{72}\right]$$
$$= 0.187$$

$$b_2^* + b_2^{**} = \frac{1}{2}\left[\frac{93}{116} - \frac{93}{190} + \frac{38}{72} - \frac{55}{249}\right]$$
$$= 0.310$$

$$a^* = \tfrac{1}{8}[\Sigma p_i - 4 \cdot 0.187 - 4 \cdot 0.310]$$
$$= 0.300$$

$$\frac{b_2}{v} = \frac{0.310}{0.813} = 0.381 \qquad \text{(true value is 0.286)}$$

$$\frac{a}{v} = \frac{0.300}{0.813} = 0.369 \qquad \text{(true value is 0.357)}$$

$$\frac{c}{v} = 1 - 0.381 - 0.369 = 0.250 \qquad \text{(true value is 0.357)}$$

$$b_2 = 0.381\left[\frac{-1}{(1 - 0.05)} \log 0.187\right]$$
$$= 0.655 \qquad \text{(true value is 0.4)}$$
$$a = 0.635 \qquad \text{(true value is 0.5)}$$
$$c = 0.429 \qquad \text{(true value is 0.5)}$$

For attribute 2 as dependent:

$$b_2^* = \frac{1}{4}\left[\frac{34}{159} - \frac{5}{199} + \frac{23}{81} - \frac{14}{111} + \frac{38}{76} - \frac{26}{81} + \frac{93}{152} - \frac{48}{141}\right]$$
$$= 0.199$$

$$b_1^* + b_1^{**} = \frac{1}{2}\left[\frac{93}{152} - \frac{34}{159} + \frac{48}{141} - \frac{5}{199}\right]$$
$$= 0.357$$

$$a^* = \tfrac{1}{8}[\Sigma r_i - 4 \cdot 0.199 - 4 \cdot 0.357]$$
$$= 0.025$$

$$\frac{b_1}{v} = \frac{0.357}{0.801} = 0.445 \qquad \text{(true value is 0.421)}$$

$$\frac{a}{v} = \frac{0.025}{0.801} = 0.031 \qquad \text{(true value is 0.053)}$$

$$\frac{c}{v} = 1 - 0.445 - 0.031 = 0.524 \qquad \text{(true value is 0.526)}$$

$$b_1 = 0.445 \left[\frac{-1}{(1 - 0.05)} \log 0.199 \right]$$
$$= 0.737 \qquad \text{(true value is 0.8)}$$
$$a = 0.051 \qquad \text{(true value is 0.1)}$$
$$c = 0.867 \qquad \text{(true value is 1.0)}$$

The estimates of effects in this case show an overestimate of the effect of 2 on 1, and an underestimate of the effect of 1 on 2. The random shocks are better estimated in this example than are the parameters of effect. The parameters of effect in this example lie between the true values of each. Whether these results are general properties of the estimation method is not clear. In this example, an extension of this sample was used also, giving the results shown in Table 7.

TABLE 7
Randomly generated data with two interdependent attributes
(2000 cases)

		Time $(20 \cdot 0.05) = 1$			
		1	2	3	4
Time $(1 \cdot 0.05) = 0.05$	1	380	108	14	54
	2	187	195	28	112
	3	248	86	62	70
	4	119	127	48	162

The unweighted and weighted estimates are given in Table 8, together with the true values and the weighted estimates for the 1000-case sample.

The estimates of effect from the 2000-case sample remain between the true values of 0.8 and 0.4, but are farther apart than are those from the 1000-case sample (the same 1000 cases are included as half of the 2000-case sample, and thus influence its estimates). Further work, however, is necessary to determine the possible biases introduced by the approximation (the approximation is that of assuming linear change in the independent attribute).

STATISTICAL INFERENCE AND INTERACTION TERMS

Because the procedures used with panel data for estimating b_i^* are analogous to those used in estimating a', b', and c' with cross-sec-

TABLE 8

Parameter (change in 1)	True values	1000-Case Un-weighted	Weighted	2000-Case Un-weighted	Weighted
$\dfrac{b_2}{v}$	0.286	0.381	0.433	0.356	0.406
$\dfrac{a}{v}$	0.357	0.369	0.320	0.385	0.338
$\dfrac{c}{v}$	0.357	0.250	0.247	0.259	0.255
b_2	0.4	0.655	0.629	0.590	0.587
a	0.5	0.635	0.467	0.638	0.487
c	0.5	0.429	0.360	0.430	0.367
(change in 2)					
$\dfrac{b_1}{v}$	0.421	0.445	0.449	0.410	0.413
$\dfrac{a}{v}$	0.053	0.031	0.027	0.052	0.046
$\dfrac{c}{v}$	0.526	0.524	0.524	0.538	0.551
b_1	0.8	0.737	0.727	0.775	0.765
a	0.1	0.051	0.044	0.098	0.086
c	1.0	0.867	0.850	1.019	1.001

tional data except that the p_is themselves are based on different tabulations, the procedures used there for statistical tests for weighting and for estimating interaction terms can be used directly here. Statistical tests are based on calculating a variance that is the sum of the variances of the $p_i(t)$, as in the cross-sectional case. Weighting is carried out just as in that case, by recognizing that each difference in proportions constitutes an estimate, and each such difference may be weighted by an estimate of the inverse of its variance, just as in the cross-sectional case. Interaction terms have the effect of a new attribute x_{ij} created from two original attributes, and their effects are estimated through quantities b_{ij}^* which bear in estimation the same relation to the quantities b_i^* that the quantities b_{ij}' have to b' in the cross-sectional case.

CONCLUSION

In the present paper an exposition of an approach to causal analysis of attribute data has been presented, including some new estimating procedures for panel data. The model on which the approach is based allows comparison of causal parameters obtained from cross-sectional data with those obtained from panel data, and allows as well the introduction of interaction terms orthogonal to the effects of the original attributes.

When weighting is used in estimates, the approach becomes identical to multiple regression analysis with a proportion as the dependent variable, and variables having values of 0 or 1 as the independent variables. The measures of relative effects, b'_i, are identical to regression coefficients in such a regression analysis.[8] The approach thus provides a linkage between cross-tabulations as frequently used for attribute data, and regression methods, frequently used for data with continuous variables.

BOUDON, R.
    1967   *L'analyse Mathematique de Faits Sociaux*. Paris: Librairie Plon.

BOYLE, R. P.
    1966   "Causal theory and statistical measures of effect: A convergence." *American Sociological Review* 31: 834–851.

COLEMAN, J. S.
    1964   *Introduction to Mathematical Sociology*. New York: Free Press.
    1968   "The mathematical study of change." Pp. 428–478 in H. M. Blalock and A. B. Blalock (Eds.), *Methodology in Social Research*. New York: McGraw-Hill.

KISH, L.
    1965   *Survey Sampling*. New York: Wiley.

MCDILL, E. L. AND COLEMAN, J. S.
    1965   "Family and peer influences in college plans of high school students." *Sociology of Education* 38 (Winter): 112–126.

MCPARTLAND, J. M.
    1969   "Relative influence of school and of classroom desegregation on the academic achievement of ninth grade negro students." *Journal of Social Issues* 25 (Summer): 93–102.

PINARD, M.
    1963   "Structural attachments and political support in urban politics: The case of fluoridation referendums." *American Journal of Sociology* 67 (March): 513–526.

[8] Because path coefficients are standardized regression coefficients, the b'_i may be transformed to path coefficients through multiplication of b'_i by the standard deviation of the independent attribute over the standard deviation of the dependent attribute. Using binomial variances, this ratio is $\pi_i(1 - \pi_i)/\pi_1(1 - \pi_1)$, where π_i is the proportion in state 1 on attribute i (the independent attribute), and π_1 is the proportion positive on attribute 1 (the dependent attribute).

❧14❧

STATISTICAL SIGNIFICANCE AS
A DECISION RULE

G. William Walster
UNIVERSITY OF WISCONSIN

T. Anne Cleary
UNIVERSITY OF WISCONSIN

Many of us perform experiments in order to make rational decisions in the face of uncertainty. It is clear, however, that classical hypothesis-testing methodology does not necessarily lead a researcher to make rational decisions. The problem is not with classical methodology, but with the way it is used. We propose a modification of current practice that will enable the researcher to use classical methodology to make decisions. Although much of the theory in this paper is quite general, the specific applications and examples are limited to comparisons among the means of a fixed set of independent populations.

In the usual formulation of classical methodology, one states a null hypothesis and computes the probability of obtaining the observed data, given that the null hypothesis is true. If this probability is sufficiently small, the decision is made to reject the hypothesis. Many researchers follow this procedure, but it is not clear that they care about the decision to reject a traditionally formulated hypothesis. If a researcher does not care about this decision, what is the decision that might interest him?

When a researcher rejects a null hypothesis, he may wish to act in the future as if there exists an important deviation from that hypothesis. In addition, after a failure to reject, he may wish to act as if there exists no more than a trivial deviation from the null hypothesis. The decision to take one of these two courses of action is basically different from the decision provided by classical methodology. Because of this discrepancy between the two decisions, it is not surprising that the mechanisms for controlling the quality of classical procedures are often ineffective for the decisions of interest to the researcher.

In order for the researcher to use statistical significance as a mechanism for making the decision of interest, a meaningful relationship must exist between the degree to which the hypothesis is false (the magnitude of the effect) and the probability of observing statistical significance. Unless this relationship satisfies certain conditions, it may not be meaningful. Some have argued that in order to interpret statistical significance sensibly, one need only replace the null hypothesis by one consistent with the decision of interest. But changing the hypothesis tested will not necessarily establish the required meaningful relationship. In fact, it can be argued that the hypothesis tested is irrelevant so long as an appropriate relationship is guaranteed between the sampling distribution of a statistic and the magnitude of the effect.

How can one control the relationship between a statistic and the magnitude of an effect? In the case of hypotheses about means, a meaningful relationship can be established, if both sample size and the critical value of the statistic are chosen in a particular way. We first specify the necessary conditions for guaranteeing the quality of the decision of interest to the researcher, and then show how these can be achieved within classical methodology.

The quality of a decision-making procedure can be defined as the probability of correctly making the decision of interest. If the true magnitude of an effect is sufficiently large, a researcher will wish to have a high probability of correctly deciding that there is an important effect. On the other hand, if the true magnitude of an effect is sufficiently small, he will wish to have a high probability of correctly deciding that there is no more than a trivial effect.

Assume that a researcher is investigating whether the mean of one group is greater than the mean of another on some measure. For example, he might be asking whether a particular training program for the unemployed will raise the level of their job skills. Further, assume that he has decided to run an experiment in which subjects are randomly assigned to either a treatment or a control condition. Classically, the hypothesis tested would be that the treatment has no effect. However, most researchers run this type of experiment in order to make a decision. For example, if the treatment's effect is large enough, the researcher will recommend its adoption throughout the country. Only if the treatment can be implemented without cost or effort will he want to detect *any* positive treatment effect, regardless of the magnitude. In most cases there will be both a range of positive effects that the researcher will consider trivial and a range of larger effects that he will consider important.

Even the person interested in testing a theory will usually be able to identify a range of trivial and a range of important effects. This is not to say that he would attach no value to information about a small effect, but that it is more efficient to concentrate on larger effects at the current stage in the development of his theory. It is to be expected that different researchers will not agree on the magnitudes of effects that they consider trivial and important. For example, the magnitude of an effect that is considered important by a theoretician may be considered trivial by a person asking whether to implement a costly program. Regardless of the researcher's point of view, however, he must make a judgment about the magnitude of effects of interest.

In order to talk about magnitudes of effects, one needs a usable index of the magnitude of an effect. In most situations in the behavioral sciences, the fact that two populations have different means is of little interest unless the underlying variability of the populations is known, at least approximately. For example, two populations with a standard deviation of 1.0 and with a difference in their means of 10.0 generally will be considered very different, for there is almost no overlap in the populations. However, two populations with standard deviations of 100.0 and with the same mean difference will be considered very close, for there is almost total overlap. In many situations, any non-zero difference in means will be considered large or small depending upon the magnitude of the standard deviation of the underlying populations. Thus the ratio of the difference in means of two populations to their common standard deviation provides a usable index of the magnitude of an effect.

Let us call this index Δ. For the two-sample case,

$$\Delta = (\mu_2 - \mu_1)/\sigma$$

where μ_1 and μ_2 are the population means, and σ is the common standard deviation. Most researchers are able to make judgments about Δ: If the true value of Δ is less than a particular positive value, say Δ_1, the treatment has at most a trivial effect; if Δ is greater than some value, say Δ_2, the treatment has an important effect. (In the case where a nondirectional difference between μ_1 and μ_2 is of interest, researchers can specify trivial and important differences in terms of the absolute value of Δ.)

The index Δ is closely related to the noncentrality parameters of the noncentral t-distribution and the noncentral F-distribution. In the case of a directional effect, the noncentrality parameter of the noncentral t-distribution is

$$\delta = \frac{(\mu_2 - \mu_1)}{\sigma} \cdot \sqrt{N/2} = \Delta \sqrt{N/2}$$

In the case of a nondirectional effect, the noncentrality parameter of the noncentral F-distribution is

$$\delta^2 = \frac{(\mu_2 - \mu_1)^2}{\sigma^2} (N/2) = \Delta^2(N/2)$$

In both cases N refers to the number of observations in each group.

In the fixed-effect analysis-of-variance situation, Δ^2 can be easily generalized to an index of the magnitude of any single contrast (a planned comparison). For example, say the contrast of interest is $\sum_{i=1}^{I} c_i \mu_i$, where I is the number of cells in the design, μ_i is the population mean of the ith cell, and c_is are the contrast coefficients with $\sum_{i=1}^{I} c_i = 0$. The noncentrality parameter for the contrast is

$$\delta^2 = \frac{N\left[\sum_{i=1}^{I} c_i \mu_i\right]^2}{\sigma^2 \sum_{i=1}^{I} c_i^2}$$

Let us now define two new means. Let μ_1^* be the weighted average of the means with positive coefficients and μ_2^* be the weighted average of the means with negative coefficients:

$$\mu_1^* = \frac{\Sigma c_i \mu_i}{\Sigma c_i} \quad \text{for} \quad c_i > 0$$

and

$$\mu_2^* = \sum \frac{c_i \mu_i}{\Sigma c_i} \quad \text{for} \quad c_i < 0$$

In a manner analagous to the two-sample case, we can define

$$\Delta = \frac{\mu_2^* - \mu_1^*}{\sigma}$$

The noncentrality parameter can then be written in terms of Δ^2:

$$\delta^2 = Nk\Delta^2 \quad \text{where} \quad k = \frac{\left[\sum_{i=1}^{I} |c_i|\right]^2}{4\Sigma c_i^2}$$

Notice that if the contrast coefficients are $(+1, -1)$ then $k = \frac{1}{2}$ and the relationship between δ^2 and Δ^2 is the same as in the two-sample case.

Because the development of an index of the magnitude of a source of variation with more than one degree of freedom requires some careful consideration of the purpose of investigating a source, this generalization of Δ is not considered here.

Now that the researcher is able to specify the magnitudes of the effect that are of interest to him, he will wish to exercise control over the probabilities of correctly drawing the conclusion that there is a trivial or an important effect. Using D_1 to denote the decision to act in the future as if $\Delta \leq \Delta_1$, and D_2 to denote the decision to act as if $\Delta \geq \Delta_2$, the probability of making D_1 or D_2 correctly will satisfy the following inequalities:

$$P[D_1|\Delta \leq \Delta_1] \geq P[D_1|\Delta = \Delta_1]$$
$$P[D_2|\Delta \geq \Delta_2] \geq P[D_2|\Delta = \Delta_2]$$

Thus letting $P_1 = P[D_1|\Delta = \Delta_1]$ and $P_2 = P[D_2|\Delta = \Delta_2]$, a researcher can specify lower bounds on the probability of correctly making D_1 or D_2 by specifying particular values of P_1 and P_2. By stating P_1 and P_2, the researcher has specified the conditions that a decision rule must satisfy.

Now we wish to make the observation of a statistic greater than some critical value equivalent to making D_2 and the observation of a statistic less than the critical value equivalent to making D_1. Therefore, the particular choice of the critical value will influence the probability of making D_1 versus D_2. In addition, because it is necessary to control the absolute magnitude of the probability of correctly making D_1 or D_2, it is reasonable to expect that it will be necessary to specify sample size.

How will it be possible in general to determine both sample size and the critical value of a statistic, given that P_1 and P_2 have been specified? Consider two sampling distributions of a statistic (T, say) based on a sample of size N. Label the statistic T_1 when $\Delta = \Delta_1$ and T_2 when $\Delta = \Delta_2$. (For a nondirectional effect, the statistic would be

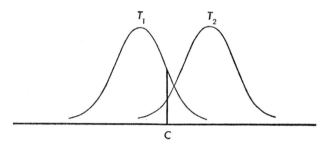

Figure 1. Sampling Distributions of $T_1(\Delta = \Delta_1)$ and $T_2(\Delta = \Delta_2)$.

T^2 and the index, Δ^2). In Figure 1, the area to the left of the critical value (C) in the distribution of T_1 is P_1. In addition, the area to the right of C in the distribution of T_2 is P_2. Thus we wish to choose both N and C such that $P[T_1 < C]$ and $P[T_2 > C]$ have particular values, those specified by the researcher for P_1 and P_2.

In order to gain a better understanding of the implications of the choice of N and C that we are recommending, consider in addition the sampling distribution of T_0 (the statistic under the null hypothesis that $\Delta \leq 0$) shown in Figure 2. The shaded area to the right of C in the distribution of T_0 is α or the probability of committing a Type I error (falsely rejecting the null hypothesis). In addition $P[T_1 > C]$, the area to the right of C in the distribution of T_1, is the power against the alternative Δ_1; and $P[T_2 > C]$, the area to the right of C in the distribution of T_2, is the power against the alternative Δ_2. Graphically these relationships can be represented on a power curve with the abscissa indicating alternative values of Δ (see Figure 3).

In classical terms our choice of N and C leads one to have power of at least P_2 against alternatives greater than Δ_2, and to have power not greater than $1 - P_1$ against alternatives less than Δ_1. Thus, if sample size and Type I error rate are chosen appropriately, rejecting the classical null hypothesis can be the rule for making the decision of

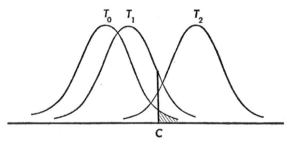

Figure 2. Sampling Distributions of $T_0(\Delta = \Delta_0)$, $T_1(\Delta = \Delta_1)$, and $T_2(\Delta = \Delta_2)$.

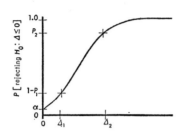

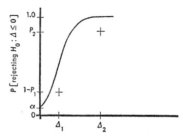

Figure 3. Power Curve Appropriate for the Decision of Interest.

Figure 4. Power Curve with Too Large a Sample Size for the Decision of Interest.

interest. In general it will be possible to choose sample size and Type I error rate such that these two conditions will be satisfied.[1]

It is both distressing and informative to consider the possible consequences of the way that many researchers choose a critical value and a sample size. First, α is usually chosen by convention to be 0.05 or 0.01. Second, as large a sample as possible is obtained. Thus, in many instances, α is essentially arbitrarily fixed and the sample size is chosen on grounds other than the magnitude of effects of interest and the importance of making correct decisions. As a result, two undesirable situations can arise without the experimenter's knowledge. First, if subjects are inexpensive and a large number are used, choice of a traditional α level may result in a power curve similar to that in Figure 4. Clearly the probability of rejecting H_0 (or equivalently deciding $\Delta \geq \Delta_2$) will be much too great in cases where $\Delta < \Delta_1$. Second, if subjects are very costly and small numbers are obtained, a traditional α will yield a power curve as in Figure 5. Here clearly the probability of rejecting H_0 is much too small in cases where $\Delta > \Delta_2$. Fixing α and letting N vary without regard to the quality of decisions of interest will result in a decision-making procedure whose outcome is more a function of sampling size than of the magnitude of effects of interest.

It should also be clear that the essential problem is not with the hypothesis being tested. If one wishes to test $H_0 : \Delta \leq 0$, there will be

[1] A Fortran computer program can be obtained from the authors. The program computes both sample size and the critical value of the variance-ratio statistic for any fixed-effects analysis-of-variance contrast or source of variation given the specified values of P_1 and P_2. A number of sources (for example Dixon and Massey, 1957; Cohen, 1969) contain power tables for sample size calculations. However, these tables are restricted to Type I error rates from 0.01 to 0.10. If a researcher happens to specify values of P_1 and P_2 which lead to an α in the range of these tables, an approximation to the appropriate critical value and sample size can be obtained without the computer program.

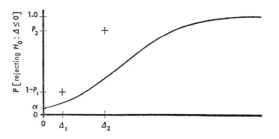

Figure 5. Power Curve with Too Small a Sample Size for the Decision of Interest.

an appropriate α and N which will lead to sensible decisions. However, it is equally clear that one could also test $H_0 : \Delta \leq \Delta_1$ or $H_0 : \Delta \leq \Delta_2$ and arrive at precisely the same decision rule.

In order to illustrate the technique that we are recommending, consider how two different researchers might approach the same problem. The first researcher is interested in whether a costly training program should be implemented on a national scale. In order to make his decision, he designs an experiment in which subjects are randomly assigned either to an experimental group that receives the training or to a no-treatment control group. Because of the cost of implementing the program, it cannot be justified unless it has a relatively large effect. To this researcher, a Δ of less than 0.5 is trivial ($\Delta_1 = 0.5$). Only a Δ greater than 2.0 is important to him ($\Delta_2 = 2.0$). Once he has specified these two values of Δ, he must choose the lower bounds on the probabilities of making the decision correctly. He wants the probability of correctly deciding that the effect is trivial to be at least 0.95 ($P_1 = 0.95$) and the probability of identifying an important effect to be at least 0.99 ($P_2 = 0.99$). Using these input values, our computer program gives the appropriate sample size as sixteen per group and the critical value of the variance-ratio statistic as 10.5 (the Type I error rate would be 0.003).

Our second researcher is a theoretician. He also runs a two-group experiment, but because he is not faced with the cost of a nationwide implementation of the program, he is interested in much smaller effects than the first researcher. However, because there are costs associated with pursuing a theory that leads to sufficiently small predicted effects, he does not set $\Delta_1 = 0$. He sets Δ_1 at 0.2 and Δ_2 at 0.8. For lower bounds on the probabilities of making the correct decision, he chooses 0.95 for P_1 and 0.99 for P_2. For these input values, the program gives the appropriate sample size as ninety-one per group, and the critical value of the variance-ratio statistic as 9.1 (the Type I error rate would be 0.003).

It is interesting to note that it is not uncommon for the theoretician working in a laboratory to run a small number of subjects per group, while the applied researcher engaging in field testing has hundreds per group. Our analysis indicates that if the two researchers in our example had used such sample sizes, statistical significance would be inappropriate as a rule for making the decision of interest.

REFERENCES

COHEN, J.
   1969   *Statistical Power Analysis for the Behavioral Sciences.* New York: Academic Press.
DIXON, W. J. AND MASSEY, F. J.
   1957   *Introduction to Statistical Analysis.* New York: McGraw-Hill.

PART FOUR

MATHEMATICAL
SOCIOLOGY

☙15☙

MATHEMATICAL FORMALIZATION OF DURKHEIM'S THEORY OF DIVISION OF LABOR

Kenneth C. Land

COLUMBIA UNIVERSITY AND RUSSELL SAGE FOUNDATION

This chapter is a revised form of a paper read at the Annual Meetings of the American Sociological Association, August, 1968. It is based on a chapter in Kenneth C. Land, "Explorations in Mathematical Sociology," unpublished Ph.D. dissertation, The University of Texas at Austin, 1969. The encouragement and assistance of Harley L. Browning and the staff of the Population Research Center of The University of Texas at Austin is gratefully acknowledged. Also, Hubert M. Blalock, Jr., and the editors of this volume made valuable comments on earlier versions of the paper. Any remaining errors and inaccuracies are, of course, the sole responsibility of the author.

Modern sociology has a considerable intellectual heritage in the "classics" of social theory. Moreover, each generation of sociologists must make its own terms with the legacy of Marx, Weber, Durkheim, Pareto, and a host of other social theorists of the past several centuries. It is in this sense that the present treatment of Durkheim's theory of the causes of the division of labor (1933, pp. 233–350) should be taken. For, in spite of the fact that many outstanding contemporary sociologists have exposited on this particular contribution of Durkheim (see, for example, Schnore, 1958; Merton, 1934; Parsons, 1949), no scholar has yet systematically formalized a coherent body of the essay as a mathematical model and subjected it to a rigorous empirical evaluation by estimating the parameters of the model. This is the task of the present chapter. First, Durkheim's theoretical concepts and propositions are reviewed. Second, the dimensions of the concepts are analyzed and the verbal propositions are restated. Third, the propositions are mapped onto a model consisting of algebraic and differential equations, and the logical properties of the model are elaborated. Fourth, an observation record is examined for its relevance to the model. Finally, the free parameters of the model are estimated from the observation record and the fit of the mathematical structure to the observation record is evaluated. That is, in this paper, the properties of a dynamic system implied by Durkheim's theory are studied for the purposes of making explicit the processes which, more often than not, are implicit in Durkheim's verbal treatise. The long-range goal of this effort is to bring the theory into closer correspondence with the empirical processes it is designed to explain. In short, the present essay is an illustration of the interplay of the dual processes of theoretical specification and parameter estimation. Because an author's perception and organization of a classical social theory are vital steps in the methodology of theoretical formalization, we begin with a review of these aspects of Durkheim's theory.

DURKHEIM'S THEORY

Durkheim's analysis of the division of labor begins in Book I (1933, pp. 49–229) with a distinction between two forms of social organization, mechanical and organic. According to Durkheim, the first type describes the relatively undifferentiated mode of social organization found in small isolated populations which have achieved little control over their environment. The basis of solidarity in this type of society is likeness or similarity. That is, social unity is a kind of mechanical cohesion, as in rock forms, and it is maintained by homogeneity. Furthermore, there is minimal division of labor as most members are engaged in the same activity such as hunting or fishing. On the other hand, Durkheim observed that modern Western societies were increasingly characterized by differentiation of social activities, and the concept of the organic type of social organization was designed to refer to the structural characteristics of these societies. The basis of solidarity in this class of society, as in living organisms, is the intricate interdependence of specialized parts. That is, men engage in different and complementary activities which impel them to exchange goods and services for subsistence. It is out of this mutual interdependence that the solidarity of the society develops.

Having established the ideal types of mechanical and organic societies, Durkheim's concern in Book II of *The Division of Labor in Society* is the elaboration of the causal processes which transform populations from one mode of social organization to another. A crucial concept in Durkheim's theory of the dynamics of changes in social organization is the dynamic or moral density of societies. He postulated (1933, p. 257) that:

> The division of labor develops . . . as there are more individuals sufficiently in contact to be able to act and react upon one another. If we agree to call this relation and the active commerce resulting from it dynamic or moral density, we can say that the progress of the division of labor is in direct ratio to the moral or dynamic density of society.

Thus, according to Durkheim, as the rate of social intercourse increases in a population, the segmentation (separation) of the constituent social units begins to break down. However, the direct measurement of dynamic density for large-scale societies, defined as above, would seem to be quite a difficult task. Durkheim (1933, p. 257) circumvents this problem by further postulating that dynamic density is dependent on material density and that material density can be used to measure dynamic density:

> But this moral relationship can only produce its effect if the real distance between individuals has itself diminished in some way. Moral density cannot grow unless material density grows at the same time, and the latter can be used to measure the former.

Having posited the above relationship, Durkheim further explicates the meaning of material density by pointing to its dependence on two variables. First, material density increases with increasing concentration of population, especially urbanization. Second, material density increases with the development of more rapid and numerous means of communication and transportation. In Durkheim's words (1933, pp. 257–260):

Whereas lower societies are spread over immense areas according to population, with more advanced people population always tends to concentrate. . . . The formation of cities and their development is an even more characteristic symptom of the same phenomenon. . . . Finally, there are the number and rapidity of ways of communication and transportation. By suppressing or diminishing the gaps separating social segments, they increase the [material] density of society. . . . Since this visible and measurable symbol reflects the variations of what we have called moral density, we can substitute it for this latter in the formula we have proposed.

According to Durkheim, an increase in the material density of societies produces an increase in the division of labor because it induces an increase in dynamic density. Another factor contributing to an increase in dynamic density is an increase in the size of the society. Because of the negative cases of China and Russia, however, Durkheim cautions that an increase in the size of a society in itself is not sufficient to induce an increase in the division of labor. Rather, an increase in size must be accompanied by an increase in material density in order to be sufficient to increase the division of labor (1933, pp. 260–262):

If condensation of society produces this result [an increase in the division of labor], it is because it multiplies intrasocial relations. But these will be still more numerous, if, in addition, the total number of members of society becomes more considerable. If it comprises more individuals at the same time as they are more intimately in contact, the effect will necessarily be reenforced. Social volume, then, has the same influence as density upon the division of labor. . . . In the same way, if the number of social units has influence on the division of labor, it is not through itself and necessarily, but it is because the number of social relations generally increases with that of individuals. But, for this result to be attained, it is not enough that society take in a great many people, but they must be, in addition, intimately enough in contact to act and react upon one another. . . . The increase of social volume does not, then, always accelerate the advances of the division of labor, but only when the mass is contracted at the same time and to the same extent.

On the basis of the reasoning outlined above, Durkheim arrives at the following proposition (1933, p. 262):

The division of labor varies in direct ratio with the volume and density of societies, and if it progresses in a continuous manner in the course of societal development, it is because societies become regularly denser and generally more voluminous.

Durkheim was not satisfied simply to note the covariation of the population size and density and the means of transportation and communication with the division of labor of a society. Rather, he went on to address himself to the question of what produces the differentiation of societies. That is, Durkheim was also interested in specifying the mechanism that would produce differentiation under the prescribed conditions. Here he adduces competition as an intervening variable between increases in the size and density of societies and increases in the division of labor. Specifically, he extends Darwin's observation that, in a scarce environment, increased contact of animals leads to increased competition to the human species. Darwin's argument is that the resulting "struggle for existence" produces the differentiation of species. Similarly, Durkheim argues that social units offering or consuming the same goods and services are potential competitors. Furthermore, Durkheim maintains that increased social interaction is sufficient to transform the potential competition into an active struggle. Finally, Durkheim notes, the division of labor is the means by which human societies resolve the dilemma of competition. That is, increased differentiation is the societal alternative to a fight to the finish. In Durkheim's words (1933, pp. 266–270):

If work becomes divided more as societies become more voluminous and denser, it is not because external circumstances are more varied, but because struggle for existence is more acute. Darwin justly observed that the struggle between two organisms is as active as they are analogous. Having the same needs and pursuing the same objects, they are in rivalry everywhere. As long as they have more resources than they need, they can still live side by side, but if their number increases to such proportions that all appetites can no longer be sufficiently satisfied, war breaks out, and it is as violent as this insufficiency is more marked; that is to say, as the number in the struggle increases. It is quite otherwise if the coexisting individuals are of different species or varieties. As they do not feed in the same manner, and do not lead the same kind of life, they do not disturb each other. The chances of conflict thus diminish with chances of meeting, and the more so as the species or varieties are more distant from one another. . . . Men submit to the same law. In the same city, different occupations can coexist without being obliged mutually to destroy one another, for they pursue different

objects. . . . The division of labor is, then, a result of the
struggle for existence, but it is a mellowed *denouement*. Thanks
to it, opponents are not obliged to fight to a finish, but can
exist one beside the other. Also, in proportion to its development, it furnishes the means of maintenance and survival to a
greater number of individuals who, in more homogenous
societies, would be condemned to extinction.

Finally, it should be noted that since his purpose is to explain
the transformation of societies from one mode of social organization
to another, Durkheim's theory of necessity must be dynamic, that is, it
must be capable of explaining changes in the variables over time. In
this respect, note that Durkheim (1933, p. 262) postulated a mechanism
of change as an intrinsic aspect of his theory via a feedback link from
an increase in the division of labor to an increase in the concentration of
societies:

If society, in concentrating, determines the development of
the division of labor, the latter, in its turn, increases the concentration of society.

VERBAL RESTATEMENT OF DURKHEIM'S THEORY

A difficulty confronting any formalization of a classical social
theory is that many specific models may often be formalized from a
single classic because of its generality of application and diffuseness of
structure. That is to say, classical social theorists were often satisfied
with ill-defined concepts and indeterminate theoretical structures because these characteristics suited the expansiveness of their goals and
their penchant for a rather loose fit to empirical data. The modern
social theorist, therefore, can rarely claim to have captured the "complete" meaning of a classic in his more rigorous restatements of classical
social theory. At best, he can choose the goals of his formalization and
attempt to show how the classic implies his restatement when viewed
from that perspective. The generally encountered difficulties of formalization must be surmounted in the present treatment of Durkheim's
theory of the causes of the division of labor. Thus, the essence of my
concern in the remainder of this paper is to restate Durkheim's theory
in such a manner as to maximize its correspondence to trends of the
division of labor in the modern world and, at the same time, to assure
its logical consistency as a system of theory.

In broad terms, the division of labor has become increasingly
complex and intricate in modern societies. As noted above in the review

of his theory, Durkheim postulated a mechanism of change as an intrinsic aspect of his theory such that an initial increment in dynamic density would tend to reinforce itself by means of a feedback loop from an increase in the division of labor to dynamic density. Hence, it would seem, at first glance, that Durkheim's assumptions would adequately mirror recorded trends in the division of labor. It will be shown, however, that a formal model based solely on these assumptions is inherently unstable since an initial increment in dynamic density would rapidly increase both itself and the division of labor to infinitely large values. Quite obviously, this has not been the experience of any recorded society. A more accurate appraisal of experience is that although the division of labor has generally increased over time it has also shown a tendency to adjust itself to given levels of population, urbanization, and technology. Hence, it is necessary to incorporate into the reformulation features that allow the model to adjust itself to an equilibrium state. This will involve verbal propositions containing statements about the "appropriate" level of one variable for a given value of another variable.

Before restating the propositions of Durkheim's theory, we should clarify the meaning of its concepts relative to the present investigation. First, there is the concept of dynamic density; according to Durkheim, this term refers to the actions and reactions of persons upon each other. A specific action-reaction sequence between two individuals can be called an *interact*. The number of interacts in a society per unit of time is called the *dynamic density*. The dimensions of the dynamic density concept are:

$$\frac{number\ of\ interacts}{time}$$

Durkheim was keenly aware of the difficulty of measuring dynamic density empirically; for this purpose he introduced the concept of *material density*. The level of the material density of a society is the product of the levels of population size, urbanization, and efficiency of the technology of communication and transportation. The dimensions of the concept are:

$$population\ size \times \frac{population\ in\ urban\ areas}{population\ size} \times efficiency\ of$$
$$communication\ and\ transportation$$
$$= population\ in\ urban\ areas \times efficiency\ of$$
$$communication\ and\ transportation$$

Durkheim proposes to use this concept to measure the dynamic density of a society. Hence, the rationale for this definition of material density is that *some* level of each of the three variables is a necessary condition to any level of dynamic density. That is, without a population, obviously there can be no dynamic density, nor can there be dynamic density without some level of concentration of the population. Finally, without some means of communication and transportation—some form of language and the ability to move one's body, at a minimum—there can be no dynamic density. On the other hand, although an increase in any one of the three variables in itself is not sufficient to produce an increase in dynamic density, Durkheim maintained that a simultaneous increment in all three variables is a sufficient condition.

It is instructive to think of the analogous experimental situation in which one is manipulating several independent variables and studying the consequences for a dependent variable. Under these circumstances, a linear function represents each independent variable as sufficient to induce an increment in the dependent variable, that is, an increment in the dependent variable on the order of the independent variable's coefficient in the linear function. On the other hand, a multiplicative function of changes in the independent variables mirrors the experimental situation in which an isolated increment in any one independent variable will not produce an increase in the dependent variable, but a simultaneous increment in all independent variables does yield an increase in the dependent variable; stated in another way, a zero value of change in any one independent variable will annihilate the effect of a change in any other independent variable.

In order to assume that dynamic density is measured by material density, there must be a correspondence of the dimensions of the two concepts. Obviously, the dimensions outlined in the definitions given above are not identical. Hence, Durkheim's proposal that material density can be used to measure dynamic density must be taken to mean that the dimensions take on the following functional relationship:

$$\frac{number\ of\ interacts}{time} = K \times population\ in\ urban\ areas \times efficiency\ of$$
$$communication\ and\ transportation$$

where K is a constant representing the rate at which the concentrated portion of the population utilizes the means of communication and transportation for interaction and carries the dimensions (rate of use of means of communication and transportation)/time. Thus, the dimensions of the two concepts agree when a coefficient of transformation is included in the equation. In other words, the dimensions of the concepts are identical in a functional as opposed to a definitional sense.

Two other concepts complete the set dealt with in Durkheim's theory. First is the level of competition in the society. This variable presents no conceptual or measurement problems, however, since its effects will be "absorbed" into other variables which are conceptually more tractable and on which observations are available. The second concept is the division of labor. Classically, there are two general ideas associated with this concept: occupational differentiation and functional interdependence, that is, the exchange of goods and services among occupational groups. It can be argued, however, that the first phenomenon implies the second. That is to say, an increase in the degree of differences of individuals with regard to sustenance activities (that is, an increase in occupational differentiation) implies an increase in the degree of their functional interdependence. In short, if the members of a society are to maintain their existence, then they must have a supply of certain essential goods. Furthermore, if their sustenance activities have been specialized, then they must increase their rate of exchange of goods and services in order to have the essential goods and services.

On the other hand, if the rate of exchange of goods and services increases (that is, if functional interdependence increases), then it follows that individuals *may* engage in different activities (that is, occupational differentiation may increase) although it is not necessary that they do so in order to maintain a given level of functional interdependence. Thus, an increase in functional interdependence is a necessary but not sufficient condition for an increase in occupational differentiation. On the basis of the review of his theory presented in the preceding section, it would seem that Durkheim himself preferred this interpretation. In brief, occupational differentiation creates functional interdependence and functional interdependence is the basis of social solidarity in organic societies, according to Durkheim. As a consequence of this reasoning, we utilize the following definition of the division of labor in the present essay: The level of the *division of labor* in a society is the degree of differences among members of the society with regard to their sustenance activities. A specific measure of this concept and its dimensions are examined below.

The concepts are now at hand to facilitate a restatement of the postulates in Durkheim's theory. Because the meaning of some of the conditions which are imposed on the theory becomes clear only when its mathematical structure is studied, discussion of certain aspects of the restatement are postponed to the next section of this chapter. It is important, however, to lay the foundation for the mathematical model by verbally restating those aspects of Durkheim's theory explored in the remainder of the essay.

There are two basic methodological principles which guide the present formalization of Durkheim's verbal statements (see Simon, 1957, for a similar use of these principles). First, it is assumed that the relationships of density, competition, and division of labor as described by Durkheim represent an adaptive system. That is to say, it is assumed that for given values of the parameters of the system each variable will adjust to a value which is "appropriate" to the values of the other variables. Second, it is assumed that the processes described in Durkheim's theory can be distinguished according to their relative speeds of consummation. In other words, those processes which relate changes of the variables most rapidly can be represented as instantaneous relative to the other slower processes. Neither of these assumptions does violence to Durkheim's original presentation.

The basic relations with which we begin are that the level of competition in a society is a monotonic increasing function of the level of dynamic density, that the level of the division of labor in a society is a monotonic increasing function of the level of competition, and that there is a feedback loop from the level of the division of labor to the level of dynamic density. In order to study the possible approaches of such a set of relationships to equilibrium points if any exist for the system, further assumptions need to be made about the time relations and adjustment levels among the variables. First, it is assumed that the level of competition in a society adjusts itself to the level of dynamic density almost instantaneously. This assumption can be defended by an argument, similar to Durkheim's original defense of the proposition, that an increase in the number and concentration of individuals consuming similar items will very rapidly increase demand for the items. Hence, the level of competition in a society will increase almost coincidentally with the increase in density. The adjustment of the division of labor to an increase in the level of competition may not be quite so rapid, and therefore it is postulated that this relationship takes time for completion. The feedback from an increment in the division of labor to the level of dynamic density also may not be simultaneous, and we again postulate an adjustment over time. Furthermore, since it is desired to deal with the equilibrium levels of dynamic density and the division of labor, one must consider whether the given level of each variable is "appropriate" to the level of the other. Hence, we shall have to consider changes in each of these variables as dependent upon its own given values.

On the basis of the reasoning outlined above, Durkheim's theory is restated in the following three propositions:

The level of dynamic density in a society will tend to increase if its existing level is lower than that "appropriate" to the level of the division of labor. That is, if there is an increase in the level of the division of labor and the level of dynamic density is no longer in equilibrium with the level of the division of labor, then there will be a subsequent increase in the level of dynamic density which will tend to move it back toward equilibrium with the new level of the division of labor. Finally, this postulated relationship will require time for its adjustment.

The level of competition in a society depends upon, and increases with, the level of dynamic density in the society. It is also postulated that the level of competition adjusts itself almost simultaneously to the level of dynamic density in the society.

The level of the division of labor in a society will increase if its existing level is lower than that "appropriate" to the level of competition in the society. Furthermore, it is postulated that the adjustment of the division of labor to the level of competition in a society requires time to be effected.

LAND-DURKHEIM MODEL

In order to transform the verbal postulates of the last section into a mathematical model, let us consider the following variables, all functions of time: $U(t)$—the level of urbanization in a society; $T(t)$—the level of efficiency of the technology of communication and transportation in the society; $P(t)$—the size of the society (population); $D(t)$—the level of dynamic density in the society where the value of density at time t is computed by the formula, $D_t = D_{t-1} + k(\Delta U)^a(\Delta T)^b(\Delta P)^c$, the symbol Δ representing the change in the value of the variable from $t - 1$ to time t; $C(t)$—the level of competition for scarce goods among the members of the society; and $L(t)$—the level of the division of labor in the society. The postulates stated verbally in the last section can be represented (in the same order) by the following three equations, where dx/dt represents the derivative of x with respect to time:

$$\frac{dD(t)}{dt} = f[D(t), L(t)] \tag{1}$$

$$C(t) = g[D(t)] \tag{2}$$

$$\frac{dL(t)}{dt} = h[C(t), L(t)] \tag{3}$$

In words, equation (1) states that the time rate of change in dynamic density is a function of the existing level of dynamic density and the level of the division of labor. Also, equation (2) states that the level of competition is a function of the level of dynamic density. Finally, equation (3) states that the time rate of change in the level of the division of labor is a function of the level of competition and the existing level of the division of labor. Note, however, that the verbal postulates of the last section contained more information than this. They made assertions about the directions of the relationships.

Specifically, it was assumed that when the level of dynamic density is appropriate to the level of the division of labor, that is, when $dD/dt = 0$ (when dynamic density is not changing over time), then an increase in L will produce an increase in the appropriate level of dynamic density. Stated otherwise, dD/dt varies directly (when dD/dt approximates zero) with L. Mathematically, this corresponds to placing the restriction on the function f that the partial derivative of f (where $f = dD/dt$) with respect to L is greater than zero or $\partial f/\partial L > 0$. With respect to equation (2), we assumed in the previous section that C was a monotonic increasing function of D. This corresponds to the restriction that the derivative of C with respect to D be greater than zero ($dC/dD = dg/dD > 0$). Further, it was assumed for equation (3) that when $dL/dt = 0$ (when the division of labor is appropriate to the level of competition), then an increase in C will produce an increase in L. Mathematically, this restriction is that $\partial h/\partial C > 0$ (where $h = dL/dt$). Finally, in order that dD/dt and dL/dt will not continue increasing without limit subsequent to an initial increment in L and D, the restraints that $\partial f/\partial D < 0$ and $\partial h/\partial L < 0$ must be imposed on f and h. It is appropriate to remark here that these conditions are the only constraints on the system for which some basis cannot be found in a faithful exegesis of Durkheim. They arise, instead, from the assumption that the system is adaptive, which is evidently how Durkheim viewed his representation. In summary, the restrictions on the postulates implied in our verbal propositions are expressed by the following partial derivatives; expressions (4) and (5) apply to equation (1), expression (6) applies to equation (2), and expressions (7) and (8) apply to equation (3):

$$\frac{\partial f}{\partial L} > 0 \tag{4}$$

$$\frac{\partial f}{\partial D} < 0 \tag{5}$$

$$\frac{dC}{dD} = \frac{dg}{dD} > 0 \tag{6}$$

$$\frac{\partial h}{\partial C} > 0 \tag{7}$$

$$\frac{\partial h}{\partial L} < 0 \tag{8}$$

In order to facilitate further study of the present mathematical model, we shall first reduce the system to two differential equations by collapsing equations (2) and (3). Substituting equation (2) into (3), we have

$$\frac{dL}{dt} = h[g(D), L] = e(D, L) \tag{9}$$

and since $dg/dD > 0$ and $\partial h/\partial C = \partial h/\partial g > 0$, the proper restriction on equation (9) is

$$\frac{\partial e}{\partial D} = \frac{\partial h}{\partial D} = \frac{\partial h}{\partial g} \cdot \frac{dg}{dD} > 0 \tag{10}$$

Moreover, the condition corresponding to expression (8) for equation (9) is

$$\frac{\partial e}{\partial L} = \frac{\partial h}{\partial L} < 0 \tag{11}$$

The mathematical model is now reduced to equations (1) and (9) and the corresponding restrictions. Practically all of the formal properties of Durkheim's theory are contained in these mathematical relationships. However, we have not as yet specified the precise functional forms of equations (1) and (9). Furthermore, there is precious little in Durkheim's theory to guide one in the specification of the structural relationships. Hence, any additional elaboration of the model will go considerably beyond Durkheim's verbal treatment. The motivation for a further specification of the model is clear. Put simply, unless the functions f and e are given a definite form, we are essentially limited to qualitative deductions from the model. Furthermore, we most assuredly will not be able to utilize empirical parameter estimates to evaluate or reformulate the system in anything more than a qualitative fashion. In short, we will not be able to extract a specific mathematical structure from the general mathematical model.

In light of the above discussion, we shall proceed now to a specification of the form of equations (1) and (9) as linear and to an investigation of the properties of the resulting model. In particular, a linear specification of the functions f and e yields:

$$\frac{dD}{dt} = a_1 - b_{11}D + b_{12}L \tag{12}$$

$$\frac{dL}{dt} = a_2 + b_{21}D - b_{22}L \tag{13}$$

where D and L are defined as before, a_1, a_2 are positive and constant over time, and b_{11}, b_{12}, b_{21}, b_{22} are positive and constant for each time period (the signs of the postulated structural relationships modify the signs of the b coefficients).

Equations (12) and (13) should be considered only as a first approximation to an adequate representation of the dynamics of the division of labor. Formally, the equations are described as a linear differential equation system with constant coefficients. It is the simplest type of differential equation system. Although empirical evidence may lead to a number of successive modifications of equations (12) and (13), it is probably best to begin with as simple a system as possible and move to more complex representations only as they are demanded.

Consider the structural properties of equations (12) and (13). First, as the signs of the following partial derivatives demonstrate, the system satisfies conditions (4), (5), (10), and (11):

$$\frac{\partial}{\partial L} \frac{dD}{dt} = +b_{12} \tag{14}$$

$$\frac{\partial}{\partial D} \frac{dD}{dt} = -b_{11} \tag{15}$$

$$\frac{\partial}{\partial D} \frac{dL}{dt} = +b_{21} \tag{16}$$

$$\frac{\partial}{\partial L} \frac{dL}{dt} = -b_{22} \tag{17}$$

This implies that the equations possess all the properties that were postulated in the verbal restatement of Durkheim's theory. Second, note that the dynamic properties of the equations are theoretically meaningful. For example, given a zero value for the density variable, equation (13) would describe a decrease in the division of labor until $a_2 = b_{22}L$, at which point the division of labor would cease changing and dL/dt would become zero. Equation (12) describes a similar dynamic relationship for density. Finally, it should be noted that the dimensions of the coefficients in equations (12) and (13) are meaningful. Thus, a_1 represents the number of units of change in density per unit time when the values of density and the division of labor are zero while a_2 has a similar meaning for the division of labor. On the other hand, b_{11} and b_{22} represent the number of units change per unit time in D and L respectively for each existing unit of D and L. That is, b_{11} and b_{22} represent the dependency of changes in D and L on their own values. Similarly, b_{12} and b_{21} represent the number of units change per unit time in D and L respectively for each existing unit of L and D. These coefficients are measures of the *direct* dependence of D and L on each other. In comparison, the ratios b_{12}/b_{11} and b_{21}/b_{22} represent the *relative* dependence of changes in each variable on itself and the other variable.

In order to facilitate further analysis of the present set of differential equations, it will be convenient to introduce some additional notation. First, equations (12) and (13) are denoted as follows:

$$\frac{dx_1}{dt} = a_1 + b_{11}x_1 + b_{12}x_2 \tag{18}$$

$$\frac{dx_2}{dt} = a_2 + b_{21}x_1 + b_{22}x_2 \tag{19}$$

where $x_1 = D$, $x_2 = L$, a_1, a_2, b_{12}, b_{21} are positive constants, and b_{11}, b_{22} are negative constants. Further parsimony of representation may be obtained by calling the vector of derivatives of the x_i with respect to t, $\mathbf{x}'$; the vector of the constants a_i, $\mathbf{A}$; the vector of the x_{it} where the subscript t denotes the time of observation, $\mathbf{x}_t$; and the matrix of the constants b_{ij}, $\mathbf{B}$. Utilizing this matrix notation, equations (18) and (19) are represented by

$$\mathbf{x}' = \mathbf{A} + \mathbf{Bx}_t \tag{20}$$

The representation of our model of Durkheim's theory as a linear differential equation system with constant coefficients allows us to make use of the considerable mathematical theory of such systems. Specifically, the following sections of this chapter review the mathematical results concerning the solution, equilibrium, and stability properties of equation (20).

In order to estimate the parameters of a system of differential equations, the system must first be solved. Fortunately, systems of linear differential equations with constant coefficients can be solved completely and explicitly. In particular, the solution of the present system is:[1]

$$\mathbf{x}_t = \mathbf{e}^{Bt}\mathbf{x}_{t-1} - \mathbf{B}^{-1}\mathbf{A} \tag{21}$$

where the matrix $\mathbf{e}^{Bt}$ is defined as the infinite sum

$$\mathbf{e}^{Bt} = \mathbf{I} + \mathbf{Bt} + \frac{\mathbf{B}^2\mathbf{t}^2}{2!} + \frac{\mathbf{B}^3\mathbf{t}^3}{3!} + \cdots \tag{22}$$

Equation (21) is in a form susceptible to linear regression analysis as follows:

$$\mathbf{x}_t = \mathbf{A}^* + \mathbf{B}^*\mathbf{x}_{t-1} \tag{23}$$

Furthermore, given empirical estimation of equation (23), there are a number of procedures for deriving estimates of the parameters of equation (20).

---

[1] Those wishing a copy of the derivation of the system of equations can obtain it by writing directly to the author.

An equilibrium position is one in which the values of the variables remain stationary. The equilibrium and stability characteristics of equation (20) are best revealed when the system is transformed into normal form. Therefore, if we find $\mathbf{N}$, the Jordan normal matrix of $\mathbf{B}$, and $\mathbf{P}$ such that $\mathbf{B} = \mathbf{P}^{-1}\mathbf{NP}$, and if we let $\mathbf{z}_t = \mathbf{Px}_t$, $\mathbf{C} = \mathbf{PA}$, then by multiplying both sides of equation (20) on the left by $\mathbf{P}$ and combining, we get

$$\mathbf{Px'} = \mathbf{PA} + \mathbf{PBP^{-1}Px}_t$$

or $$\mathbf{z'} = \mathbf{C} + \mathbf{Nz}_t \qquad (24)$$

Now it can be shown that if the matrix $\mathbf{B}$ has distinct eigenvalues λ_i, then the matrix $\mathbf{N}$ has diagonal form with the eigenvalues of $\mathbf{B}$ on its main diagonal (see Nering, 1963, pp. 100–101). Further, the condition for equilibrium that we would like to investigate is $dx_i/dt = 0$, or

$$\mathbf{z'} = 0 = \mathbf{C} + \mathbf{Nz}_t \qquad (25)$$

which implies that

$$-\mathbf{C} = \mathbf{Nz}_t \qquad (26)$$

Looking at the elements in the matrices, we have:

$$-c_1 = \lambda_1 z_1 \qquad (27)$$

$$-c_2 = \lambda_2 z_2 \qquad (28)$$

If the $\lambda_i \neq 0$ (we have assumed that the $\lambda_i \neq 0$ in the estimation procedure), then equations (27) and (28) specify a unique equilibrium point for the system (20). Finally, if the real parts of the λ are negative, then the equilibrium point specified by equations (27) and (28) is stable (see Coddington and Levinson, 1955, pp. 371–375, for a proof of this statement).

OBSERVATION RECORD

In order to estimate empirically the parameters of the linear differential equation system which has been posited to govern the dynamics of Durkheim's theory, it would be desirable to have lengthy time series of annual observations on the two primary variables of the model—density and the division of labor. However, since the basic observations on these two variables—population size, percentage of population in urban areas, efficiency of technology of communication and transportation, distribution of labor force among occupations—are made no more frequently than every ten years and that for only a few modern Western nations, we shall have to be satisfied with far less than ideal data conditions. The ten-year interval of census observations is not a severe restriction given that the variables of the theory are aggregate societal characteristics which would exhibit little change on a yearly basis. The more restrictive characteristic of the available data in Table 1 is the fact that the time series are not long; rather, they are disturbingly short.

TABLE 1

Time Series Values for Four Variables, United States, 1900–1950

Year	Degree of Urbanization[a]	Degree of Occupational Differentia- tion[b]	Technological Efficiency[c]	Population Size[d]
1900	39.7	92.2	78.5	76,212,168
1910	45.7	94.7	165.7	92,228,496
1920	51.2	95.7	288.4	106,021,537
1930	56.2	96.7	440.3	123,202,624
1940	56.5	97.2	497.4	132,164,569
1950	59.0	97.8	674.9	151,325,798

[a] Source: Labovitz and Gibbs, 1964, Table 5. The degree of urbanization is defined as the percentage of the population residing in urban places. Urban places in this case are defined as consisting of 2,500 or more persons under the "old" urban definition of the U.S. Census.

[b] Source: Labovitz and Gibbs, 1964, Table 1.

[c] Estimated work output in billions of horsepower hours. Source: Labovitz and Gibbs, 1964, Table 3.

[d] Source: 1960 United States Census, Volume 1, Part A, Table 3.

The data used below for parameter estimation and appraisal of the goodness of fit of the Land-Durkheim model are in the form of a time series of six decennial observations from an earlier study by Labovitz and Gibbs (1964). The observed variables are (1) percentage of population that is urban, or *degree of urbanization*, and (2) *occupational differentiation* in the United States, 1900–1950 (see Table 1). Strictly speaking, in order to use these observations in an empirical evaluation of the Land-Durkheim model, it must be *assumed* that alternative measures of the concepts of density and the division of labor would be linear transformations of the present set. Hence, it is important to inquire into the relationship of the observations in Table 1 to the definitions of the theoretical concepts given above.

Consider first the concept of dynamic density and its measurement by the percentage of the population residing in urban places. Earlier, the following formula was given for the measurement of dynamic density at time t from the component factors of material density:

$$D_t = D_{t-1} + K(\Delta U)^a(\Delta T)^b(\Delta P)^c \qquad (29)$$

where the symbol Δ represents the change in the values of urbanization, efficiency of the technology of communication and transportation, and population size from time $t - 1$ to time t. Now, the use of the percentage of the population that is urban as a measure of dynamic density corresponds to setting the exponents b and c to zero and to setting the exponent a and the constant K to unity in equation (29). This assumes that the changes in the values of the other two variables in each decade of the time series was greater than zero.

If accurate observations on all three components of the density measure were available, then it would be possible to compute equation (29) and to study its characteristics. However, no satisfactory measures of the efficiency of the technology of communication and transportation are available. On the other hand, Labovitz and Gibbs (1964) present several measures of general technological efficiency for the United States, 1900–1950, and show that all the measures are highly intercorrelated. One of these series, work output, measured in terms of the estimated work output in billions of horsepower-hours, is reproduced in Table 1. Labovitz and Gibbs (1964, p. 7) argue that work output is an indicator of the efficiency of technological processes. Furthermore, assuming that the efficiency of the technological processes of communication and transportation is highly correlated with the efficiency of technological processes in general, this measure can be utilized as an index of the former.

In light of the lack of sufficient data to compute the theoretically prescribed measure of dynamic density, equation (29), there are advantages to be gained by using the degree of urbanization inasmuch as the percentage of the population in urban places is a measure with desirable ratio scale characteristics. First, however, the measure must meet the assumptions outlined above. One assumption is that the population and technology variables possess a non-zero value of change for each decade of the time series. An examination of the data in Table 1 reveals that this assumption is met by the observations.

A second assumption is that other possible measures of dynamic density are linear transformations of the degree of urbanization. Since it has been assumed above that the exponent of the change in urbanization is unity, one possible alternative class of measures of density would be those in which the exponents of change in technology and population size are also unity. Furthermore, a sufficient condition that this class of measures be linear transformations of the degree of urbanization is that there exist a high correlation between the measures. For the data of Table 1, this condition is met. Therefore, it may be concluded that the percentage of population in urban places is a measure of dynamic density, which is a linear transformation of a large class of possible measures of the concept. Furthermore, by manipulation of the unspecified constant, K, in the measurement formula for dynamic density, equation (29), the fact that the correlations of urbanization with technological efficiency ($r = 0.81$) and population size ($r = 0.97$) are high implies that it would be possible to bring the values of the theoretically derived measure of density quite close to the values of the degree of urbanization. Therefore, parameters estimated from the measure used here are not completely unrelated to the parameters which would be computed from a more detailed measure.

One remaining question regarding the use of the proposed measure of urbanization should be addressed. That is, do alternative measures of urbanization exist which are more desirable than the degree of urbanization? In a recent paper, Gibbs (1966) proposed two alternative measures of urbanization: the scale of urbanization and the scale of population concentration. Both measures attempt to measure the urban size hierarchy as well as the concentration of the population in urban places. Gibbs demonstrates (1966, p. 175), however, that the product moment correlation coefficients of the degree of urbanization with the scale of urbanization and the scale of population concentration for the eighteen decennial points in time, 1790–1960, United States, are 0.9797 and 0.9981, respectively. These results imply that it is sufficient to consider the degree of urbanization as a measure of population concentration since other possible measures are linear transformations of this measure for the time period under consideration in the United States.

Consider now the data of Table 1 on occupational differentiation in the United States, 1900–1950, as a measure of the division of labor concept. Earlier, the division of labor was defined as the degree of differences among members of the society with regard to their sustenance activities. A detailed classification of each person in the labor force by occupation would be sufficient for an accurate measurement of this concept. The detail of the available data is somewhat less than ideal. The measures of occupational differentiation reported in Table 1 are based upon the 253 occupations reported in the 1900 census data (Labovitz and Gibbs, 1964, p. 6).

The measures of occupational differentiation in Table 1 were computed according to the following formula (Labovitz and Gibbs, 1964, p. 6):

$$\frac{1 - [\Sigma X^2/(\Sigma X)^2]}{1 - 1/N} \tag{30}$$

where X is the number of individuals in each occupational category, and N is the number of occupational categories. This formula can be interpreted as a measure of the dispersion of the labor force among the occupational categories. Indeed, Carter and Rockwell (1966) have shown that formula (30) is a measure for qualitative classifications analogous to that of variance for quantitative distributions. The maximum possible value of the numerator is $1 - 1/N$, which is the denominator. Thus, the measure may be interpreted as a percentage, and, consequently, it has the properties of a ratio scale.

Formula (30) is also meaningful in terms of the theoretical definition of the division of labor. That is, the maximum degree of differences among members of a society with regard to sustenance activities would exist when exactly $1/N$ of the labor force was contained in each occupation. This corresponds to the denominator of formula (30) while its numerator gives a measure of the actual dispersion in a given occupational classification. In brief, the dimensions of the measure of occupational differentiation are (actual differences of sustenance activities of labor force)/(maximum possible differences of sustenance activities of labor force). These are theoretically meaningful dimensions.

Finally, it should be noted that an increase in the number of occupations implies an increase in the degree of occupational differentiation. However, Labovitz and Gibbs (1964, p. 7) have shown that although the number of reported occupations increased from 253 in 1900 to 372 in 1950, the product moment correlation coefficient is 0.99 for formula (30) computed on both the constant and variable numbers of occupations. Therefore, at least during the period 1900–1950, it suffices to consider changes in dispersion of the labor force among a constant number of occupations.

ESTIMATED STRUCTURE

Given an appropriate statistical estimation procedure, the problem now is to fit the Land-Durkheim model to the data of Table 1. The question of an appropriate estimation method is somewhat subtle in that, even when the linear differential equation system (20) is integrated, it still consists of two simultaneous first-order linear difference equations (23). Econometricians (see Christ, 1966, pp. 298–494) have shown that unless certain simplifying assumptions can be made, the estimation of the parameters of simultaneous equation systems can be quite complex.

Consider equation (23), which has been written out in detail as equations (31) and (32):

$$x_{1t} + 0 \cdot x_{2t} = a_1^* + b_{11}^* x_{1(t-1)} + b_{12}^* x_{2(t-1)} \qquad (31)$$

$$0 \cdot x_{1t} + \quad x_{2t} = a_2^* + b_{21}^* x_{1(t-1)} + b_{22}^* x_{2(t-1)} \qquad (32)$$

Equations (31) and (32) can be described as two first-order linear difference equations in which $x_{1(t-1)}$ and $x_{2(t-1)}$ are two predetermined variables while x_{1t} and x_{2t} are *jointly dependent*, that is, their values are determined simultaneously at time t, which makes the estimation of the parameters of equations (31) and (32) a qualitatively different problem from the classical experimental situation in which one must estimate the parameters of a single equation determining the value of one dependent variable. Fortunately, in the present context, the fact that the non-zero values of the left-hand side of equations (31) and (32) are on the diagonal allows a reduction of the problem of estimating its parameters to the classical case. That is, the set of equations (31) and (32) are *just-identified*. Technically, they satisfy the *rank condition* for identifiability (see Christ, 1966, p. 320, for a statement of this condition), and the rank condition is sufficient for the just-identification of a structural parameter if all structural equations are just-identified (see Christ, 1966, pp. 402–404).

On the basis of the preceding analysis of equations (31) and (32), the parameters were estimated by a standard least-squares multiple regression computer program on the CDC 6600 computer (see Veldman, 1967, pp. 295–307 for a description of the computational procedure and a listing of the Fortran program). This procedure yields the following equations as the empirically fitted counterpart of equations (31) and (32):

$$x_{1t} = -169.079 + 0.096x_{1(t-1)} + 2.288x_{2(t-1)} (R = 0.983) \quad (33)$$

$$x_{2t} = 69.946 + 0.109x_{1(t-1)} + 0.221x_{2(t-1)} (R = 0.989) \quad (34)$$

where the multiple correlation coefficient in each case is placed beside the equation.

The fit of the Land-Durkheim model as judged by the sizes of the multiple correlation coefficients of equations (33) and (34) is quite good. Only 3 and 2 per cent, respectively, of the variance in the data is unaccounted for by the equations. However, the time series of observations is extremely short. There are, in fact, only three degrees of freedom in the estimation of the parameters of equations (31) and (32). Hence, it is not possible to put too much confidence in the multiple correlation coefficients as a statistical test of the fit of the model to the data. In brief, although the sizes of the correlation coefficients imply that we should not reject the model as inadequate, the brevity of the time series of observations implies that we cannot make a firm decision about the empirical adequacy of the model at the present time.

Before proceeding to an analysis of the parameter estimates, it would be well to examine the residuals of equations (33) and (34). It is well known that a high positive or negative autocorrelation of the residuals of time series structural equations may strongly bias the estimates of the structural parameters (see Christ, 1966, pp. 482–488). Therefore, in order to have confidence in the parameter estimates of equations (33) and (34), the residuals of the equations should first be examined as another aspect of testing the goodness of fit of the model.

Durbin and Watson have worked out a statistical test which is appropriate to testing for serial correlation of disturbances in a regression equation (see Christ, 1966, pp. 525–528). It was designed for equations in which all of the "independent" variables are strictly exogenous, that is, determined by other variables outside the system under consideration, rather than predetermined, that is, determined within the system under consideration by previous values of the variables, as in equations (33) and (34). However, the test is approximately valid for systems with predetermined variables (Christ, 1966, p. 527), and it is in this sense that the test is applied here. The Durbin-Watson d-statistic is computed according to the formula (Christ, 1966, p. 525):

$$d = \frac{\sum\limits_{2}^{N} (\hat{v}_t - \hat{v}_{t-1})^2}{\sum\limits_{1}^{N} (\hat{v}_t)^2} \tag{35}$$

where $\hat{v}$ is the computed value of the residual at time t, and N is the number of points in the time series.

The computed residual values for equations (33) and (34) and the data in Table 1 are

for x_{1t}:		and for x_{2t}:	
	0.014		0.005
	−0.782		−0.156
	1.402		0.023
	−1.066		−0.243
	0.261		0.214

The application of formula (35) to these residual values gives the d-statistic 2.103 for x_{1t} and 1.792 for x_{2t}. Now, the sampling distribution of d has not been computed for samples as small as the present series of six observations. Therefore, it is not possible to apply a simple rule for the rejection or acceptance of the null hypothesis of random disturbances in equations (33) and (34). However, the distribution of d is symmetrical with a mean value of 2 (Christ, 1966, pp. 525–526). Therefore, for a sample of six observations, it would be reasonable to expect the d values to approximate 2. As an illustration of the typical range of d, for a sample size of fifteen and two independent variables, the region for failing to reject the null hypothesis at the 0.01 level of significance is 1.25 − 2.75. Since the computed d values for equations (33) and (34) differ from 2 by only 0.1 and 0.2, respectively, we cannot reject the null hypothesis of random disturbances. Indeed, the computed residuals are small enough that they could easily have arisen from random measurement error.

The primary goal of an empirical analysis of the Land-Durkheim model is not equations (33) and (34). Rather, the central interest is in transforming the estimated parameters of equations (33) and (34) to arrive at estimates of the fundamental change parameters of equation (20), which has been assumed to represent the basic structure producing the observed values of the variables. In brief, equation (20) with unspecified parameter values is a *dynamic model* of the relationship between density and the division of labor. On the other hand, empirically estimated values of the parameters may be said to specify a given *dynamic structure*—in this case, the structure of the United States, 1900–1950—which is a particular manifestation of the more general theoretical processes described by the model. On the basis of the evidence given above regarding the good fit of the model to the data and the lack of evidence of high serial correlation of disturbances, we now proceed to derive estimates of the parameters of equation (20) from the parameters of equations (33) and (34).

Operating on equations (33) and (34), a procedure with the time intervals of observations defined so that $\Delta t = 10$, yields the following fitted structure:

$$\frac{dx_1}{dt} = -23.444 - 0.078x_1 + 0.148x_2 \qquad (36)$$

$$\frac{dx_2}{dt} = 6.052 + 0.007x_1 - 0.070x_2 \qquad (37)$$

where the eigenvalues of the estimated B matrix are $\lambda_1 = -0.0412$ and $\lambda_2 = -0.1062$. Since the number of time intervals between observations, Δt, has been set to ten in the estimation process, the estimated coefficients of equations (36) and (37) are relative to *annual* units of time. In the first equation, for example, the parameter 0.148 represents the number of units of change per year in the degree of urbanization for each existing unit of occupational differentiation.

A number of observations are in order concerning the Land-Durkheim model in the light of the estimated parameters of equations

(36) and (37). First, note that the elements of the estimated B matrix of equations (36) and (37) possess the signs postulated in the model. That is, each variable has a positive effect on the other variable and a negative feedback on itself. Second, the ratios $b_{12}/b_{11} = 1.89$ and $b_{21}/b_{22} = 0.1$ indicate that changes in the degree of occupational differentiation are relatively more dependent on its own current values than on the values of the degree of urbanization while the converse is true for urbanization. Third, the signs of the eigenvalues of the estimated B matrix indicate that the system of relationships has been stable for the United States over the period 1900–1950. That is, the estimated structure is such that neither the degree of urbanization nor the degree of occupational differentiation has increased or decreased explosively over time. Indeed, it would be disquieting if the equation system indicated otherwise. In brief, the estimated B matrix conforms highly with the theoretically predicted properties of the Land-Durkheim model.

Finally, it should be noted that the estimated parameters of the constant vector A are within the bounds of theoretically meaningful limits. This is particularly true in light of the fact that the estimated sizes of the elements of the A vector are partially a function of the value assigned to Δt—the number of time intervals between observations—in the estimation method. That is, as Δt increases, the values in the A vector approach zero.

THEORETICAL AND EMPIRICAL ADEQUACY

The empirical accuracy of the Land-Durkheim model is encouraging. Although the time series of observations is not long enough to give firm evidence regarding the estimated parameters and fit of the model, it is nevertheless true that the model would not fit even so short a series *if* the "real" structure of relationships among the variables was greatly different from the postulated structure; for example, if the "real" structure was grossly nonlinear. Briefly, we can conclude from the present analysis that the causal structure relating density and the division of labor is approximately linear at least for the United States 1900–1950. However, to the present empirical assessment of the Land-Durkheim model we must append a plea for longer time series of observations on the variables and, in particular, observations on other societies so that the generality of the linear model across societies can be evaluated.

On the theoretical side, the major problem of the Land-Durkheim model lies in the lack of specification of the theoretical relationships of competition to density and the division of labor as well as the failure to specify rules of correspondence of the concept to some operational procedure. The consequent underidentification of the position of competition in the causal structure impairs the estimation of theoretically important parameters of the model. Again, this implies a need for further data and analysis before we can place confidence in the relationships originally prescribed by Durkheim and formalized and corroborated in the present study.

Finally, it should be noted that this paper has sought only to formalize Durkheim's theory of the causes of the division of labor and to ascertain the extent to which it could account for trends in existing observations on the United States. In particular, we have not made any comparisons of Durkheim's theory with other representations of the causes of the division of labor. Yet, obviously, Durkheim's theory must be shown to compete well with other explanations before it can be accepted as a more or less adequate representation of the phenomenon.

REFERENCES

CARTER, L. F. AND ROCKWELL, R. C.
    1966   "The concept of variation in qualitative systems." *Proceedings of the Southwestern Sociological Association.*

CHRIST, C. F.
    1966   *Econometric Models and Methods.* New York: Wiley.

CODDINGTON, E. A. AND LEVINSON, N.
    1955   *Theory of Ordinary Differential Equations.* New York: McGraw-Hill.

COLEMAN, J. S.
    1968   "The mathematical study of change." In Hubert M. Blalock, Jr., and Ann B. Blalock (Eds.), *Methodology in Social Research.* New York: McGraw-Hill.

DURKHEIM, E.
    1933   *The Division of Labor in Society.* Translated by George Simpson. New York: Free Press.

GIBBS, J. P.
    1966   "Measures of urbanization." *Social Forces* 45: 170–177.

GIBBS, J. P. AND BROWNING, H. L.
    1966   "The division of labor, technology, and the organization of production in twelve countries." *American Sociological Review* 31: 81–92.

GIBBS, J. P. AND MARTIN, W. T.
    1962   "Urbanization, technology, and the division of labor: International patterns." *American Sociological Review* 27: 667–677.

LABOVITZ, S. AND GIBBS, J. P.
    1964   "Urbanization, technology, and the division of labor: Further evidence." *Pacific Sociological Review* 7: 3–9.

MERTON, R. K.
    1934   "Durkheim's *Division of Labor in Society.*" *American Journal of Sociology* 40: 319–328.

NERING, E. D.
    1963   *Linear Algebra and Matrix Theory.* New York: Wiley.

PARSONS, T.
   1949   *The Structure of Social Action.* New York: Free Press.
SCHNORE, L. F.
   1958   "Social morphology and human ecology." *American Journal of Sociology*
          63: 620–634.
SIMON, H. A.
   1957   *Models of Man.* New York: Wiley.
VELDMAN, D. J.
   1967   *Fortran Programming for the Behavioral Sciences.* New York: Holt, Rine-
          hart, and Winston.

16

STATUS DYNAMICS

Thomas J. Fararo
UNIVERSITY OF PITTSBURGH

This work was supported in part by funds provided by a Faculty Research Grant from the Social Science Research Council and by a research grant (GS-2538) from the National Science Foundation. I am grateful to Jacqueline Cohen and Joseph Seldin for their critical reactions to an earlier draft.

In recent years, theorists in sociology and social psychology have emphasized the role of balancing or equilibrating principles in social behavior. This emphasis has been especially noticeable in the area of status-related phenomena, where one is familiar with the terms *status consistency*, *status crystallization*, and *rank balance*. (See, for example, Galtung, 1966; Kimberly, 1966; Lenski, 1954; Zelditch and Anderson, 1966.)

This chapter is part of an attempt to place the setting for and the analysis of problems of equilibration of statuses within a unified mathematical framework. Such an attempt must begin with an analysis of the concept of status to arrive at a mathematical representation suitable for the kinds of models involved. An analysis of the status concept, which is primarily axiomatic and algebraic, is reported elsewhere (Fararo, 1968). The first section of this chapter constitutes an elaboration and sociological interpretation of the relevant portions of this prior work.

The history of attempts to apply "social physics" methods to social science warns us that the undertaking is hazardous in two respects. First, on the face of it the approach has the appearance of another naive attempt to reduce complex theoretical problems of sociology to simple-minded physical analogies. Second, even if the mathematical methods are theoretically appropriate to the substantive area, the complexity of the problems involved in *applying* the theoretical models may imply that the approach fails to attain empirical relevance.

As to "mere analogy," three aspects of the present work rule out this hazard. First, the existence of an appropriate measurement basis is a firm guard against mere formal manipulation of equations lacking empirical interpretation. Second, standard sociological notions are imbedded in the formalism. Third, not only concepts but also representations of well-verified mechanisms at work in the real world are incorporated into the system.

The second hazard, concerning application difficulties, cannot be argued away; our ability to estimate parameters, for instance, is severely limited. But this much can be said in favor of pursuing mathematical models in the "classical" manner even where precise parameter estimates or simplified versions of the general phenomena (for testing purposes) are hard to find: such an approach also involves a "qualitative theory," in which problems of equilibrium and stability of a system are analyzed. In addition, there is a feedback from the theoretical conclusions (or, more likely, from the intuitions acquired in analyzing the models) to the conceptualization of the measurement basis. Such a feedback may lead to procedures that make the measurements simpler, more appropriate, or of wider scope. (For a related discussion, see Blalock, 1969.)

One cannot be certain that the approach developed along these lines will be empirically fruitful, but at present it does seem to offer a natural mathematical way of framing and studying theoretical problems in status dynamics.

The intuitive notion of a status variable can be framed as follows. In a given population, the individuals are *differentiated* in terms of some characteristic and, simultaneously, the different ways in which they may be characterized are *differentially evaluated*. This conception seems common to an enormous portion of the sociological literature on status. For example, it is expressed in Parsons (1953), Barber (1957), and Tumin (1967). According to this conception, a society (or, more generally, a social system) will have a stratification system consisting of a plurality of such status variables. Further, it is ordinarily assumed that, in some sense, there is a shared value basis for the differential evaluations. The mobility of an individual in the system consists in his successive occupancies of profiles in terms of the status variables. It is usually assumed that in a natural way the typical individual wants to move up in the system, because of his participation in the common value basis. Further, it is agreed that an individual possessing discrepant statuses along the parts of his profile will be motivated to try to make them congruent.

If the preceding paragraph is taken as a kind of minimal sociological consensus concerning status variables, we can proceed to outline a mathematical approach based upon this consensus. First, the informal idea of differentiation and differential evaluation will be imbedded in a conceptualization producing ratio-level status variables. Second, a collection of such variables will be taken to define a stratification frame within which mobility is defined in a natural way. Third, the minimal mechanics of mobility, that is, the mechanisms moving an individual through the system in time, will be imbedded in a set of differential equations. Fourth, the system of equations will be analyzed for its qualitative consequences in terms of equilibrium and stability.

REPRESENTATION OF STATUS

Our first problem, then, is to pass from the sociological consensus about the meaning of a status variable to an exact quantitative formulation consistent with the sociological background meaning.

The approach to status measurement taken here is that the sociological researcher will always begin with qualitative facts of the kind "Mr. A thinks x is better than y," where the individual and the xs and ys will vary; and that any claim to quantitative representation must begin with this qualitative basis and with the undeniable fact that there is scatter or variability among individuals as to preferences. Thus, our assumptive base will refer to the existence of discrete choices made by individuals and to the existence of variability among individuals. Then it will deduce that a suitable quantitative representation exists, provided that these individual choices satisfy certain justifiable assumptions.

Let A be a set, the members of which we term *actors*. In any application, this will be the population from which we draw the concrete individuals making choices. Let C be a set whose elements are thought of as the various values a characteristic can assume. We call C a *characteristic*, and the elements of C are called *states*. A typical member of C can be denoted by x. It is desirable that C be compound in the sense that the states are described in terms of several aspects. For example, rather than x = college graduate, one prefers x = liberal arts graduate of an Ivy League school, since the multiple-aspect description reveals more about differential evaluations. Individuals are differentiated in terms of characteristics. A typical such differentiation is given by specifying for each individual in a population how he stands on a certain characteristic. Mathematically, this will be represented by a "mapping" or a "function" with domain the set of actors A, and range the set of states of a characteristic C. We let c be the mapping. One can think of c as a table whose first column contains names of individuals and whose second column lists for each individual a state of a given characteristic. Thus $c(\alpha)$ is the way in which actor α in A is characterized in terms of C. We term the mapping c a *characterization*.

Let S be any nonempty, finite subset of C. For example, S could contain a sample of occupations, if C is the occupational characteristic. Our first assumption is that each actor α in A is associated with a system of probability functions denoted P_S^α such that for any x in S, with probability $P_S^\alpha(x)$ the actor α chooses x when his alternatives comprise S. A special case of importance is $S = \{x, y\}$, a set of two distinct states and the actor must choose between them. In this case, we write

$$p^\alpha(x, y) = P_{\{x,y\}}^\alpha(x) \tag{1}$$

as an abbreviation for the cumbersome notation on the right. This is the probability that actor α prefers x to y. Because we assume a probability distribution, in the special case of two elements we have

$$p^\alpha(x, y) + p^\alpha(y, x) = 1 \tag{2}$$

which can be taken to restrict the empirical interpretations to cases in which the individual must make a selection. "Indifference" will be treated as probability one-half in pairwise preference.

Our next assumption is that, for any subset S of C,

$$P_S^\alpha(x) = P_S^\beta(x) \qquad \text{every } x \text{ in } S \tag{3}$$

as α and β vary over A. That is, the probability functions are the same for all individuals. In contrast to the assertion that probability functions exist, which is relatively innocuous, this assumption requires some justification, which will be presented subsequently. We can now drop the actor superscript, and write $P_S(x)$ and $p(x, y)$ for various probabilities.

One empirical interpretation is as follows. Let C be the set of all occupations in the United States, and let S be a sample of them. Let A be the adult members of the United States population. Ask a random sample to rank the elements of S. Estimate $p(x, y)$ by the fraction of people placing job x above job y. (The justification for this estimation is given subsequently.)

This concludes our representation of the qualitative base of differential evaluation: people make choices between "states" serving as ways in which they can be characterized, but they exhibit scatter in their preferences. The sets A and C, the existence of a characterization c and the probability functions, represent these facts.

Next, we postulate that a *general* principle of choice behavior will apply to *this* choice behavior, and that our general principle is an axiom proposed by Luce (1959). It is this connection with Luce's axiom that provides the basis for the quantitative representation of the evaluations by individuals and it is this part of the development that has been discussed elsewhere (Fararo, 1968). Therefore, the discussion is rather abbreviated and intuitive.

One intuitive interpretation of Luce's axiom can be put this way: conditional probability has independent empirical meaning. We explicate this with an example used by Luce. Suppose a man visits regularly a certain restaurant which has a menu consisting of certain items forming a set, denoted S. Suppose he has probability $P_S(x)$ of choosing x = roast beef. This can be estimated by the relative frequency of choosing roast beef in successive visits to the restaurant, choosing from the identical menu. Consider the probability that he chooses roast beef, given he chooses meat. Denote this by $P_S(x|T)$, where T is the set of meat offerings on the menu. This can be estimated by the dividing the number of times he selected roast beef by the number of times he selected meat. Now suppose the restaurant, for whatever reason, offers him a new menu listing only those meats in T. The probability that he chooses roast beef is $P_T(x)$. It is estimated by the relative frequency of choosing roast beef from the new menu. Luce's axiom says that

$$P_T(x) = P_S(x|T) \qquad (4)$$

for all offerings x in T. The left side of equation (4) is a probability defined relative to one situation while the right side is defined relative to a different situation. The two are *postulated* to be identical. While Luce offers plausibility grounds for this axiom, more important in the light of the present paper is whether this proposed general choice principle has any empirical justification. This may be put as follows: are the testable consequences of this axiom upheld in data gathered to test the axiom? The answer appears to be yes, if one examines the treatment of the axiom and its comparison with data found in a recent treatise on mathematical psychology (Atkinson, Bower, and Crothers, 1965). We take these data, together with Luce's plausibility arguments, as together tentatively supporting the hypothesis that Luce's axiom is a general choice principle.

If we could be absolutely sure that the principle was general, then its application to our problem would be a mere matter of a special case. Since we take a tentative attitude toward the axiom, we must assume a similar standpoint toward any special cases and argue as follows. It is reasonable to propose that when individuals are confronted with choice situations involving properties or characteristics (as in the ranking of occupations), they satisfy Luce's axiom. But for a concrete application, of course, one should test the consequences following the paradigm of Atkinson, Bower, and Crothers.

Why should we use Luce's axiom? Basically because of the following consequence. If Luce's axiom holds over a domain C of alternatives then there exists a ratio-level scale over C, denoted v, such that for any finite subset S of C,

$$P_S(x) = \frac{v(x)}{\sum_{y \in S} v(y)} \tag{5}$$

That is, the probability that the individual chooses x from S is the "valuation" of x divided by the sum of the valuations of all alternatives in S. Since this is a ratio scale one can select some state of C, say a, and arbitrarily let $v(a) = 1$.

Coupling this with the differentiation of actors along C, which is represented by our characterization map c with domain A and range C, we see that we have a representation of the differentiation, via c, and a representation of the differential evaluation, via v. By the status of actor α in A in terms of C we mean the valuation of *his* standing on C. Translated into mathematics, this means that the status of α is $v[c(\alpha)]$, where $c(\alpha)$ is in C. Calling the defined status of this actor $s(\alpha)$, we have

$$s(\alpha) = v[c(\alpha)] \qquad \text{all } \alpha \text{ in } A \tag{6}$$

Thus s is our defined status variable. It is defined for the population A, based on the characteristic C, on the differentiation or characterization c, and on the valuation v. Thus all the intuitive components of the consensus usage appear to be built into this definition.

Our final adjustment is practical. How can one actually estimate v and so s? Using pairwise preferences, Luce showed that we have

$$v(x) = \frac{p(x, a)}{p(a, x)} \qquad \text{all } x \text{ in } C \tag{7}$$

where a is the state chosen for the unit. One way to use formula (7) requires a pairwise preference situation. This is a highly restricted type of situation. It would make application to status phenomena virtually impossible outside laboratory settings. To extend the empirical range of this formula, then, we need a way of estimating $p(x, y)$—and so v, and so s—from data of the kind more readily obtained in sociological research, namely rankings. Fortunately, Luce has already done the axiomatic work and the empirical tests confirm his ranking theory (see Atkinson, Bower, and Crothers, 1965). Roughly speaking, the Luce Ranking Postulate is that the choice axiom applies at each level of choice to an ever-diminishing choice set S. The result is that $p(x, y)$, interpreted as the probability that x is preferred to y, is equal to the probability of a ranking in which x is placed ahead of y. The distinction here is that a ranking is a *context* of choice, which is not empirically identical to a choice between two things; according to Luce's postulate and the confirming data, however, this context does not change the probability. Thus if we take the fraction of individuals placing x above y as an estimate of the probability that x is placed before y (which is justified by our assumption that the individuals choose with identical probabilities), then by the Ranking Postulate this estimates $p(x, y)$. Therefore we can obtain estimated valuations $v(x)$, using formula (7), and so estimates of the statuses of individuals by using formula (6).

To sum up, the basic assumptions of our ratio-level status measurement are as follows. Individuals will be making choices from finite sets of alternatives. They will display variability. They choose in accordance with Luce's axiom. This axiom applies to ranking situations as described by Luce. A homogeneous system of probabilities as between individuals is assumed. Given these assumptions, it is a logical consequence that a ratio-level scale representing the evaluations exists. Given a conception of status as comprising differential evaluation and differentiation, we pass to its formal definition in terms of the valuation.

Of these assumptions, those bearing upon Luce's axiom are taken as warranted by empirical tests. The only remaining point of discussion is the reminder that Luce's axiom applies to each chooser and deduces that this chooser has the scale v. Our uniformity assumption, adopted for the stratification context of the axiom's application, then implies that all the actors have this same v scale. This is a quantitative version of the sociological idea of a fundamental value system in a society. On the one hand, the individuals internalize this system through socialization and on the other hand, the fact that they each sustain a rather idiosyncratic passage through various parts of the social structure means that this shared value system ordinarily will not translate into identical preferences. The connection of the shared v scale with the scatter implied by the probability distribution is intended to accommodate this theoretical perspective. In a sense, this is a quantitative version of the ideas presented in Parsons and Smelser (1956); in effect, we place the same v inside each actor in the system, but allow this to "translate" into observable variability.

For example, the statement, "engineers enjoy twice as much prestige as do artists in the United States," is meaningful in our system. It is represented by $v(\text{engineer}) = 2v(\text{artist})$. This implies by formula (5) that the probability that the engineer is considered better than the artist is given by

$$\frac{v(\text{engineer})}{v(\text{engineer}) + v(\text{artist})} = \frac{2v(\text{artist})}{3v(\text{artist})} = \frac{2}{3}$$

By the connection with rankings this means that we expect two-thirds of the sample to place "engineer" before "artist" in a ranking task. Conversely, given that two-thirds of the sample place the engineer before the artist in a ranking task, we know that the respective v scale values lie in the ratio

$$\frac{2/3}{1/3} = 2$$

so that $v(\text{engineer}) = 2v(\text{artist})$. In applications, of course, we will start with estimated probabilities and infer the valuation v, which will provide an estimate of the status variable s.

MOBILITY

It is clear that s can change if either the characterization c changes or the valuation v changes. Let T be an interval of the real line and let t in T be interpreted as moment t. In a mathematical model, the above structure is assumed to exist at each moment t and so we have

$$s_t(\alpha) = v_t[c_t(\alpha)] \quad \text{for all } \alpha$$

If for all t, the characterization of an actor α is constant, we say that the actor α is *characterization-stationary*. If for all t, we have the same valuation v, we say that we have a *stationary value system*. If for all t, the status of a given actor is constant, we say that the actor is *status-stationary*. It follows that if an actor is characterization-stationary in a stationary value system his status is stationary.

Thus to provide mechanisms to change status we must provide a way in which an individual actor changes characterization, or a way in which the valuation changes. (In this chapter, statuses change in stationary value systems, so that only characterizations are subject to change.) The analytical study of models for changing status by using devices related to these ways is termed the *field of status dynamics*. For example, to change characterization may require power, and so power in relation to status is part of status dynamics.

Our intuition suggests that the theory must deal with several status variables. For example, one variable is based on a characteristic related to possessions, another variable is based on a characteristic related to ethnicity, another variable is based on a characteristic related to education, and so forth.

Thus, in the general case, we have a representation

$$\mathbf{s} = (s_1, \ldots, s_j, \ldots, s_n)$$

and we term $\mathbf{s}$ *the status vector*, with s_j based on a characteristic C_j.

Just as in the case of a single variable, when we have a status vector we assume the structure exists at each moment t. The value of the status vector at time t for actor α is that actor's position at that time. Thus, the position of α in A at time t is given by

$$\mathbf{s}(t; \alpha) = [s_{1t}(\alpha), s_{2t}(\alpha), \ldots, s_{jt}(\alpha), \ldots, s_{nt}(\alpha)]$$

where $s_{jt}(\alpha)$ is the term

$$v_j[c_{jt}(\alpha)]$$

assuming a stationary value system. In words: the jth component of actor α's position at time t is the valuation of his standing on the jth characteristic, where the valuation is shared among the actors in A and is time-invariant. Concretely, $c_{jt}(\alpha)$ might be "liberal arts graduate of an Ivy League School" or "lawyer in a Wall Street firm at a middle level of authority." The precise nature of the components will depend upon the operationally defined characteristics C_j. The important theoretical point is that not this characterization itself but its valuation provides the actual value of the status variable (for that actor at that time). Perhaps if we call the vector of characterizations $[c_{1t}(\alpha), c_{2t}(\alpha), \ldots, c_{nt}(\alpha)]$ the *profile*, it will be clear that in a stationary value system the individual's position changes only because of changes in his profile. But not all changes in profile are changes in position, since two distinct profiles might differ only trivially (that is, they have the identical valuation in each component).

In studying individual mobility, we hold the actor α fixed and let t vary. In this context, we can drop the notation for the actor to write the simpler form

$$\mathbf{s}(t) = [s_1(t), s_2(t), \ldots, s_n(t)]$$

with a single actor understood.

The path in n-dimensional space traced out by the vector $\mathbf{s}(t)$ as t varies is termed the *status trajectory:* the succession of positions held by an actor through time. When the vector has just two components we have a geometric image of the trajectory as shown in Figure 1.

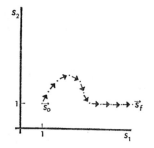

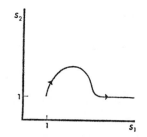

Figure 1. An Illustrative Status Trajectory

Figure 2. The Status Trajectory of Figure 1 as Generated by a Solution to a System of Differential Equations

The individual at time t_0 is at position $\mathbf{s}_0$ as shown in the figure; the arrows show the successive positions as time flows, culminating at $\mathbf{s}_f$. We see that initially this actor is upwardly mobile on both variables (arrows pointing upward and to the right), then he begins losing status on the second variable while still gaining on the first (arrows downward and to the right); finally, he remains fixed on the second variable while moving steadily upward on the first (arrows parallel to the s_1-axis and pointing to the right). A similar picture could be drawn for three variables; for higher dimensions we use intuitions obtained in the lower dimensions.

In the field of status dynamics, the aim is to create models such that one has an intelligible explanatory basis for the movement shown by the arrows. Put another way, the aim is to introduce mathematical representations of motivational processes (or other processes) inducing the shifts forming the status trajectory. Any such process, seen in terms of how it moves an individual in the "space," is termed a *mechanism*. As we shall see below, this dynamical viewpoint allows us to regard status inconsistency as a mechanism: a driving force for change in position.

Status dynamics may be regarded as the field in which we introduce functions of status and possibly of other variables, collectively denoted by the vector $\mathbf{u}$, in such a way that we have a system of the form

$$\frac{d\mathbf{s}}{dt} = f(\mathbf{s}, \mathbf{u}) \tag{8}$$

This shows, on the left side, the rate of change of position, which (by standard mathematical definition) is just the derivative of each component of the vector. (Thus this is a system of differential equations in vector form.) The right side shows a function of status and of "input" to the actor. This is the total mechanism, which depends on where the individual is and what is happening to him. To see how this form can generate a status trajectory, multiply both sides by dt (thought of as a small interval of time). This gives

$$d\mathbf{s} = f(\mathbf{s}, \mathbf{u})\, dt \tag{9}$$

In looking at expression (9), we think of a movement, of magnitude and direction given by a "little vector," $d\mathbf{s}$, which is induced by the mechanism $f(\mathbf{s}, \mathbf{u})$ acting through an interval of time dt. For example, starting at $\mathbf{s}_0$ with input $\mathbf{u}_0$, the mechanism becomes, $f(\mathbf{s}_0, \mathbf{u}_0)$, which when multiplied by a suitable dt gives the first motion out of $\mathbf{s}_0$ as shown in Figure 1. By applying the mechanism again at this new location we drive the system to its next location, and so forth. At point $\mathbf{s}_f$ we would find that the mechanism is still operative, but induces no motion out of that position. This would be an equilibrium position.

The above paragraph provides the interpretation that one would use in a numerical simulation. It is in greatest fidelity to the discrete jumps shown in an actual status trajectory. But in analytical work, it is simpler to idealize to methods which generate the trajectory as a smooth curve as in Figure 2, where we see the curve corresponding to the actual status trajectory of Figure 1.

In general, in postulating mechanisms we start from some intuitive basis which is translated into a system of differential equations. Eventually, we can hope to formalize several recurrent principles used in such postulations to the extent that the form of a model is partially determined by general considerations of status dynamics, that is, valuation-characterization changes and their causes. We cannot expect to logically derive specific mechanisms from purely general principles, but we can expect principles that make the construction less arbitrary.

In particular we can provisionally use the general principle that the mobility at any time is a sum of several positive and negative *mobilizers*, where the latter refers to some category of cause for changing characterization. In particular, there are two classes of mobilizers of general interest. The first is termed the class of *natural mobilizers*, meaning what would happen if no extrinsic causal factors induced characterization change; in particular, since characterizations $c_{jt}(\alpha)$ of actor α are valued by him as $v_j[c_{jt}(\alpha)] = s_{jt}(\alpha)$ it follows that if he were able, he would attempt to change $c_{jt}(\alpha)$ such that the value of his assigned profile would be higher. Thus a natural mobilizer induces upward mobility. On the other hand, comparisons with other statuses form the class of *equilibrational mobilizers*. These ideas are best understood in the context of a specific model, to which we now turn.

SETTING UP A MODEL

This section provides an example in which the mechanism $f(\mathbf{s}, \mathbf{u})$ is proposed on intuitive, "mobilizer" grounds rather than constrained by detailed dynamical postulates, in the above sense.

Galtung (1966) provides a comprehensive discussion of "rank-equilibration" and includes two axioms referring to what I will call natural mobility and to equilibration, respectively. Galtung's first axiom is that an individual will attempt to maximize his status. His second axiom states that an individual will try to equilibrate upward his various component statuses. By including the phrase *equilibrate upward* in his second axiom, Galtung includes an upward mobility bias even in respect to equilibration. However, we know that individuals sometimes equilibrate downward in the broad sense that a low status may induce low levels of aspiration for other statuses. Thus, the system studied here will posit that equilibration can act in either direction; its basic motivational component is the "setting of things in balance." Basically, in this model the status trajectory is produced by a tug-of-war between natural mobilizers inducing movement upward, equilibrational mobilizers inducing movements toward balance, and external constraints. Depending upon the relative importance of these mechanisms in a system, and his initial position, a man can be driven up the ladder (arrows up and to the right in the plane) or down the drain (arrows down and to the left in the plane). It is significant that this explains both upward and downward mobility by appeal to the same mechanisms.

The system is stated first in complete form, and then is derived in the sense of showing in detail how it arises from sociological considerations. In order to present the basic ideas with a minimum of mathematical complexity, the system is taken to be in two dimensions. Let

$$\frac{ds_1}{dt} = a_1 s_1 + b_1(s_2 - s_1) - c_1$$

$$\frac{ds_2}{dt} = a_2 s_2 + b_2(s_1 - s_2) - c_2 \tag{10}$$

where the parameters a_i, b_i and c_i ($i = 1, 2$) are positive.

In vector form the system is given by:

$$\frac{d\mathbf{s}}{dt} = A\mathbf{s} - \mathbf{c}, \tag{11}$$

where

$$\mathbf{c} = \begin{pmatrix} c_1 \\ c_2 \end{pmatrix}$$

$$\mathbf{s} = \begin{pmatrix} s_1 \\ s_2 \end{pmatrix} \tag{12}$$

$$A = \begin{pmatrix} a_1 - b_1 & b_1 \\ b_2 & a_2 - b_2 \end{pmatrix}$$

and so $f(\mathbf{s}, \mathbf{u}) = A\mathbf{s} - \mathbf{c}$, in this model. This is a linear model since f is linear. It has a constant input, $\mathbf{u} = \mathbf{c}$.

The equations (10) arise as follows. If the actor were unconstrained by other actors in the system or by nonsocial factors, the mechanism $f(\mathbf{s}, \mathbf{u})$ could be taken as

$$\frac{ds_i}{dt} = a_i s_i \qquad (a_i > 0, i = 1, 2) \tag{13}$$

with a_i thought of as some fraction. This implies ever-increasing status in each component. This is plausible because the actor acts in accordance with his values and there are no constraints on his manipulating his characterization to ever increase its value in each dimension. But this means ever-increasing status. For example, keeping in mind the analytical restriction to this single mechanism, a typical trajectory would be as in Figure 3, using $a_1 = a_2$ for illustrative purposes.

On the other hand, suppose our actor is a pure equilibrator; that is, the mechanism involves only comparisons "horizontally" along his statuses. When he finds agreement between his actual and expected statuses he is satisfied with that characterization, while disagreement creates an imbalance he attempts to resolve by changing his characterization. Once again we assume that the motivation to change charac-

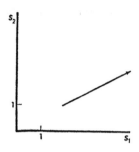
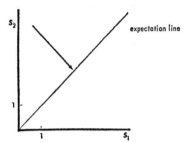

Figure 3. A Typical Trajectory   Figure 4. A Typical Trajectory
Based on a Natural Mobilizer   Based on An Equilibrational Mobilizer

terization can be converted into change (that is, for a pure equilibrator
the environment does not constrain the actor's mobility).

To convert these ideas into an exact mechanism, let us assume
that the equilibrated statuses all lie on an expectation line in the plane.
For instance, if absolute equality is expected, then the 45°-line is the
expectation line (see Figure 4). A more general model would be based
on the assumption, "the higher I am here on s_1, the higher I ought to be
there on s_2," which is any monotone-increasing curve in the plane. Taking a line through the origin as the model is an attempt to keep the
mathematics simple. Analytically the line is given by a function of the
form

$$e(s_1) = ks_1 \qquad\qquad (14)$$

with k positive. Positions on this line are equilibrated, other positions
are not. At any time, when the actor is at status s_1 then he expects to
be at ks_1 on the second variable. It is reasonable to assume that the
magnitude and direction of induced movement on this second variable
will be proportional to the amount of the discrepancy:

$$\frac{ds_2}{dt} = b_2(ks_1 - s_2) \qquad (b_2 > 0) \qquad (15)$$

Thus, if at a particular time the individual's position is $\mathbf{s} = (s_1, s_2) =
(s_1, ks_1)$, the mechanism does not induce change. If, on the other hand,
s_2 is less than ks_1, then he is induced to move upward on s_2 to catch up
to the expected status (based on where he is on s_1 at the time). If s_2
is above ks_1, so that he is above his expected place, the mechanism becomes negative, and he is induced downward on the second variable. At
a particular moment, the level of aspired s_2-status will be given by this
mechanism: thus a low s_1 status will induce (via the balance process) a
low level of aspired s_2-status, in keeping with our desire to build this

phenomenon into the model. On the other hand, the aspirations can be ambitious, as when ks_1 is well above s_2.

Applying the same reasoning symmetrically to s_1 based on s_2, we merely traverse the expectation line from the s_2-axis horizontally to find the expected s_1-status, which will be $(1/k)s_2$. Thus the mechanism here will be of the form

$$\frac{ds_1}{dt} = b_1(s_2/k - s_1) \qquad (b_1 > 0) \qquad (16)$$

with identical reasoning as to the induced movement. If we put $k = 1$ for the simplest possible dynamic model, we obtain the mechanism, from equations (15) and (16),

$$\frac{ds_1}{dt} = b_1(s_2 - s_1)$$

$$\frac{ds_2}{dt} = b_2(s_1 - s_2) \qquad (17)$$

Figure 4 shows a typical trajectory produced by this mechanism, taking $b_1 = b_2$. Note that when $s_1 = s_2$ we obtain zero derivatives, and so the actor is not induced to move out of such a position. To combine the facts that the actor is naturally driven upward by acting in accordance with his values and he also is an equilibrator, one uses the additivity rule to combine the mobilizers of equations (13) and (17), to obtain

$$\frac{ds_1}{dt} = a_1 s_1 + b_1(s_2 - s_1)$$

$$\frac{ds_2}{dt} = a_2 s_2 + b_2(s_1 - s_2) \qquad (18)$$

Finally, let us assume that other actors and the surrounding environment constrain the actor's mobility. For simplicity, let us suppose this constraining input to the actor to be constant in time. Then the mechanism (18), with the negative inputs $-c_1$ and $-c_2$, becomes the differential equation system (10).

To summarize, equation system (10) represents on the left side the mobility of the actor; the actor's mobility is equal to the sum of certain mobilizers (inducing change in status) which appear on the right. These mobilizers consist in, first, a natural upward drift because of the actor's values and his behavior in accordance with these values; second, an equilibrating effect due to a desire to have statuses in different dimensions equal; and, third, a constraining environment, including other actors, who act in such a way that we regard their combined effect on our actor as a constant input pushing his status downward.

This model, it is emphasized, is only one among a family of mechanisms that could be postulated. An obvious change in the signs of the parameters, for instance, induces new models. For example, with $c_i < 0$ the constraint terms now become pushes in the upward direction, and we have a model of a situation in which, aside from equilibration, the actor faces no block to his naturally upward mobility. Similarly, a ceiling on the statuses could be assumed. This leads to difficult nonlinear models, relative to which the present model can be regarded as an approximation.

In the next section an analysis of the system (10) is provided to illustrate the kinds of questions one can ask and answer in this kind of work.

ANALYSIS OF THE MODEL

Given any system of the form (8), that is,

$$\frac{d\mathbf{s}}{dt} = f(\mathbf{s}, \mathbf{u})$$

there are three kinds of questions we pose: What form do the status trajectories take? Is there an equilibrium position and is it unique? And is a given equilibrium position a stable equilibrium? For our purposes the qualitative analysis based on the second and third questions is of greater significance than an analysis based on the first question, since this kind of analysis generalizes to nonlinear models which cannot be solved in the sense of the first question.

First, we treat the problem of equilibrium. The meaning of a position being an equilibrium position is this: if an actor is ever in this position, say $\mathbf{s}_e$, then he stays there given the mechanisms of the system and unchanged parameter values. The point of this definition is that there is no assertion that the actor will be in equilibrium or will gravitate toward it if he is not there. It is purely a matter of what the mechanisms of the system imply concerning a position. The stability or instability of this position is a separate question. Correspondingly, the mathematical definition of an equilibrium point of a system of the form

$$\frac{d\mathbf{s}}{dt} = f(\mathbf{s}, \mathbf{u})$$

is simply any solution of the system

$$\frac{d\mathbf{s}}{dt} = \mathbf{0}$$

Since in the status model

$$\frac{d\mathbf{s}}{dt} = A\mathbf{s} - \mathbf{c}$$

the equilibrium positions are the status vectors satisfying

$$A\mathbf{s} = \mathbf{c} \tag{19}$$

Applying the inverse of A to both sides of equation (19), we obtain

$$\mathbf{s}_e = A^{-1}\mathbf{c} \tag{20}$$

Computationally, we must have a nonvanishing determinant, denoted Δ. This, for the matrix of equation system (10), is given by

$$\Delta = (a_1 - b_1)(a_2 - b_2) - b_1 b_2 \tag{21}$$

Summarizing:

PROPOSITION 1. *If $\Delta \neq 0$, the status system has a unique equilibrium point given by equation (20).*

Since the actor is an equilibrator, we ask: Is it the case that the components of $\mathbf{s}_e$ are at the same level, that is, if $\mathbf{s}_e = (s_{1e}, s_{2e})$, must we have $s_{1e} = s_{2e}$? By equation (20) we obtain

$$s_{1e} = \frac{1}{\Delta} [(a_2 - b_2)c_1 - b_1 c_2]$$

$$s_{2e} = \frac{1}{\Delta} [(a_1 - b_1)c_2 - b_2 c_1] \tag{22}$$

and therefore we can prove the following:

PROPOSITION 2. $s_{1e} = s_{2e}$ *if and only if* $a_2/a_1 = c_2/c_1$.

According to equation system (22), $s_{1e} = s_{2e}$ if and only if

$$(a_2 - b_2)c_1 - b_1 c_2 = (a_1 - b_1)c_2 - b_2 c_1$$

and so if and only if

$$a_2 c_1 - (b_2 c_1 + b_1 c_2) = a_1 c_2 - (b_1 c_2 + b_2 c_1)$$

Therefore, $s_{1e} = s_{2e}$ implies and is implied by $a_2 c_1 = a_1 c_2$.

The answer to our question, then, is that an equilibrium point need not be one which shows identity of components. Further, for an actor characterized with the ratio a_2/a_1, the condition of dissatisfied equilibrium ($s_{1e} \neq s_{2e}$) is that the constraining inputs show a ratio

$c_2/c_1 \neq a_2/a_1$. (But recall that an equilibrium may be unstable; a point to be developed later.)

To illustrate, consider the special system in which

$$a_1 = a_2$$
$$b_1 = b_2$$

Such a system will be termed *symmetric*, with parameters a and b. We have:

PROPOSITION 3. *Provided that* $b \neq a/2$, *the symmetric system has a unique equilibrium point.*

To see this, note that in the symmetric case

$$\Delta = a^2 - 2ab$$

and the condition $\Delta \neq 0$ of Proposition 1 becomes

$$a - 2b \neq 0$$

By Proposition 2, only if the equilibrium of a symmetric system is exposed to symmetric inputs ($c_1 = c_2$) will it be a happy equilibrium ($s_{1e} = s_{2e}$).

Since the reader may not find the proofs psychologically compelling—we are saying that the system is built around an equilibration toward the expectation line (identity of components in this model) and yet there may exist an equilibrium in which the statuses are unequal— let us consider one numerical example.

Let the system be symmetric and let

$$a = 1 \qquad b = 3 \qquad c_1 = 1 \qquad c_2 = 2$$

By Proposition 3, since $a \neq b/2$, we have an equilibrium position; by Proposition 2, since $c_2/c_1 \neq a/a = 1$, the position will not be on the expectation line.

Numerically, we find that the system (10) becomes

$$\frac{ds_1}{dt} = 3s_2 - 2s_1 - 1$$

$$\frac{ds_2}{dt} = 3s_1 - 2s_2 - 2$$

The equilibrium condition of vanishing derivatives gives the algebraic system

$$3s_2 - 2s_1 - 1 = 0$$
$$3s_1 - 2s_2 - 2 = 0$$

for which the solution is found to be $s_{1e} = \frac{8}{5}$, $s_{2e} = \frac{7}{5}$. Substitution of these values in the equations

$$ds_1 = (3s_{2e} - 2s_{1e} - 1)\, dt$$
$$ds_2 = (3s_{1e} - 2s_{2e} - 2)\, dt$$

shows indeed no displacement, that is, we get $ds_1 = 0$, $ds_2 = 0$, for any time interval dt. Thus the point $(\frac{8}{5}, \frac{7}{5})$ is an equilibrium point and it is not on the expectation line $s_{1e} \neq s_{2e}$. Yet, is it stable?

We now examine the stability conditions for the systems with $\Delta \neq 0$. Stability means that if our actor finds himself at some time t_0 in a position, say $\mathbf{s}(t_0)$, such that this is *not* the equilibrium $\mathbf{s}_e$, then

$$\mathbf{s}(t) \to \mathbf{s}_e$$

as $t \to \infty$. That is, he gravitates toward the equilibrium. We could put this another way: suppose he is in equilibrium and a random shock throws our actor out of equilibrium $\mathbf{s}_e$; will he return to it or not? If yes, then we have a stable system; if not, we have an unstable system.

We first change coordinate systems (see Figure 5) to put the equilibrium point $\mathbf{s}_e = (s_{1e}, s_{2e})$ at the origin:

$$s_1' = s_1 - s_{1e},\ s_2' = s_2 - s_{2e}$$

Then system (10) becomes by substitution, recalling that $d\mathbf{s}_e/dt = \mathbf{0}$,

$$\frac{ds_1'}{dt} = (a_1 - b_1)s_1' + b_1 s_2'$$
$$\frac{ds_2'}{dt} = (a_2 - b_2)s_2' + b_2 s_1' \tag{23}$$

When the system (10) is in equilibrium, the system (23) is at the origin. The advantage of system (23) is that, first, standard theorems apply to it and, second, it is easier to discuss the interpretations for the parameters by appeal to it. Thus, before discussing stability let us use equations (23) to discuss the interpretation of the parameters a_i, b_i ($i = 1, 2$), by following a mode of reasoning similar to that used by Rapoport (1960) for an arms race model.

To provide an interpretation for a_1 (the analysis for a_2 being analogous) consider a time (say $t = 0$) when we have

$$s_1'(0) = s_2'(0) \neq 0$$

At this time, then, the statuses are out of equilibrium. Then system (23) gives for the first variable

$$\frac{ds_1'(0)}{dt} = a_1 s_1'(0)$$

and so

$$\frac{1}{a_1} = \frac{s_1'(0)}{ds_1'(0)/d}$$

THOMAS J. FARARO

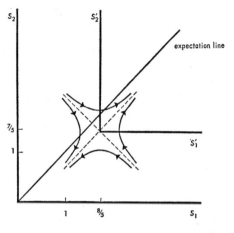

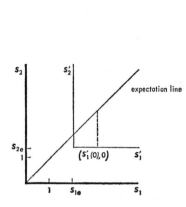

Figure 5. The Equilibrium   Figure 6. An Example of an Unstable
Point as the Origin of the New   System
Coordinate System

Now $s_1'(0)$ is where the actor *is* and $ds_1'(0)/dt$ is how fast he is *leaving* this state (of the first variable). The ratio has the dimension of time. Thus it can be thought of as a *holding time:* at fixed $s_1'(0)$, if the holding time is large, the mobility out of $s_1'(0)$ is slow; if the holding time is small, the mobility out of $s_1'(0)$ is fast. Since a_1 is the reciprocal of the holding time of s_1, large a_1 implies rapid mobility out of an arbitrary level of s_1 and small a_1 implies slow mobility out of an arbitrary level of s_1. Thus a_1 can be construed as measuring the *escapability* of status s_1: the degree to which a characterization underlying s_1 can be changed. A similar interpretation applies to a_2.

Let us consider b_i, with $i = 2$ for illustrative purposes. Let

$$s_2'(0) = 0, \; s_1'(0) > 0$$

for some time, $t = 0$ (as shown in Figure 5). Then the actor has a catching up problem on the second dimension, as shown by the dotted line in Figure 5. Equations (23) under these conditions give, for s_2',

$$\frac{ds_2'(0)}{dt} = b_2 s_1'(0)$$

and so

$$\frac{1}{b_2} = \frac{s_1'(0)}{ds_2'(0)/dt}$$

Now the right side has the dimension of time. The value $s_1'(0)$ determines where the actor wants s_2' to be at time $t = 0$: his equilibration-induced aspired status on s_2 at this time. The derivative in the denominator measures the mobility on this second status at this time. Thus for fixed $s_1'(0)$, when the ratio is small, the mobility is rapid, while if the ratio is large, the mobility is slow. Thus small values of $1/b_2$ mean rapid movement toward a momentarily aspired status; large values of $1/b_2$ mean slow movement toward the aspired status. Therefore, a high value of b_2 means rapid movement toward a momentarily aspired status, while small values of b_2 mean slow movement toward it. Thus $1/b_2$ can be thought of as an apparent catching up time, and b_2 itself measures a rather complex aspect of the $s_1 - s_2$ interaction: the extent to which the actor moves on s_2 toward a level induced by a given level of s_1, because of his desire to move to attain equal levels. Thus b_2 may be thought of as the responsiveness of s_2 to s_1: if b_2 is nearly zero, movement on s_2 is relatively unresponsive to any aspect of s_1, whereas a large b_2 means the mobility on s_2 is very much attributable to aspirations induced by s_1.

Let us return now to the question of stability. Our basic result is the following:

PROPOSITION 4. *If an equilibrium point exists, it is unstable.*

The mathematical meaning of the proposition is that for any system (23) there exist initial conditions (say, near the equilibrium) such that in these initial conditions the system moves away from the origin. Thus the equilibrium of system (10) represented by the origin in system (23) is an unstable equilibrium.

Proof. We can use the standard theorem on linear systems (see Brauer and Nohel, 1967; Rabenstein, 1966; Sanchez, 1968) that the origin of system (23) is stable if and only if both roots of

$$\lambda^2 - S\lambda + \Delta = 0$$

have negative real parts, where $S = (a_1 + a_2) - (b_1 + b_2)$ for our system (23).

The theorem is known to imply that the system is stable if and only if $S < 0$ and $\Delta > 0$. These two conditions can be rewritten in terms of the parameters of the model:

$$(a_1 + a_2) - (b_1 + b_2) < 0$$
$$(a_1 - b_1)(a_2 - b_2) - b_1 b_2 > 0$$

If this latter expression is divided by the positive quantity $b_1 b_2$ we obtain

$$\frac{(a_1 - b_1)(a_2 - b_2)}{b_1 b_2} > 1$$

and this can be written

$$(\omega_1 - 1)(\omega_2 - 1) > 1$$

where $\omega_i = a_i/b_i$. Thus the origin is stable if and only if

(a) $a_1 + a_2 < b_1 + b_2$

(b) $(\omega_1 - 1)(\omega_2 - 1) > 1$

$\qquad\qquad\qquad\qquad\qquad\qquad\qquad\qquad\qquad$ (24)

We proceed to analyze all possible cases in terms of ω_i relative to 1. If $\omega_i = 1$ (any i) then equation (24b) fails. If $\omega_i > 1$, $\omega_j < 1$ ($i \neq j$), then $(\omega_1 - 1)(\omega_2 - 1) < 0$ and so equation (24b) fails. If $\omega_1 > 1$, $\omega_2 > 1$, then $a_1 > b_1$ and $a_2 > b_2$, so that $a_1 + a_2 > b_1 + b_2$ and equation (24a) fails. If $\omega_i < 1$, then since $\omega_i \geq 0$,

$$0 < 1 - \omega_i \leq 1 \qquad (i = 1, 2)$$

Thus if both $\omega_1 < 1$ and $\omega_2 < 1$,

$$0 < (1 - \omega_1)(1 - \omega_2) \leq 1$$

and so equation (24b) fails. Thus for all possible values of the parameters ($a_i > 0$, $b_i > 0$) we conclude that the stability conditions are not satisfied, and so Proposition 4 holds.

A geometric picture of the system's behavior near equilibrium is provided in Figure 6 in order to illustrate the movement away from equilibrium characteristic of an unstable system. This is the previously used example of the symmetric system with parameters $a_1 = a_2 = 1$, $b_1 = b_2 = 3$, $c_1 = 1$, $c_2 = 2$. As indicated earlier, the equilibrium position exists at $\mathbf{s}_e = (\frac{8}{5}, \frac{7}{5})$. However, we see now that if the actor is deflected from this equilibrium or begins outside of it, he does not gravitate toward it. For four possible initial positions relative to the equilibrium, we have four different trajectories shown in Figure 6. Two of these trajectories are skid row motions in which both statuses are steadily declining as time passes. The other two trajectories are upwardly mobile movements on both variables, although the actor is not experiencing a "happy" state of affairs because most of the time his position is not balanced (according to his own expectations).

Other types of trajectory are possible, but the example should suffice to give some concreteness to the idea of an unstable system. Further, it illustrates that this model can explain both social success and social failure in the same terms; roughly speaking, it says that the difference between success and failure depends upon where you begin. It thus gives due weight to the initial position in the system. However, we see immediately what it cannot explain: how it is that anybody ever stays put. In other words, the model is only partially successful in dealing with well-known status phenomena.

DISCUSSION

The major aspect of the above model which accounts for its failure to keep individuals in place under some conditions is that it does not adequately attend to the role of the ascribed statuses. These ascribed statuses are constants for all time in which the model is at work generating a trajectory in the time-varying statuses. But expectations for the time-varying statuses will exist based upon ascribed statuses. The effect of these ascription-induced expectations is to set up relatively permanent levels of aspiration on both of the time-varying statuses. Recent soon-to-be published work (Fararo, 1970) indicates that, depending upon the actor's ascribed statuses, a special position in the plane will be singled out, exerting a steady pull on the actor in its direction. All trajectories, whether upwardly or downwardly mobile, experience a more-or-less strong braking effect, making a stable equilibrium possible.

Ideally, a dynamic model should account for the observed influence of the initial position, for instabilities in status phenomena, and for the undeniable fact that people have a tendency to stay put. The only way to accommodate all these facts appears to be in a general nonlinear model. The advantage of such a model is that it will very often have multiple equilibria, some of which are stable and some of which are unstable. Furthermore, in a nonlinear theory one can introduce very sophisticated refinements of the stability notion; for example, there will be a region of stability around an equilibrium position, so that only sufficiently large shocks out of equilibrium will induce mobility away from it. No special effort is needed to produce nonlinear models: they arise as soon as one imposes a ceiling on any status variable (for instance, on organizational position). The difficulty, of course, is in the analysis of the models.

It appears that the best strategy for future work in status dynamics would be to set up a sociologically meaningful nonlinear model incorporating known mechanisms and ceilings on statuses where needed, and then to utilize methods of linear approximation, as indicated by Kemeny and Snell (1962) in their discussion of ecological dynamics. As soon as one linearizes, the ideas and methods used in the preceding sections become relevant. The difference is that there will be a separate analysis for each of the equilibrium points of the nonlinear model.

Aside from this general orientation to nonlinearity, there are many specific steps and tasks on which mathematically oriented sociologists can work. They can, for example, attempt to set down some axioms on the characterization-valuation basis that will determine the general form of status system models; study a class of more general models in two dimensions by letting the expectation be an arbitrary linear form and by letting the expectation be time-varying in form; introduce power into the system, both in terms of a representation or measurement theory and in terms of the equations; conceptually and geometrically analyze the interpretation of the parameters to make their meanings more vivid; construct simulation studies in which concrete trajectories are produced for a variety of numerical values for the parameters of the models; study this approach from the standpoint of empirical application, using the very important methodological guides provided in a recent monograph by Blalock (1969) on the application of dynamic models; analytically study the problems of comparative statics, in which one examines how the equilibria change when the parameters are shifted; begin working on the same problems in three or more dimensions; examine and criticize the status measurement theory of the first section with a view to determining its probable scope of application; and create stochastic processes which are probabilistic versions of the deterministic models.

REFERENCES

ATKINSON, R. C., BOWER, G. H. AND CROTHERS, E. J.
    1965   *An Introduction to Mathematical Learning Theory.* New York: Wiley. Chapter Four.
BARBER, B.
    1957   *Social Stratification.* New York: Harcourt, Brace, and World.
BLALOCK, H. M., JR.
    1969   *Theory Construction.* Englewood Cliffs, N.J.: Prentice-Hall.
BRAUER, F. AND NOHEL, J. A.
    1967   *Ordinary Differential Equations, A First Course.* New York: Benjamin.
FARARO, T. J.
    1968   "Theory of status." *General Systems* 13: 177–188.
    1970   "Theoretical studies in status and stratification." *General Systems* 15 (in press).
GALTUNG, J.
    1966   "Rank and social integration: A multidimensional approach." In J. Berger, M. Zelditch, Jr., and B. Anderson (Eds.), *Sociological Theories in Progress.* Volume I. Boston: Houghton Mifflin.
KEMENY, J. G. AND SNELL, J. L.
    1962   *Mathematical Models in the Social Sciences.* Boston: Ginn. Chapter Three.
KIMBERLY, J. C.
    1966   "A theory of status equilibration." In J. Berger, M. Zelditch, Jr., and B. Anderson (Eds.), *Sociological Theories in Progress.* Volume I. Boston: Houghton Mifflin.
LENSKI, G. E.
    1954   "Status-crystallization: A non-vertical dimension of social status." *American Sociological Review* 19: 405–413.

LUCE, R. D.
   1959   *Individual Choice Behavior.* New York: Wiley.
PARSONS, T.
   1953   "A revised analytical approach to the theory of social stratification."
          In R. Bendix and S. M. Lipset (Eds.), *Class, Status and Power.* New
          York: Free Press.
PARSONS, T. AND SMELSER, N.
   1956   *Economy and Society.* New York: Free Press.
RABENSTEIN, A. L.
   1966   *Introduction to Ordinary Differential Equations.* New York: Academic
          Press.
RAPOPORT, A.
   1960   *Fights, Games and Debates.* Ann Arbor: University of Michigan Press.
SANCHEZ, D. A.
   1968   *Ordinary Differential Equations and Stability Theory: An Introduction.*
          San Francisco: Freeman.
TUMIN, M. M.
   1967   *Social Stratification.* Englewood Cliffs, N.J.: Prentice-Hall.
ZELDITCH, M., JR. AND ANDERSON, B.
   1966   "On the balance of a set of ranks." In J. Berger, M. Zelditch, Jr., and
          B. Anderson (Eds.), *Sociological Theories in Progress.* Volume I. Boston:
          Houghton Mifflin.

𝕏17𝕏

STRUCTURE OF
SEMANTIC SPACE

Andy B. Anderson

PURDUE UNIVERSITY

I would like to thank Professor Fromkin and the staff of the Behavioral Science Laboratory in the Krannert Graduate School of Industrial Administration, Purdue University, for the use of the laboratory. Support for the research came from grant MH-17210-01 from the National Institute of Mental Health. I am also indebted to the editors of this volume and the anonymous reviewers for their many valuable and insightful criticisms.

The semantic space hypothesized by Osgood, Suci, and Tannenbaum (1957) concerns psychological aspects of meaning. Against a background of traditional learning theory, meaning is defined as a representational mediation process. The semantic differential operationalizes this concept of meaning with seven-point bipolar adjectival scales against which a concept is judged. A distinction may be drawn between the psychological and methodological issues attending the

308

semantic differential. The psychological issues involve theoretical validity. Is the meaning of *meaning* as presented in the semantic space hypothesis theoretically sound? The methodological issues involve the validity of the measuring instrument rather than that of the theory. It is within the second set that this research finds its problem.

The above distinction greatly oversimplifies the question. The two sorts of issues are not independent. Nevertheless, it is useful at this point to make clear the scope of the investigation. Semantic space is characterized by three orthogonal bipolar dimensions having a common origin in a symmetric Euclidean space. Tests of these structural characteristics generally consist of factor analytic studies of responses to semantic differential schedules. Factor analyses of semantic differential data have resulted in factor structures which are impressively consistent over a variety of subjects, scales, and concepts. Moreover, the generality extends across social, cultural, and linguistic boundaries (Osgood, 1965). It seems clear that responses to the semantic differential are consistent with the semantic space model. However, it is not clear whether these traits result because of characteristics of human semantic judgment or because of characteristics of the measuring instrument used to elicit the judgment. In short, do particular structural characteristics of semantic space result from the use of the semantic differential as a measuring instrument? A factor analysis of responses to the semantic differential cannot provide a means for evaluating the question. One cannot ascertain from the resulting factor structure whether it reflects the nature of human semantic judgment or the restrictions placed on that judgment by the schedule. To an important degree the major characteristics—dimensionality, orthogonality, symmetry, bipolarity, and common origin—came about through assumption rather than empirical investigation.

One of the characteristics which has received some criticism and subsequent research is that of bipolarity (Carroll, 1959; Ross and Levy, 1960; Green and Goldfried, 1965). Osgood, Suci, and Tannenbaum themselves recognized the need to test the bipolarity assumption (1957, pp. 327–328), and they clearly anticipated the instrument effect issue when they asked, "Does the semantic differential force the subject to use unnatural bases of judgment?" Again, they asked, "If subjects were asked to make judgments of similarity and difference among concepts *without* use of the semantic differential, would approximately the same distances among the concepts appear, in a space having the same number of dimensions?" (1957, p. 143).

Two noteworthy attempts have been made to answer this question. Rowan (1954) had subjects rate ten concepts on a form of the semantic differential. Each subject also was presented with all 120 possible triads of the ten concepts and asked to choose in each triad the two most similar concepts. A "similarity space" was generated by defining a distance function, $d_{ij} = 1 - P_{ij}$, where P_{ij} is the percentage of the times that i and j are chosen most similar out of the total number of triads in which they both appear. In factoring the matrix of cross-products between concept vectors (origin at the centroid), Rowan found some of the latent roots to be negative. Although distortion was slight, this did indicate that the concepts would not map into a Euclidean space. Wilson (1954), setting the distance function $1 - P_{ij}$ equal to d_{ij}^2 rather than d_{ij}, reanalyzed Rowan's data and produced a closer fit to a Euclidean model. Rowan's factor analysis yielded three factors for both spaces, with equivalent concept orderings along the three dimensions. However, in the similarity space only the evaluative factor could be clearly identified. The potency and activity factors seemed to coalesce. The third factor was specific to one concept. Osgood et al. (1957) pointed out a major shortcoming of this approach: the results are limited to the unique set of ten concepts used. Increasing the number of concepts cannot solve the problem because the method of triads and similar techniques become more impractical as the number of stimuli increases. The authors, recognizing the dilemma, indicated the need for more work on the problem.

Other problems limited these attempts to examine the issue at hand. The semantic differential is based on a spatial model of semantic similarity. The more similar two concepts are, the closer spatially they will be. Therefore, the definition of a distance function is crucial. Technically, the distance measures used by Rowan and Wilson are indices of distance and not scaled distances. Torgerson (1958) pointed out that such indices "are simply a matter of definition, there is no internal basis for selecting one definition over another" (p. 295). At this early stage in the development of multidimensional scaling, solutions came at the price of rather severe formal requirements. In order to generate the spatial configuration implied by a set of responses, it was necessary to make assumptions about the data which were difficult if not impossible to justify. This problem was a major stumbling block in the way of attempts to verify the results of factor analyses on the semantic differential. However, recent work in the area of multidimensional scaling has made it possible to reapproach the problem.

METHOD

If the structural characteristics of semantic space are not artifacts produced by using the semantic differential, then one should find the same structural characteristics in a space generated using some other method for obtaining judgments of semantic similarity and difference. A two-stage method is implied. First, judgments of semantic similarity must be represented as a spatial configuration. Second, the obtained configurations must be analyzed so as to reflect on the tenability of the hypothesis that semantic space is Euclidean with three orthogonal, bipolar dimensions symmetric about a common origin.

The first stage, representing semantic judgments as spatial configurations, is composed of three tasks. First, a set of concepts must be chosen. Second, a method must be devised for obtaining judgments of semantic similarity among the concepts. Third, a means must be found for expressing the similarity judgments as a spatial configuration of the concepts. The third task will be examined first. The particular technique of nonmetric multidimensional scaling used in this research grew from work by Shepard (1962a; 1962b) in which he explored the use of spatial models of psychological similarity. If stimuli are represented as points in a multidimensional space, Shepard reasoned, the perceived similarity between any two stimuli should be directly related to the distance between the points. The more similar two stimuli are judged to be, the nearer they will be in the space. Of course, the degree of similarity must be reflected in some measurement. Shepard calls the measurements *proximities*. Then, a monotonic transformation of the proximity measures is needed in order to obtain spatial distances. However, for all but a few problems, there was no reason to select any one function in preference to any other.

Shepard decided to make no assumption about the form of the function, other than the requirement that it be monotonic. The simultaneous inequalities imposed by maintaining the rank order of the proximity measures force the configuration to solution. But N points can always be mapped into a space of $N - 1$ dimensions. Therefore, the criterion of minimum dimensionality is imposed. The remarkable outcome of this approach is that the condition of monotonicity, coupled with a requirement of minimum dimensionality, is generally sufficient to lead to a unique metric solution. In other words, given a subject's judgments of similarity on a set of objects (measurement at the ordered distance level), Shepard's technique will produce a configuration of object-points in a metric space such that the interpoint distances are monotonically related to the subject's judgments of similarity.

The technique was updated by Shepard's colleague, Kruskal (1964a; 1964b). Kruskal provided the technique with a measure of goodness of fit. Given a set of similarity judgments (δ_{ij}), the problem is to find a configuration having interpoint distances which fit the data best. To define best fit, Kruskal developed a quantitative measure of nonmonotonicity called *stress*. The best fitting configuration in a space of a given dimensionality is that configuration which minimizes stress. The output of the program is the set of coordinates giving the location of each point such that stress is minimized. Each space is normalized with the root-mean-square distance from points to the origin at the centroid being equal to 1.000, thus allowing for comparability between configurations.

The spatial models of psychological similarity and semantic similarity are homologous. Therefore, the technique provides a solution to one of the fundamental problems encountered in this research by furnishing a means of generating a spatial configuration from similarity data. However, the configurational comparison is to no avail unless there is reason to believe the data are related on a fundamental level to semantic judgment in the semantic space theory. The obtrusive question confronting the research is the selection of the set of stimuli.

The previously cited studies by Rowan and Wilson simply selected an arbitrary set of ten concepts. Undoubtedly, the approach used by Osgood *et al.* is to be preferred. The authors tested across an extremely wide variety of concepts. However, the magnitude of such an undertaking makes it prohibitive, particularly in light of the analytic model proposed. With only ten concepts, there are $\binom{10}{2} = 45$ similarities to evaluate. As the number of stimuli increases, the number of similarities quickly becomes unmanageable. The dilemma was clear. Two considerations were paramount: (1) the number of stimuli had to be fairly small, hopefully under fifteen; and (2) the stimuli should hold some claim to generality. In order to satisfy these requirements a compromise was accepted which possibly introduces a bias to the analysis in favor of the semantic space hypothesis. To be specific, concept-points were selected from the bipolar adjectives in the semantic differential. Twelve adjectives were selected representing two scales from each of the three factors. For each factor the pivot scale was selected: *good–bad* for the *evaluative* factor, *hard–soft* for the potency factor, and *active–passive* for the *activity* factor. For the second scale on each factor, scales were chosen that had a maximum loading on their respective factor and minimum loadings on the other two factors. For evaluative, the second scale was *clean–dirty*. *Strong–weak* represented potency, and *fast–slow* represented activity.

The selected concept set, although it avoids a dilemma, forces some qualifications on the interpretation. It is possible that judgments of similarity on all pairs from this set will yield spaces having the structural characteristics assumed in semantic space, even if these structural characteristics do not hold in general. The compromise must be kept in mind during the interpretation of results. Nevertheless, it should be recalled that the research problem has to do with methodological validity, not psychological validity. The issue is not whether "real" semantic space has the stated structural characteristics. The investigation is concerned with the extent to which these structural characteristics are imposed by the semantic differential. Therefore, using bipolar adjectives as the concept set is not nearly as open to criticism as it would be if the study were questioning the psychological soundness of the theory. These adjectives, after all, are absolutely fundamental to the semantic space hypothesis in at least two ways. First, they are basic to the Osgood *et al.* theory of the nature and dynamics of human semantic judgment. Second, the bipolar adjectives operationally define semantic space. Therefore, the judgments of semantic similarity between pairs of selected adjectives should have implications reaching beyond the unique set of concepts used.

An additional problem concerns the justification for representing adjectives as points in a multidimensional space. Concepts, it could be argued, have values on adjective scales, and thus have a fixed location, but adjectives only label scales and do not have a fixed location. At one level, the objection is undoubtedly valid. Osgood *et al.* conceptualize meaning as a compound reaction of bipolar, adjectival components, and this does not necessarily assume that the adjectives have specific locations. However, the authors of the semantic differential have used adjectives as concepts to be judged against bipolar scales (Osgood *et al.*, 1957, pp. 152–153). The procedure operationally defines the connotative meaning of the adjective as a point in semantic space. Representing adjectives as points, it would appear, is not in itself in conflict with the semantic space theory. There is another line of reply which is more directly to the point of the criticism. While it may be true that the semantic space theory does not insist on specific coordinate locations of the adjectives, certain facts regarding those locations and the relationships between the locations are either explicitly stated in the theory or are directly deducible from explicitly stated assumptions. The model assumes that the bipolars are equidistant from the origin. Therefore, two adjectives which are in the same direction on the same factor (*good* and *clean*, for example) are assumed to be at the same spatial location regardless of what that location is. Moreover, since the factors are assumed to have an angular separation of 90 degrees, it is possible using the Pythagorean theorem to express the distance between adjectives from different factors (*fast* and *bad*, for example) in terms of the distances between the adjectives and the origin, regardless of what those distances are. Therefore, it seems reasonable to assume that a hypothetical configuration can be constructed which is, in the strict geometric sense, similar to the configuration implied by the semantic differential. If the configuration is normalized in the manner described previously it becomes a suitable hypothesis against which to compare the similarly normalized configurations generated from experimental data.

Once the twelve concept-points have been specified, a task must be designed which will elicit from subjects the similarity measures, δ_{ij}, for the $\binom{12}{2} = 66$ adjective pairs. Symmetry is assumed in the sense that $\delta_{ij} = \delta_{ji}$. In addition, identity similarities, δ_{ii}, between each concept and itself, are assumed to be zero. Each subject was given a deck of sixty-six small cards. Each of the sixty-six possible pairs of adjectives appeared at the top of one of the cards. At the bottom of each card were two blanks labeled "prelim score" and "final score." The subject was asked: (1) to rate each adjective pair on a 100-point similarity scale, ties being allowed, (2) to write the ratings in the "prelim score" blanks, (3) to array the cards, (4) to examine the array checking to see if the "prelim scores" accurately expressed his opinion, (5) to write final scores in the appropriate blanks. Analysis was based on the final ratings. It is well to state again that the scores are assumed to constitute measurement at the level of ordered distances. That is, the scores are used only to rank the sixty-six pairs on the basis of similarity. But, the distances produced when the Shepard-Kruskal technique is applied to the similarity data are distances in a metric space, and can be treated as ratio level measurement. The forty-two subjects were paid volunteers taking undergraduate sociology courses at Purdue University. Although data will be examined in summary form, each subject's responses were used to generate a separate configuration of the twelve adjective-points.

The second stage of the analysis consists of a comparison of the obtained configurations to the configuration postulated in the semantic space model. The semantic space is a Euclidean space defined by three general bipolar factors which are orthogonal and symmetric about a common origin. Figure 1 is a diagram of the model. The four adjectives representing the evaluative dimension can be symbolized by E1, E2, E3, and E4 where E1-E2 have similar meanings, as do E3-E4. In a like manner, the four potency adjectives can be written as P1-P2 and P3-P4, and the activity concepts as A1-A2 and A3-A4. If the semantic space hypothesis is to be supported, these adjective-points should be distributed approximately as shown in Figure 1.

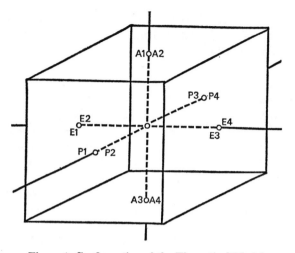

Figure 1. Configuration of the Theoretical Model

Before beginning a discussion of the analysis it is appropriate to enter two observations. The first point concerns the use of the idealized model of semantic space as a standard of comparison. Clearly, there is no problem in deducing this ideal-type configuration; Osgood, Suci, and Tannenbaum are quite explicit on this matter. Nevertheless, one must be aware of the fact that this criterion configuration sets an exceedingly rigorous standard for the data to meet. To illustrate, it is known that the three dimensions in the factor analytic studies do not exhaust the ways in which meanings vary. Moreover, the scales, almost without exception, do not have pure loadings on their respective factors. In short, deviations from this ideal-type model would be expected to occur even using the semantic differential as a measuring instrument. Any interpretation must be tempered by the realization that using the model as a criterion for comparison is quite unrealistic. Its purpose, in this study, is to serve as a frame of reference and not as a critical standard.

The problem requires a comparison between obtained configurations, or characteristics of the obtained configurations, and the configuration hypothesized by the semantic space theory. The first step is to generate the spatial configurations implied in the similarity data. Once the configurations are produced, the question becomes one of finding techniques for comparing configurations which will reflect on the tenability of the particular structural assumptions in question. The difficulty at this point is that there exists no ready arsenal for comparisons of spatial configurations as there does for comparisons of central tendency, dispersion, and other such traditional topics in statistical analysis. It is necessary, therefore, to improvise measurements to reflect various aspects of configurational agreement, most of which have no known sampling distribution.

The analysis is in four parts. The first examines the dimensionality data, the second evaluates the bipolarity assumption, the third concerns the assumption of symmetry about a common origin, and the fourth investigates overall configurational similarity.

The assumption that the space is three-dimensional Euclidean can be evaluated by examination of data coming directly from the Shepard-Kruskal program. Each case will be analyzed in Euclidean spaces of dimensionality 5 through 1. The stress figure indicates how well the data map into the space of each given dimensionality. Kruskal has suggested criteria for evaluating the stress values based on his experience with both experimental and synthetic data. Stress of 20 per cent or more is considered a poor fit. Stress of 10 to 19.99 per cent is considered fair. From 5 to 9.99 per cent rates as good. Between 2.5 and 4.99 per cent is excellent. Below 2.5 per cent is approaching perfection, where perfect means that there is a perfect monotonic relationship between similarities and distances (Kruskal, 1964a, p. 3).

To examine the bipolarity assumption, the means of each of the sixty-six interpoint distances are examined. The six distances corresponding to the distances between bipolar opposites should be the largest in the distance matrix. These data also provide some insight into factor consistency. If the semantic space hypothesis holds, the six distances between the adjectives assumed to be similar in meaning should be the smallest in the matrix of interpoint distances. For example, *good* and *clean* should be relatively close together in the space. Similarly, the adjectives which are theoretically opposite, but not bipolar opposites, should be comparatively far apart. For example, *good* and *dirty* should be widely separated. Attention is given to deviant cases.

The third analysis concerns symmetry and common origin. The symmetry assumption implies that bipolars are equidistant from the origin. However, this characteristic becomes involved with the assumption of common origin. If a line from one bipolar to its polar opposite does not go through the origin, then the fact that they are equidistant from the origin is not proof of symmetry. Both problems are considered. Distances from each bipolar to the origin are calculated. For each pair of bipolars, the distance between one of the pair to the origin is compared to the distance between the other and the origin. A ratio of the smaller to the larger is formed. If the assumption of equidistance holds, the ratio should approach 1.00.

The notion of common origin implies that if a straight line is drawn between each pair of bipolars, the lines will intersect at the origin. The three points representing the two bipolars and the origin should be colinear. To illustrate the analysis, assume the bipolar pair *good–bad* is being examined. Suppose a triangle with vertices at *good*, *bad*, and the origin. Let D_{gb} be the distance between *good* and *bad*, and D_{go} and D_{bo} the distances between *good* and the origin and *bad* and the origin, respectively. The law of cosines states that

$$D_{gb}^2 = D_{go}^2 + D_{bo}^2 - 2D_{go}D_{bo}\cos_{gb}$$

Equivalently, $\cos_{gb} = (D_{gb}^2 - D_{go}^2 - D_{bo}^2)/(-2D_{go}D_{bo})$

The cosine gives the size of the angle formed by the two vectors, one from *good* to the origin and the other from *bad* to the origin. Under the hypothesis this angle should be 180 degrees, yielding a cosine of -1.000. Of course, if this condition obtains, it is really not possible to have a triangle as described.

A fourth and final analysis is directed to the rather amorphous problem of overall configurational correspondence. Given two sets of twelve points each set in Euclidean space, how can one obtain an indication of the degree to which they have similar configurations? The selected measure of configurational agreement is the Pearson product moment correlation coefficient. To compare two configurations, a correlation coefficient is calculated between the two sets of sixty-six interpoint distances. The more the two configurations resemble one another, the higher the correlation coefficient will be.

RESULTS AND SUMMARY

How well do the adjective-points map into a Euclidean space of three dimensions? Table 1 gives the means and standard deviations of

TABLE 1
Mean Stress by Dimensionality

| | Dimensionality | | | | |
	5	4	3	2	1
Mean	0.068	0.070	0.106	0.195	0.406
S.D.	0.024	0.024	0.031	0.047	0.076

the stress values obtained from solutions in Euclidean spaces of dimensionality 1 through 5. In the three-dimensional space, mean stress is slightly above the *good fit–fair fit* cutting point of 0.100 suggested by Kruskal. Forcing a two-dimensional solution almost doubles mean stress, putting that figure just under the *fair fit–poor fit* cutting point. On the other hand, going from a three-dimensional to a four-dimensional

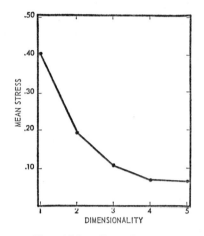

Figure 2. Plot of Mean Stress by Dimensionality

solution does not greatly reduce mean stress. Figure 2, the plot of mean stress by dimensionality, graphically illustrates the findings. The data are consistent with the hypothesis of a three-dimensional Euclidean space. Additional information supporting the tenability of the three-dimensional solution can be found in Klahr's (1969) work, which provided estimates of the statistical significance of stress values obtained from Kruskal's nonmetric multidimensional scaling. Using Monte Carlo simulation, Klahr randomly generated many sets of data, scaled them, and studied the distribution of stress. For sets of twelve points scaled in three dimensions, only 5 per cent of the randomly generated configurations had stress values below 0.118, a figure slightly larger than our mean stress of 0.106 for twelve adjective-points in three dimensions. Therefore, the remaining analyses are based upon the three-dimensional solutions.

How well does the assumption of bipolarity hold? Table 2 gives the sixty-six interpoint distances in normalized form for the semantic differential model. The matrix of mean interpoint distances is given in Table 3. In general, the assumption of bipolarity is supported. Of the six largest mean distances, four are between bipolars, and the smallest bipolar distance (*fast–slow*) ranks as the tenth largest in the matrix. The mean bipolar distance is $\bar{X} = 1.841$.

The data in Table 3 reflect indirectly on questions concerning the factor structure hypothesized in the semantic differential. In Table 2, which represents the semantic space model, the distances fall into three groups. Group I represents distances between bipolar opposites (*good–bad*) and distances between adjectives which are assumed to be

TABLE 2
Interpoint Distance Matrix for Theoretical Model

Concept	Good	Bad	Clean	Dirty	Hard	Soft	Strong	Weak	Active	Passive	Fast	Slow
Good												
Bad	2.000											
Clean	0.000	2.000										
Dirty	2.000	0.000	2.000									
Hard	1.414	1.414	1.414	1.414								
Soft	1.414	1.414	1.414	1.414	2.000							
Strong	1.414	1.414	1.414	1.414	0.000	2.000						
Weak	1.414	1.414	1.414	1.414	2.000	0.000	2.000					
Active	1.414	1.414	1.414	1.414	1.414	1.414	1.414	1.414				
Passive	1.414	1.414	1.414	1.414	1.414	1.414	1.414	1.414	2.000			
Fast	1.414	1.414	1.414	1.414	1.414	1.414	1.414	1.414	0.000	2.000		
Slow	1.414	1.414	1.414	1.414	1.414	1.414	1.414	1.414	2.000	0.000	2.000	

TABLE 3
Mean Interpoint Distance Matrix

Concept	Good	Bad	Clean	Dirty	Hard	Soft	Strong	Weak	Active	Passive	Fast	Slow
Good												
Bad	1.877											
Clean	0.781	1.836										
Dirty	1.706	0.825	1.825									
Hard	1.390	1.367	1.455	1.316								
Soft	1.338	1.546	1.199	1.622	1.854							
Strong	1.099	1.489	1.264	1.396	0.809	1.706						
Weak	1.633	1.281	1.581	1.410	1.809	0.906	1.847					
Active	1.053	1.606	1.238	1.500	1.056	1.678	0.727	1.868				
Passive	1.544	1.369	1.493	1.550	1.679	0.955	1.736	0.773	1.840			
Fast	1.107	1.572	1.341	1.501	1.065	1.732	0.850	1.818	0.669	1.794		
Slow	1.562	1.345	1.531	1.518	1.653	1.074	1.656	0.816	1.769	0.786	1.800	

opposite in meaning but which are not bipolar opposites (*good–dirty*). There are twelve distances in Group I. To support the semantic space hypothesis, the twelve distances should be the largest of the sixty-six. Group III represents the six distances between adjective pairs assumed to be similar in meaning: *good–clean, bad–dirty*, and so on. The six Group III distances should be the smallest of the sixty-six. The forty-eight cross-factor distances are in Group II, and they should be in between the extremes of Group I and Group III.

The means of the three groups are as follows: Group I, $\bar{X}$ = 1.805; Group II, $\bar{X}$ = 1.382; Group III, $\bar{X}$ = 0.796. Although these means are in the order hypothesized, the data cannot be accepted as supporting the factor structure of the semantic differential. Of the twelve largest values in the matrix, ten represent Group I distances. At least one of the Group I distances is exceeded by the following Group II distances: *fast–soft, strong–passive, active–weak*, and *fast–weak*. Although the mean of the Group II distances ($\bar{X}$ = 1.383) is close to the 1.414 hypothesized, there is substantial variation (S.D. = 0.278). The mean of the Group III distances ($\bar{X}$ = 0.796) is the lowest of the three groups, as it should be. However, this represents a rather apparent discrepancy from the hypothesized interpoint distance of zero. Moreover, Table 3 reveals only four of the six smallest mean distances to be from Group III. The following Group II distances are smaller than at least one of the Group III values: *active–strong, fast–strong, passive–weak, weak–slow*. All of the above discrepancies involve pairs of points one of which represents the activity factor and one of which represents the potency factor. The activity and potency dimensions evidently tend to coalesce, a pattern sometimes encountered in using the semantic differential.

Are the factors symmetric about a common origin? Are the bipolars equidistant from the origin? The distance between each concept and the origin was calculated. For each of the bipolar pairs, the distance between one of the bipolar adjectives and the origin was compared with the distance between the other bipolar and the origin. A ratio of the smaller to the larger was formed. According to the semantic space model, the ratio should approach 1.00. Table 4 gives the means and standard deviations of these ratios for each bipolar pair.

TABLE 4
Equidistance Ratios

	Bipolars					
	Good Bad	Clean Dirty	Hard Soft	Strong Weak	Active Passive	Fast Slow
Mean	0.865	0.895	0.916	0.846	0.897	0.883
S.D.	0.111	0.075	0.068	0.089	0.068	0.090

The data are relatively consistent with the assumption of equi-distance. Although there are individual cases which deviate markedly, the tendency is toward equidistance. The standard deviations indicate that the individual ratios are not widely dispersed about the means.

Taking each pair of bipolars plus the origin as a set of three points, are the three points colinear? An angle is formed by dropping vectors from each adjective-point in a bipolar set to the origin. If the three points—the two adjective-points plus the origin—fall on a straight line, then the angle cosine will be −1.00, or an angle of 180 degrees. The means and standard deviations for each bipolar pair are presented in Table 5.

TABLE 5
Angle Cosines

	Bipolars					
	Good Bad	Clean Dirty	Hard Soft	Strong Weak	Active Passive	Fast Slow
Mean	−0.800	−0.648	−0.746	−0.793	−0.732	−0.652
S.D.	0.205	0.412	0.277	0.212	0.207	0.297

The cosine data only marginally support the hypothesis. The mean cosines vary from −0.648, representing an angle of only approximately 130 degrees, to a mean cosine of −0.800, corresponding to an angle of roughly 143 degrees. In addition, the relatively large standard deviations reflect considerable deviation about the means. However, the distributions of individual cosines are highly skewed with the result that a comparatively small number of highly discrepant angles affect the means. The distribution of the *good–bad* cosines, for example, has nineteen of forty-two cosines in the −0.900 to −1.000 range, even though the mean is only −0.800. The other scales have similar distributions. Although the importance of the individual variation cannot be discounted, the character of the cosine distributions suggests that the data can be accepted as only marginally supporting the hypothesis.

Overall, how well do the subject's configurations correspond to the configuration representing the semantic space model? To compare any two configurations a Pearson product moment correlation coefficient can be calculated between the two sets of sixty-six interpoint distances. The correlation between the set of mean distances (Table 3) and the distances implied by the model (Table 2) is $r = +0.75$, a relatively high positive correlation. Previously, it was stated that to use the model configuration as a criterion is to use a standard of comparison from which notable deviation should be expected. Even data from the seman-tic differential will be at variance with the exact theoretical configuration. Moreover, in correlating against the model it is important to realize that the interpoint distances in the model configuration have, in effect, only three values. Therefore, the Pearson r is somewhat compromised as a measure of configurational similarity. In light of these qualifications, the correlation can be taken as evidence in moderate support of the semantic space hypothesis. However, once again a qualification must be entered concerning individual variation. Although the overall agreement between the model distances and the means of the data distances is fairly high, the extent of configurational agreement varies greatly from individual to individual, with the average correlation between individual configurations and the model configuration being only $\bar{r} = +0.57$.

SUMMARY

Qualifications on the research have been stated. At this point two shortcomings are worth noting. In regard to the sample, it is not possible to avoid the implications resulting from size and method of selection. Strictly speaking, one cannot generalize beyond this particular set of subjects.

The choice of concepts raises questions discussed previously. The judgments of semantic similarity were made on adjectives drawn from the semantic differential. Does this bias the outcome in favor of the theory? If one recalls that the interest is methodological, not psychological, the issue is less important. The reasoning was given. Nevertheless, it is theoretically possible that judgments of semantic similarity on other concept sets could give results, even for the methodological issue, differing from those reported in this paper. If this qualification has importance, perhaps it can be stated in the following implication. Findings in accord with the semantic model cannot be taken as *decisive* confirmation. It is equally true that findings contrary to the model would seem to be a formidable contraindication.

For the most part the data are consistent with the assumption that semantic space is a three-dimensional Euclidean space. There is some evidence of coalescence between the activity and potency factors. Although the stress data do not support the tenability of a two-dimensional solution, the coalescence is in line with what the authors of the semantic differential observed occasionally to happen. The bipolarity assumption is supported, in spite of much case-to-case variation. Some bipolar distances are exceeded by non-bipolar distances, and the bipolar distances vary across scales. Nevertheless, the bipolars tend to be maximally separated. The data are consistent with the assumption that bipolars are equidistant from the origin. The assumption that bipolars fall on straight lines running through the origin is only marginally supported. Considerable individual variation is noted. The correlation data, in light of the qualifications discussed, indicate overall configurational similarity between the data configurations and the hypothesized configuration. Once again, the conclusion must be qualified because of variation between subjects.

In summary, the research did not establish sufficient reasons for concluding that the structural characteristics implied by the semantic space theory are due to instrument effects in the semantic differential. Since an unpublished pilot study came to a similar conclusion, the assumption of a "three-dimensional Euclidean space composed of bipolar factors symmetric about a common origin" appears to be supported against the charge of instrument effects (Anderson, 1969). However, there is an additional conclusion of substantial sociological relevance. For many applications of the semantic differential in social research, the researchers are interested in how meanings of certain concepts vary within a group, or how two groups differ on the meanings of certain concepts. One argument given for using the semantic differential in such work is that the data can be handled as swarms of points in a three-dimensional space and differences can be measured by using the Euclidean distance function. This involves some strong mathematical assumptions about the space and the mapping function. Throughout this analysis, in spite of general support for the model, enough variation was found to suggest that for any particular case the assumptions needed to handle semantic differential data as points in a three-dimensional Euclidean space may not be warranted. The applications in social research for which the semantic differential seems most promising are precisely the ones requiring the most severe set of assumptions. The research suggests that the problem of meeting these assumptions be given consideration.

REFERENCES

ANDERSON, A. B.
    1969   "Structural assumptions of semantic space: A nonmetric multidimensional scaling analysis." Institute for the Study of Social Change, Purdue University, Working Paper Number 21. (Mimeo).
CARROLL, J. B.
    1959   "Review of Osgood, Suci, and Tannenbaum, *The Measurement of Meaning.*" *Language* 35: 58–77.
GREEN, R. F. AND GOLDFRIED, M. R.
    1965   "On the bipolarity of semantic space." *Psychological Monographs* 79: 1–31.

KLAHR, D.
  1969   "A Monte Carlo investigation of the statistical significance of Kruskal's nonmetric scaling procedure." *Psychometrika 34* (September): 319–330.
KRUSKAL, J. B.
  1964a "Multidimensional scaling by optimizing goodness of fit to a nonmetric hypothesis." *Psychometrika* 29 (March): 1–27.
  1964b "Nonmetric multidimensional scaling: A numerical method." *Psychometrika* 29 (June): 115–129.
OSGOOD, C. E.
  1965   "Cross-cultural comparability in attitude measurement via multilingual semantic differentials." Pp. 95–105 in I. D. Steiner and M. Fishbein (Eds.), *Current Studies in Social Psychology*. New York: Holt, Rinehart, and Winston.
OSGOOD, C. E., SUCI, G. J. AND TANNENBAUM, P. H.
  1957   *The Measurement of Meaning*. Urbana: University of Illinois Press.
SHEPARD, R. N.
  1962a "The analysis of proximities; Part I." *Psychometrika* 27 (June): 125–140.
  1962b "The analysis of proximities; Part II." *Psychometrika* 27 (September): 219–246.
ROSS, B. M. AND LEVY, N. A.
  1960   "A comparison of adjectival antonyms by simple card-pattern formation." *Journal of Psychology* 49: 133–137.
ROWAN, T. C.
  1954   "Some developments in multidimensional scaling applied to semantic relationships." University of Illinois (unpublished doctoral dissertation).
TORGERSON, W. S.
  1958   *Theory and Method of Scaling*. New York: Wiley.
WILSON, K.
  1954   *Multidimensional Scaling of Data Obtained by Method of Triads*. Control Systems Laboratory, University of Illinois. (Mimeo)

ERRATUM FOR
1969 VOLUME

On page 110 of *Sociological Methodology 1969* Step B3 should read as follows: "Otherwise, solve for p_{30}, using the positive or negative square root of the quantity under the radical, according to which one satisfies equation (15)." An analogous correction of Step G3 is required, substituting (16) for (15). The consequences of this mistake are not trivial. The entire lower half of Table 3 is wrong as are all the illustrative results presented subsequently in the paper, since they are derived from Table 3. I am preparing a full set of corrigenda which I will supply on request. My thanks to Arthur S. Goldberger for a suggestion which led to the discovery of this mistake (as well as to a method of solving the equations superior to the one in which the mistake occurred).

OTIS DUDLEY DUNCAN

NAME INDEX

A

ABRAMSON, N., 211
ABU-LUBAN, B., 171n
AGGER, R. E., 171n
ALTHAUSER, R. P., 167
ANDERSON, A. B., 324
ANDERSON, B., 283
ANDREWS, F. M., 3, 9
ATKINSON, R. C., 288, 289
ATTNEAVE, F., 211

B

BARBER, B., 285
BARTLETT, M. S., 76, 81, 84–87, 91n, 93
BAYES, T., 185. *See also* Bayes' theorem; Bayesian statistics
BLALOCK, H. M., JR., 3, 39, 41, 43, 49, 50, 53, 60–63, 65, 66, 68, 76n, 83, 84, 92n, 105, 152, 161, 168n, 284, 306
BLANKENSHIP, L. V., 171n
BLUMBERG, L. U., 171n

BOHRNSTEDT, G. W., 4, 76n, 105, 165
BOWER, G. H., 288, 289
BOYLE, R. P., 218
BRETON, R., 205, 215
BROWNLEE, K. A., 44, 46
BUNGE, M., 53, 54–55

C

CAFFREY, J., 119
CAMPBELL, D. T., 3, 4, 152, 152n, 153–155, 157, 161, 167, 171, 177
CARROLL, J. B., 309, 324
CARTER, L. F., 83, 84, 276
CATTELL, R. B., 105, 126, 127
CATTON, W. R., 49
CAWS, P., 50
CHAMBLISS, W. J., 49
CHRIST, C., 78, 89, 276–278
CLAYTON, K. N., 3
CLEARY, T. A., 131, 134, 137
CODDINGTON, E. A., 272
COHEN, J., 143, 254

327

W

WALD, A., 76, 81–87, 91n, 93

WALKER, H. M., 40

WALSTER, W. G., 131, 134, 137

WALTON, J., 171n

WEBER, M., 258

WERTS, C. E., 152, 152n

WILDAVSKY, A., 171n

WILEY, G. E., 172–175

WILSON, K., 310, 312

WOLFINGER, R., 171

WOOLDRIDGE, P. J., 80n

WRIGHT, S., 4, 41, 46, 105

Z

ZELDITCH, M., JR., 283

ZETTERBERG, H. L., 48, 49, 54, 59

SUBJECT INDEX

A

Agreement, measure of, 140
American Documentation Institute, 213n
American Psychological Association, 123
Analysis: causal, *see* Causal analysis; cross-sectional, 8; factor, 119, 126–127, 201; multivariance, 198, 200–201, 214–215; parametric, 201; path, 4, 107–109, 151; preliminary, 212; regression, 7–8, 10, 26, 201, 245; two-wave model, 8; uncertainty, *see* Uncertainty analysis; variance, 201, 211–212
Axiom, definition of, 51

B

Baye's theorem, 185, 186–187
Bayesian statistics, 185; data collection and, 196–197; example of, 188–189; literature on, 197; posterior distribution in, 194–195; probability and, 191–192; results of, 195; statistical inference and, 187–188, 192–194; subjective elements of, 190–191

C

Causal analysis: measurement errors and, 12–20; models for, 3–4, 10–12; sample size and, 17–19; two-wave data of, 4–12, 26
Coefficients: concordance of, 140; intraclass correlation, 143; path, 4–5, 7–8, 10, 46; Spearman rank order correlation (rho), 144
Coefficients of agreement, bivariate, 140–141; formulas for, 147–149; interpretation of, 142–144; properties of, 145–147
Computer programs, availability of, 201, 225, 231n, 252n, 277
Confidence intervals, 185, 186
Constancy, 10

331

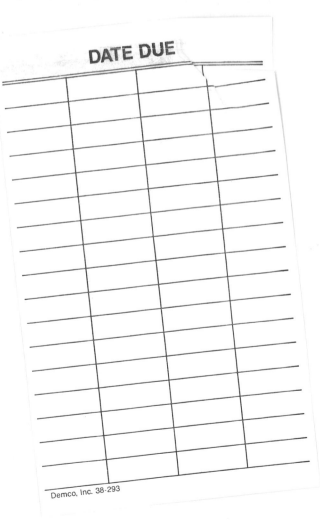

Demco, Inc. 38-293

ABP-9542